A GEOLOGY FOR ENGINEERS

A GEOLOGY FOR ENGINEERS

F. G. H. BLYTH Ph.D., D.I.C., F.G.S.

IMPERIAL COLLEGE OF SCIENCE AND TECHNOLOGY, LONDON

Edward Arnold (Publishers) Ltd London

S B N : 7131 2020 7

Printed in Great Britain by
Butler & Tanner Ltd., Frome and London

PREFACE TO FIFTH EDITION

When this book was first published it aimed at presenting a short account of geological science and some of its applications to engineering. This has proved to be a useful approach, which has been tested over many years of teaching experience with civil engineering students. Certain aspects of geology are more important than others in relation to constructional work and are therefore given more space in the text, while some (such as palaeontology) are necessarily omitted almost entirely. The book remains essentially a text-book of geology, with an emphasis on engineering applications. The civil engineer, during most kinds of construction, comes into contact with problems which are fundamentally geological. If he has some knowledge of geology he is able to understand better the nature of such a problem and to discuss its implications with geological colleagues.

The present edition follows the same lay-out as earlier editions, but contains much new material, including a largely re-written Chapter 6 (Sedimentary Rocks); additions to Chapters 1, 11 and others; a revised Chapter 13 (Water Supply); and new sections on the Roseires Dam (Chapter 14) and the Cameron Highlands Scheme (Chapter 15). There are also several new plates.

I acknowledge with thanks the permission of the Director of H.M. Geological Survey for the reproduction of photographs in Plates IVb, Vb, VIa, Xb, XIa, and XIIIa; of the Council of the Geologists' Association for Plates Ia, Ib, IIa, IXa, Xa, and XIIb; and of the Editor of the *Belfast News-Letter* for Plate XV. The new illustration in Plate IXb is an Institute of Geological Sciences photograph reproduced by permission of the Controller of H.M. Stationery Office; and that in Plate XIIa is an Institute of Geological Sciences photograph reproduced by permission of the Director. The following text-figures are also used by kind permission: nos. 36, 66, and 68 from " Structure and Surface " (Brown and Debenham); Figs. 81, and 90 from " Geology " (Professor H. H. Read and the Oxford University Press); Fig. 135 (Council of the Liverpool Geological Society). For Figs. 136, 137, and 138 I am indebted to Professor J. McG. Bruckshaw. Dr. Gilbert Wilson drew Fig. 60, and also supported many discussions with helpful criticisms and advice. I am grateful to Mr. J. Gee for expert photographic help with Plate VII and with many diagrams. I am also indebted to Dr. J. L. Knill for the diagrams of Fig. 128.

F. G. H. B.

August, 1966

CONTENTS

APPENDIX

LIST OF PLATES

A GEOLOGY FOR ENGINEERS

CHAPTER 1

PHYSICAL GEOLOGY

Introduction. It is a matter of common observation that changes are constantly in progress on the earth's surface. Rivers, fed by rain, carry their loads of sediment and dissolved matter to the sea ; coast-lines are continually being modified by the combined forces of waves and currents ; fragments produced by the breakdown of the rocks are rounded into pebbles and sand, and are deposited along shore-lines, while in the river estuaries and farther out to sea the finer particles are built up into deposits of silt and mud. Water is the active agent here, but the work done by wind is also seen in the formation of sand-dunes and in the dust-storms of more arid climates. In colder regions frost, snow and ice play their part in modelling the landscape. Conditions are not static, but everywhere there is movement and change, and with the results of these geological processes the civil engineer is constantly concerned. Coast erosion, the littoral drift of shingle, shifting sand-dunes, the silting up of rivers, the regulation of river courses and the disposal of flood waters—these are a few of the problems with which he is confronted, quite apart from the geological conditions met with in excavation, tunnelling and boring operations in engineering construction.

Denudation is the general term used for the wearing down of land areas, by processes originating and acting at the earth's surface. All rocks, when exposed for a sufficient length of time to the atmosphere, undergo decay from disintegration and decomposition, together referred to as *weathering*. Disintegration is the breakdown into small particles by the action of the mechanical agents of denudation, such as rain, frost, wind and waves, all of which are helped by gravity. Decomposition is the breakdown of mineral particles into new compounds by the action of chemical agents, such as the acids in the air and in rain and river water. By all these processes a covering layer of weathered rock is formed on a land surface ; as parts of this are continually being removed, fresh material comes under the influence of weathering. This chapter reviews some of the distinctive results of denudation and deposition produced by the various geological agents, and their bearing on the work of the engineer.

WEATHERING BY ATMOSPHERIC AGENTS

1. **Rain.** The mechanical action of rain consists mainly in the washing of loose particles of soil and rock to lower levels, a phenomenon known as *rain-wash* ; it is the means by which rivers receive much of the sediment they carry in suspension. The process is a slow one, but it is continually

1

in operation. The denuding effects of heavy showers and rain-storms may be very severe, especially in regions where a covering of vegetation is lacking. Wash-outs resulting from cloud-bursts and heavy storms cut gullies in the surface of the ground, some of considerable size, and may cause great damage by the destruction of roads and live stock. Such gullies are common in tropical and sub-tropical countries, such as South Africa. Heavy rains also promote landslides (p. 22) under certain geological conditions. Rain denudation is most effective in tropical climates.

Vegetation protects the ground from the immediate disintegrating effects of rainfall, and the clearing of wooded areas has been followed in many cases by considerable denudation of the bare ground surface. If this proceeds for a length of time, the entire covering of soil may be removed and the ground rendered useless for cultivation. (Soil erosion is discussed on p. 6.) On the other hand, where ground covered with dense vegetation is subject to sub-tropical rainfall, deep zones of weathered rock may be formed, in some cases, extending to more than 200 feet below the surface. Instances are quoted on pp. 300 and 319.

In areas of thick soil with embedded boulders, a structure produced by rain denudation is the " earth pillar," a more or less slender column of soil capped by a stone or boulder which has preserved the material below it from being washed away. Groups of earth pillars are developed on valley slopes from earthy or clayey deposits containing boulders, as in parts of Scotland, the Tyrol, and elsewhere. In soft, easily denuded formations of this kind the pillars stand for a time after intervening material has been removed by the action of rain. Deposits of loose volcanic ash have been carved into earth pillars in Turkey (Anatolia), with volcanic bombs serving as cap-stones.

Mud-flows may be formed where rain, soaking into an upland area of deep soil over a long time, has built up a high water-content in the soil. The unstable, waterlogged mass becomes mobile when sufficient pressure is developed to burst the lateral restraint at a weak point, and then moves down slopes as a mud-flow. It may displace buildings and lines of transport, before coming to rest at a lower level. In some instances valleys have been temporarily blocked by mud-flows, leading to flooding.

The chemical weathering effects of rain are seen in its solvent action on some rocks, notably limestones ; the process depends on the presence of feeble acids, derived from gases such as CO_2 and SO_2, which are present in the air in small quantities and which enter into solution in rain-water. An economic aspect of chemical weathering, discussed in a later chapter (p. 139), is the decay of building stones, especially under the atmospheric conditions which prevail in cities, where a much higher content of impurities is present in the air than in country districts.

While other rocks are susceptible in some small degree to the solvent action of rain-water, limestones frequently show marked solution effects. The calcium carbonate of the limestone is dissolved by rain-water containing carbon dioxide, and is held in solution as calcium bicarbonate, thus :

$$CaCO_3 + H_2O + CO_2 \rightarrow Ca(HCO_3)_2.$$

The surface of the Chalk (an earthy limestone), for example, commonly holds solution hollows and elongated channels or " pipes," which are filled with sand or clay from overlying deposits (Plate IVb). The sands or other sediments have collapsed into the hollows as these were formed by solution. In bare limestone districts, such as areas of the Carboniferous Limestone of Lancashire and Yorkshire, the surface of the rock is channelled by " runlets " along which rain has trickled, and presents a very irregular appearance. Joints in the rocks are widened by solution as the rain passes down over their walls, and are then known as *grikes* ; the widening, of joints (especially where vertical joints intersect) leads to the formation of *swallow holes*, rough shafts which may communicate downwards with underground caverns, also formed by solution aided by the fall of loosened blocks of limestone. Gaping Ghyll, on the slopes of Ingleborough in Yorkshire, is a well-known swallow hole with a depth of 365 feet, leading to a cavern system below.

The circulation of such water underground helps to extend caverns and channels, particularly in hard limestone formations ; streams which once flowed on the surface now flow along bedding planes and joints below ground. The Cheddar Caves of the Mendips are a good example out of many which might be given, and Cheddar Gorge itself, 420 feet deep at one point, is thought to have been a cavern eroded by an underground stream and now exposed by the collapse of its roof. As water, charged with calcium bicarbonate, trickles over the walls and drips from the roofs of caves, part of each drop evaporates and calcium carbonate is slowly re-deposited through loss of carbon dioxide from solution. In this way masses of *stalactite*, hanging from the roof or coating the walls of a cave, are formed, sometimes making beautiful slender columns where they have become united with *stalagmites* which have been slowly built up from the floor of the cave, on to which water has dripped over a long period of time. Sheet-stalactite coats the walls of many caverns.

2. **Frost.** In cold climates, the action of frost breaks off angular fragments from exposed rock surfaces, a process sometimes referred to as the operation of the " ice wedge." It is this which produces the serrated appearance in a high mountain sky-line, and aids in the formation of screes on mountain slopes. Water enters rocks along pores, cracks, and fissures ; on freezing it expands and occupies about 10 per cent greater volume, exerting a pressure of about 2000 pounds per square inch during the freezing process, which is therefore like a miniature blasting action, and brings about the disintegration of the rock. The loosened particles fall from the mass and accumulate as heaps of *scree* or *talus* at lower levels, and this material may later be consolidated into a deposit known as *breccia.* By the removal of the fragments the surface of the rock is left open to further frost action, and so the process goes on. Some of the most famous screes in England are those in the Lake District, along the eastern side of Wastwater, where the mountain slopes fall steeply to the water's edge. Joints and cleavage planes in rocks assist the action of frost and to some extent control the shape of the fragments produced.

The term *permafrost* [1] is used to denote perennially frozen ground; conditions of this kind at the present day are found within the Arctic Circle, in general, but extend in places well south of it, and sporadic areas may occur as far south as 60° N. It is estimated that one-fifth of the earth's land surface is permanently frozen. Permafrost forms an impervious layer in the ground just below the surface, and may attain a thickness of hundreds of feet; over 1000 feet has been reported from boreholes in Alaska and Spitsbergen. Permafrost requires a cold climate with a mean annual air temperature of about 30° F. for its formation and maintenance. The frozen ground conditions are primarily due to the loss of heat from the surface exceeding the amount received from solar radiation. In the Arctic, for example, the period of summer warming is short, and for many months of each year heat is dissipated to the atmosphere.

The upper limit of continuous permafrost in the soil is generally between a few inches and two feet from the surface, but well-drained coarse-grained soils may thaw annually to a depth of 4 to 6 feet during the milder season. The thawing of near-surface soils means the release of large volumes of water within their mass, and this water cannot drain away through the still frozen ground below. The surface soil then becomes a very wet mud which can flow readily down slopes, even slopes of 3° or less, because of its high water content. It is known as the *active layer*. The amount of material involved in these movements is large and movement is comparatively rapid. A landscape under such conditions is reduced to long smooth slopes and gently rounded forms.

The frozen ground may contain much ice, especially where the soil texture is of fine grain and poorly drained, the ice occurring as thin films, grains, veinlets, vertical wedge-shaped masses, layers, and irregular masses of all sizes. Some kinds of ground contain little or no ice (dry permafrost). Unfrozen zones within perennially frozen ground may occur near the surface, and may mark permeable water-bearing layers or indicate past climatic fluctuations.

Frost-heaving occurs when the freezing of the soil results in the formation of layers of segregated ice at various depths.[2] Each lens of ice is separated from the next by a layer of soil, whose water content freezes solid. The ice lenses vary in thickness from a fraction of an inch to a foot or more. The total heave of the soil surface is approximately equal to the total thickness of all the ice lenses.

Many engineering problems arise in areas of permafrost, in connection with foundations and in road construction and maintenance, as in Alaska; the disposal of sewage from large camps is difficult and contamination of surface water supplies may easily occur. Normal percolation of water downwards from the surface is prevented by the impervious frozen layer, and a concentration of organic acids and mineral salts in solution is built up in the shallow depth of soil above it.

In building on permanently frozen ground it is generally necessary to

---

[1] Due to S. W. Muller (1945. U.S.G.S. Spec. Report).
[2] W. H. Ward in *Journ. of Glaciology*, Vol. 1, No. 2, 1947, p. 80.

anchor the structures in the deeper (non-active) layers. Removal of swamps, such as occurred on stretches of the Alaska Highway, only resulted in the formation of a deeper active zone, because the swamp-layer of matted decayed vegetation formed a good insulation against frost. Two kinds of construction methods are used in permafrost areas, according to Trask (reference on p. 144) : in one, the " passive method," the frozen-ground conditions are left undisturbed and the undersides of structures are provided with additional insulation, so that heat from the structure will not cause thawing of the underlying ground ; in the other, the " active method," the frozen ground is thawed prior to construction and is kept thawed (or removed), and materials used which are not subject to heaving and settling as a result of frost action. A preliminary examination is necessary to decide which procedure should be used in given conditions.

Permafrost has been responsible for the preservation of many fossils, including complete mammals, such as the mammoths unearthed at Siberian localities.

3. **Wind.** Wind is one of the two natural agents which transport rock material against gravity, and its denuding action is seen most prominently in regions which have a desert climate. As it blows over weathered surfaces it removes small loose particles of dry and decayed rock, both in the deserts and in more temperate climates. In desert areas the particles are carried along near the ground in large numbers, giving rise to repeated dust-storms. The grains may be driven against rock surfaces standing above the level of the desert, and then act as an abrading sand-blast. Rocks are smoothed and worn by the wind-blown sand and sharp corners are rounded. Ancient monuments, as in Egypt, as well as natural rock-faces, show the effects of centuries of battering by wind-blown sand; soft bands of rock have become more deeply etched than the harder layers. Vertical rock-faces are under-cut by eddying sand near the ground and left with their upper part over-hanging ; where the wind blows from several directions in turn, stacks of rock may be eroded so that their base is narrower than their top. The blown grains accumulate in suitable situations to form sand dunes. Abrasion by a sand-blast is used in commercial processes for frosting glass, and for roughening a metal finish.

Evidences of wind action in an earlier geological age are sometimes seen, as at Mountsorrel near Leicester, where granite is covered by Triassic red marl ; when excavated, the surface of the granite was found to be smoothed and to show unmistakable signs of wind erosion, pointing to a former desert climate in England. In making this deduction we are interpreting past events in terms of processes seen at work today ; on this principle (Hutton's " uniformitarianism," 1795) events recorded in the rocks can be understood by reference to the present activity of geological agents in different places and climates.

Wind-blown (eolian) grains become worn down to well-rounded, nearly spherical forms with frosted surfaces, and from their shape are sometimes called " millet seed " grains. This rounding is more perfect than in the case of water-worn sand, and the grains are also well graded (i.e. nearly of a uniform size), since wind of a given velocity cannot move particles larger than a particular diameter. From Fig. 1, particles of 1 mm. diameter would need a wind velocity of 8 metres/sec. to move them; an average wind of say 4 metres/sec. would lift grains up to about 0·35 mm. diameter, and most wind-blown grains of the deserts are between 0·15 and 0·3 mm. Wind also exerts a winnowing action : the finer particles of dust are separated from the sand and carried over larger distances, to be deposited far away from their source (see *loess*, below).

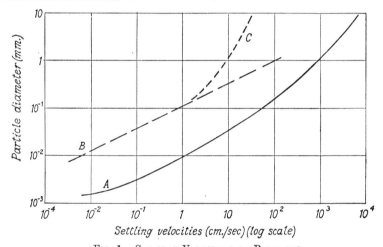

Settling velocities (cm./sec) (log scale)

Fig. 1.—Settling Velocities of Particles

in air (*A*) and water (*B*, Stokes' Law). For particles larger than $\frac{1}{10}$ mm. curve *C* gives observed velocities.

The sand is swept along until it accumulates against obstacles to form dunes. Pebbles and boulders lying on the hard floor of a desert and not lifted by the wind become smoothed and faceted by exposure to sand-storms, and frequently present three-cornered shapes, whence they are known as *dreikanter*. The surface of a desert may be worn down by the wind until a level is reached where water is present in the rocks (ground-water, p. 258). Many hollows in which *oases* are situated have been eroded down to the level of the water-table. The wet sand is the lower limit of wind action, as in the deep depressions of the Egyptian desert (p. 8).

Lines of communication may be seriously affected by wind-blown sand in arid countries. To avoid the accumulation of sand alongside railway embankments, as in the Sudan, culverts can be constructed to allow for easy passage of the wind and its load of sediment. Perhaps the most serious of all the damage caused by the action of wind is the removal of vast quantities of dry soil in many regions of the world. The " Dust Bowl " areas of Kansas and Nebraska provide an example of widespread *soil erosion* in a district of low rainfall. A century ago, this region of the Great Plains of America, between the Missouri River and the Rocky Mountains, was a short grass country supporting large herds of buffalo. Settlers used the country as a cattle-belt, and later (during the 1914–18 war) ploughed up large areas for wheat, obtaining big crops from the fertile soil. Over-cultivation developed, after repeated ploughing, and trees were cut down and swamps drained. After about twenty years the soil had become exhausted ; a series of droughts followed, and the wind began to scatter the loose dusty soil, reducing vast areas to desert. The district became a barren, wind-eroded waste, bare of vegetation and useless for cultivation until sufficient time had elapsed for new soil to be formed. Measures to promote the formation of soil were put in hand, and have slowly taken effect, and much of the area is again yielding crops.

Other instances of soil erosion have occurred, for example, in Kenya and Nigeria, largely through the overstocking of sparse grasslands with cattle and sheep, which is another contributory cause of erosion. Depletion of the scanty cover of grass soon follows and erosion of the soil begins.

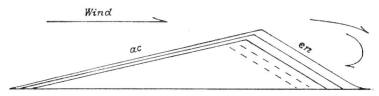

FIG. 1A.—STRUCTURE OF A SAND DUNE.

ac = accretion layer, *en* = encroachment layer ; broken lines indicate successive positions of sand-slopes.

On a minor scale, soil erosion or " blowing " has affected light soils in East Anglia.

Deposits formed by the action of wind include (i) the coastal sand-hills (or dunes) of temperate regions; (ii) desert dunes, such as *barchans* (crescentic dunes) and *seifs* (ridge dunes), and the larger sand accumulations of desert areas (e.g. the Sand Sea of the Egyptian Desert) ; (iii) *loess*.

(i) Mounds of blown sand, or *dunes*, are piled up by the wind in certain coastal regions of more humid climate as well as in desert countries. The western coasts of Europe, for example, are liable to dune formation because of the prevailing south-west wind. Accumulations of blown sand occur on the East Anglian coast and in other parts of Britain. The dunes are not stationary, but move continually and may overwhelm land areas ; stages in the advance of a sand-dune in relation to the direction of the prevailing wind are shown in Fig. 1A. Sand is blown from the back of the dune over the crest and dropped on the leeward slope at its natural angle of repose of some 30° to 35°. The dune thus migrates in the direction of the prevailing wind until arrested by some obstruction.

Evidence for the movement of coastal dunes in England is provided by old records, as at Eccles, on the coast of Norfolk. The church here was almost completely buried by sand in 1839 ; twenty-three years later the tower was uncovered as the dunes moved inland, and later the founda-tions of the tower were seen on the shore, the line of dunes having advanced still farther. The rate of movement can be estimated in this instance at about 3 feet per year ; it varies in different localities and at times may be rapid enough to warrant steps being taken to arrest the process, if valuable land areas are threatened. The stabilization of coastal dunes is frequently effected by the planting of marram grass, or rice grass, the roots of which bind the surface sand and so prevent its removal by wind. Afforestation is a larger-scale method of dealing with the same problem, as, for example, the planting of pines at Culbin on the Moray Firth ; in the Culbin area, great storms at the end of the 17th century resulted in a large tract of farmland and houses being completely buried by advancing sand. This land has now been largely reclaimed. In Wallasey, Cheshire, rubbish was dumped on an area of blown sand ; the whole became stablized in a short time and provided land for a recreation ground.

(ii) *Barchan* dunes in desert regions have crescentic shapes in plan, and are found in areas where the wind blows from a nearly constant direction, with a limited supply of sand. They are mounds of sand, up to about 100 feet in height and several times as wide, with the horns of the crescent pointing forward in the direction of the wind. Groups or colonies of barchans move slowly forward across the rocky floor of the desert where the wind and supply of sand are constant. They are found in desert areas of California, in the Libyan desert, and elsewhere.

Most dunes have a structure composed of inclined layers of sand (Fig. 1A), known as *dune-bedding*. Sand blown on to the windward slopes is compacted more than that on the leeward side, giving accretion layers (*ac*). It accumulates at a maximum rate on the summit of the dune ; the upper part of the leeward slope becomes too steep and unstable, and the sand there shears along a *slip-plane* inclined at an angle of a little over 30 degrees. More sand from the windward builds up, until another slip-plane is formed just ahead of the first, and the process continues. Each inclined layer of sand between two slip-planes is called an encroachment layer (*en* in Fig. 1A), and the dune moves forward by the addition of successive layers. Dune-bedding may be seen in sandstones formed in past geological ages, as at the Ballochmyle quarries in Ayrshire (Plate IXB), or in the Nubian Sandstone of North Africa ; the eolian grains in these rocks are rounded and frosted.[1]

The larger ridge dunes, or *seifs*, have the form of long ridges of coarser sand, several hundred feet high, which are surmounted by crests of finer sand at regular intervals. Their formation has been discussed by R. A. Bagnold.[2] The ridges extend in straight lines for great distances, sometimes a hundred miles or more, as in the region south-east of the great Qattara Depression of North Africa (west of Cairo, on the northern margin of the Sahara). The Qattara, one of a group of deep depressions excavated by wind action, lies in places at — 420 feet O.D., the local level of the water-

[1] Model dunes have been made in a wind-tunnel, and the different packings and porosity of the sand on windward and leeward slopes measured. (Unpublished thesis by J. A. Morton, Birmingham, 1964).

[2] A full account of Bagnold's researches is given in " The Physics of Blown Sand and Desert Dunes " (Methuen, 1941).

table, and contains salt-marshes at that level. The predominant winds blow from the north-north-west, and part of the material removed from the depressions has contributed to the ridge dunes and other great sand accumulations to the south. The flat floor of the desert is seen between the ridges. It has been estimated that the Sahara desert is advancing southward at the rate of a kilometre a year.

(iii) The wind-blown deposit known as *loess*, a fine calcareous clay or loam, extends from Central Europe through Russia into Asia and covers large areas in China, where it reaches its greatest thickness. It represents the finer particles which are blown from the deserts to distant regions, as mentioned above. Thus the deserts of North Africa have contributed much of this material to Europe and the Russian steppes. Generally of buff colour, it is darkened by mixture with vegetable matter, and in this condition forms the " black earth " of Russia. Loess is a porous clay or loam, and is often traversed by a network of narrow tubes which once enclosed the roots of grasses, which during growth have bound the particles of dust and silt in their grip. It resists weathering and stands in steep, sometimes vertical cliffs where, for example, it has been dissected by the action of streams.

4. Insolation. When a rock-surface is exposed to a considerable daily range of temperature, as in arid and semi-arid regions, the expansion which occurs during the day and the contraction at night, constantly repeated, have a weakening effect on the texture of the rock over a period of time. The outer heated layers tend to pull away from the cooler rock underneath, a process known as *exfoliation*. This is particularly noticeable on surfaces which face south (in the northern hemisphere), since they are subjected to the hot rays of the sun to a greater degree than would be the case for any other direction, and flakes and slabs are split off. Strain is also set up in a rock by the unequal expansion and contraction of its mineral constituents, and its texture is loosened. A more homogeneous rock, made of one kind of mineral, would not be at the same disadvantage in this respect. Under natural conditions, insolation of rock-faces results in the opening of many small cracks (of hair-like fineness) into which water enters, and so both the decomposition of the rock and its disintegration by the help of frost are promoted. This kind of weathering is prominent in climates where high day and low night temperatures are prevalent ; it may also be observed to a lesser degree in more temperate lands.

WEATHERING BY ORGANIC AGENTS

Effects which are small in themselves, but noticeable in the aggregate, are due to plants and animals. Plants retain moisture, and any rock-surface on which they grow is kept damp, thus aiding the solvent action of the water. The chemical decay of rock is also promoted by the formation of vegetable humus, an organic product of the decay of plants, which is assisted by the action of bacteria and fungi ; thus organic acids are added to percolating rain-water and increase its solvent power. The mechanical break-up of rock is helped by the roots of plants, which penetrate into cracks

G.E.— B

and crevices and tend to wedge apart the rock. The general result of these processes is the production of a surface cover of *soil*, which grades down through broken, partly decomposed rock mixed with soil (the *subsoil*), into the solid rock at no great depth (Plate Ib). Earth-worms and other burrowing animals bring to the surface large quantities of finely divided soil, which is gradually removed by transporting agents, such as rain-wash, running water, and wind. The transition from soil through subsoil to rock varies in thickness from a few inches (as on Chalk ground) to about 3 feet. Much more deeply weathered soils occur in sub-tropical countries which have a high rainfall (p. 2).

THE WORK OF RIVERS

Rivers are active agents of erosion, widening and deepening their valleys during the course of their development; their activities are enhanced in times of flood. They carry much material in suspension and re-deposit some part of it farther downstream, the rest being transported to the sea ; some matter goes into solution in the river water and ultimately helps to increase the salinity of the oceans. The energy which is imparted to sediment moved by the stream, the finer particles in suspension and the coarser (including boulders) rolled along the bed during floods, performs work by abrading the channel of the river.

The initiation of a drainage system takes place when, for example, a new land surface has been uplifted from beneath the sea, and youthful streams begin to flow over it and carve their valleys. Their courses are mainly directed by the general slope of the surface but are also controlled by any irregularities which it possesses. In the majority of cases present-day valleys have been cut by the streams which occupy them, except in so far as they have been modified by the action of ice or other agents. Stages of *youth, maturity*, and *old age* may be distinguished in the history of a river, and topographical forms characteristic of these stages may be recognized in modern landscapes. Thus there is the steep-sided valley of the youthful stream ; the broader valley and deeply dissected landscape of the more mature river system ; and the flat, meandering course of a stream in old age.

Valley Erosion. Young streams cut gorges in hard rocks and V-shaped valleys in softer rocks (profile 1, Fig. 2a), and are characteristic of many mountainous regions. Debris falls from the valley sides as it is loosened by rain and frost, to be carried away by the stream and assist in its work of abrasion. Rain-wash and soil-creep (p. 24) also contribute much material from the slopes ; this is especially the case in the more mature stages of valley development, when a mantle of soil has been formed on the land surface. Gradually as the headwaters of a river cut back into the land, its valley is deepened and widened into a broader V, and small scree-slopes form at the bottom of the valley sides (the flatter inner slopes of profile 2). The deepening and widening, if uninterrupted, continue as shown by profiles 3 and 4 in the figure, until the stage of maturity is reached, when the maximum topographical relief (i.e. difference in height between the valleys and the intervening ridges) has been produced. Later, as denudation reduces the ridges and the river enters its old age, the valley comes to have a wide, flat floor over which the river follows a winding course ; the upper slopes are convex (profile 5), and depth of relief becomes less. Such a sequence would be followed by a river in a temperate climate. Under other conditions of valley development, as in a drier climate, the slopes are cut back so that they keep their steep gradients, and the ridges between valleys are sharp instead of flat-topped.

The shape of a valley also depends on the nature of the rocks in which it is excavated. The forms illustrated in Fig. 2a would be developed in rocks

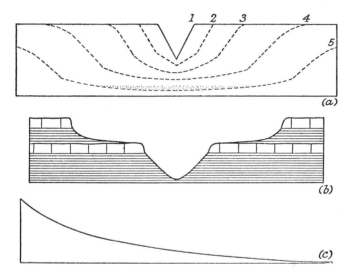

FIG. 2.—VALLEY PROFILES.

(a) Successive valley profiles during widening. (b) Valley eroded in hard and soft beds. (c) Profile along the course of a mature (graded) river. The horizontal line is base-level.

of uniform character throughout. When alternate hard and soft layers are present, erosion of the softer rock is more rapid than of the harder, and terraced slopes are developed as shown in Fig. 2b. If the rock layers are inclined and the river flows parallel to their upturned edges, instead of across them, the land surface will be carved into long hollows or vales along the softer beds, separated by ridges of harder rock which form escarpments (see Fig. 60, p. 173).

Grading and Rejuvenation. The profile taken *along* the course of a river also changes during the stream's evolution. For a young stream, actively eroding, this profile is an irregular curve, which is steeper where the river crosses more resistant rocks and perhaps forms rapids or waterfalls, and flatter where it flows over more easily eroded material. If left undisturbed by earth-movements (e.g., uplift) or other factors causing change, the river continues to reduce irregularities of gradient and to smooth out its bed until in maturity it is said to be *graded*. Its longitudinal profile is then independent of the kind of rock over which it passes, and tends towards a smooth curve (Fig. 2c) of the type expressed by the equation :

$$y = a - k.\log (p - x),$$

where y is the height of a point above datum, x its distance from the river's mouth, p the total length of the stream, and a and k are constants. For the upper course of the River Mole in Surrey, it has been shown that a curve closely fitting the longitudinal profile of the river is given by the above formula when $a = 241.5$ and $k = 65$, y being measured in feet and x and p in miles.[1] It has also been found that similar curves fit the rivers Towy,[2] Dart, and Otter, and many others.

The *base-level* of a river is the level of the sea or lake into which it discharges, for clearly it cannot cut down below this. For tributaries, base-level is the level of the main stream at their various points of entry, and as this changes in the course of time the tributaries are constantly attempting to adjust their grade to new levels. The cutting power of a river which has reached maturity or old age may, however, be revived by uplift or tilting of the land, by recession of the coast-line due to marine erosion (p. 29), or by other causes, any of which will give the stream a new fall to the sea. It begins cutting back again and lowering its bed by the newly acquired energy, and is said to be *rejuvenated*. Owing to such interruptions in their cycle of activity, not all streams become completely graded.

A good example of rejuvenation, probably due to uplift, is to be seen in the valley of the River Greta near Ingleton in Yorkshire. In its upper course this stream has a wide, mature valley ; but about $1\frac{1}{4}$ miles above Ingleton the river begins to plunge downwards in a series of waterfalls, cutting into hard rocks and displaying the energy of youth in striking contrast to the placid flow of middle age which is evident only a short distance upstream. Below Ingleton the river again assumes a meandering course.

As a river grows older it remains vigorous only in its upper reaches, where the flow is swiftest and the gradient steepest (Fig. 2c). In its lower course the speed and carrying power are reduced, and the river begins to meander from side to side of its valley. It becomes subject to seasonal floods, and under these conditions much sediment in suspension is deposited, as described later.

Waterfalls and Gorges. Waterfalls and rapids are formed where a stream in a youthful stage flows over rocks of different hardness. A hard layer is worn away less rapidly than a soft, with the result that a river's gradient is increased where it crosses a ledge of harder rock ; softer material below the resistant layer is undercut by the eddying and splashing of the water, leaving an overhanging ledge over which the stream falls (Fig. 3). As the overhang becomes greater than the strength of the rock can support, the ledge breaks away and the fall gradually recedes upstream. The Whin

---

[1] J. F. N. Green and others, " The River Mole," *Proc. Geologists' Association.* Vol. 45, 1934, pp. 35–69.

[2] O. T. Jones, " The Upper Towy Drainage System," *Q.J.G.S.*, Vol. lxxx, 1924, pp. 568–609.

Sill, in the north of England, is a layer of jointed igneous rock which frequently gives rise to waterfalls in this way, two well-known falls being High Force in Teesdale and High Cup Nick in Westmorland.

At Niagara on the Canada–U.S.A. border, the waters of Lake Erie flow down to Lake Ontario and cross a hard limestone formation (the Niagara Limestone), which lies above softer rocks ; here the river makes the world-famous falls with a drop of 180 feet. The limestone forms a broad ledge which is undercut by the river, and the falls retreat upstream as the ledge collapses from time to time. Below the falls the river flows through a gorge 7 miles long. In 63 years their position changed by 265 feet, and at this rate the time taken to erode the gorge has been about 9000 years— i.e. the gorge has been formed since the end of the Pleistocene glaciation (p. 236). The rate of recession of the falls is now reduced to 12 or 15 inches per year, because much energy is taken from the river at this point for hydro-electric power generation, affording a good example of the effect of man's interference with natural agents. The 360-feet high Victoria Falls on the Zambesi River, Rhodesia, are situated at a point where the river

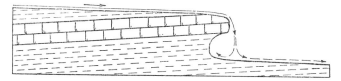

FIG. 3.—WATERFALL FORMED OVER A HARD STRATUM.
The softer beds beneath are undercut, leaving an overhanging ledge.

leaves the gently undulating surface of a lava plateau and plunges into a youthful gorge. This gorge is cut in basaltic lavas and has been eroded along lines of weakness formed by intersecting joint and fracture planes, which cause it to have a pronounced zig-zag course.

Hollows, known as *pot-holes*, may be worn in the hard rock of a river-bed by the motion of pebbles which are swirled round by eddies, especially in the neighbourhood of waterfalls. Such a water-worn rock surface is easily recognized, and if observed near but above an existing stream, it marks a former course at a higher level.

Gorges are cut by young streams which erode rapidly downwards ; especially in areas of low rainfall, weathering of the sides of the gorge takes place only slowly during its formation. In some instances, uplift of the area has helped to produce a deep gorge by maintaining the fall of the stream (see also p. 167). Where prominent joint directions or other lines of weakness in the rocks are present, they help to control the shape of the gorge. If the rock is sufficiently strong it will stand with steep or vertical walls ; with a weaker or softer rock the gorge will become widened out after a time, particularly if erosion is aided by solution, as in the case of Dovedale, Derbyshire, a gorge cut in the Carboniferous Limestone.

The Grand Canyon of the Colorado, 300 miles long and with a maximum depth of 6000 feet, is a very large erosional feature which has been formed in relatively soft rocks by a young river flowing from the Rockies, on entering an arid region. The river was rejuvenated by a geologically recent uplift, and rapid downward erosion was probably assisted by a rising land surface. The upper part of the Canyon has become widened out, though denudation of its walls by atmospheric agents has proceeded slowly on account of the arid climatic conditions and low rainfall prevailing. At the bottom of the Canyon, a steep-sided inner gorge some 1000 feet deep has been cut in harder, older crystalline rocks.

River Capture. It sometimes happens that a river which is cutting back vigorously in an easily eroded formation may approach the course of a neighbouring stream, and meet and divert the headwaters of the latter into its own channel. This process is known as *river capture*; the stream which has lost its headwaters is said to be beheaded, and dwindles in size until it has become obviously too small for the valley in which it flows, and is called a " misfit." An example is provided by the River Blackwater near Farnham, Surrey, a tributary of the Thames. The course of this now small stream once extended much farther to the south-west, whence it transported distinctive gravels containing chert, to deposit them north of the gap in the Chalk ridge at Farnham. The source rocks of the gravels prove the former extent of the river. An eastward flowing stream, the Wey, cutting back rapidly from Godalming in soft strata, tapped the upper reaches of the Blackwater and diverted the flow into its own channel. The point of the capture is marked by a right-angle bend which the river makes just east of Farnham. In north-east England the River Ouse, flowing south into the Humber, has effected successive captures of the Nidd, Ure, and Swale rivers which originally flowed east into the North Sea.

Meanders. When a river has cut down nearly to base-level it flows more slowly with a reduced gradient and begins to swing from side to side of its valley. The energy imparted to the load of sediment which it carries is expended in the widening of the valley by lateral erosion, and the course of the river develops a series of big looped curves called *meanders* (Fig. 4a). The length of a loop, when fully formed, is about sixteen times the width of the stream. On the concave side of a curve the bank is undercut and eroded, while detritus is deposited on the convex side, with the formation of banks of sand and gravel (Fig. 4b). There is evidence to show that the flow of a stream under these conditions oscillates from side to side of its channel, as indicated by the arrows in the figure ; also, the water near the stream bed flows obliquely under that nearer the surface, and one side of the bed may be much deeper than the other owing to the scouring effect of the bed current.

As the meanders progress, a *flood-plain* or *alluvial flat* is eventually developed (stage 4, Fig. 4a), and the river flows through its own deposits in the widened valley. When the meanders reach their full size they tend to shift bodily downstream, cutting into the sand and gravel of the flood-plain and rebuilding it behind them as they move forward. The river thus works in time over a large area of land, re-sorting its earlier deposits. A comparison of old and new maps of the same river will often show this shifting and change in shape of the meanders.

If a river in the meandering stage breaks through the neck of land at the end of one of the loops, as at f in Fig. 4b, and thus shortens its course, it will leave a crescent-shaped lake called an " ox-bow " or " mortlake " in the abandoned meander. Examples may be seen from a topographic map of the River Wye, e.g. near Ross, Herefordshire, where contours show the

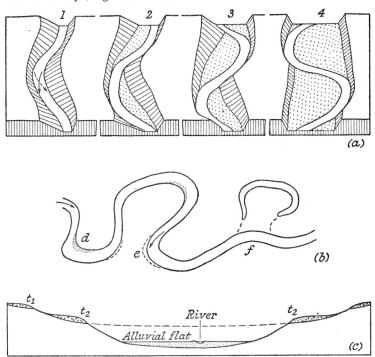

FIG. 4.—MEANDERS AND RIVER TERRACES.

(a) Stages in the widening of a valley floor and development of meanders (after Cotton).
(b) Fully developed meanders, showing deposition (d) and erosion (e) at bends. (c) Section across a valley to show alluvial flat and older river terrace deposits at $t_1 t_2$.

form of the old channel. The Wye is also remarkable in possessing a meandering course although the river flows in a gorge-like valley below Kerne Bridge. This phenomenon, known as *incised meanders*, is due to the rejuvenation of the river after it had reached a meandering stage in an earlier drainage system. Fresh energy imparted to the stream enabled it to cut downwards once more and so carve out a gorge along the great loops of its old channel.

Two other rivers which have developed meanders are the Thames and the Seine, and in both cases large parts of their lower courses have now been trained between walls and embankments, thus preventing further changes in position. The Mississippi is discussed briefly on p. 20.

The chief factors which control the formation of meanders are a low gradient and a moderate load of sediment. It has been demonstrated by means of models that if the gradient is increased beyond a limiting value, or if the load of sediment becomes too great, no meanders are developed.

River Deposits. The general term given to deposits laid down by rivers is *alluvium*, though this is often restricted to the finer material such as silt and mud, as distinct from gravels and larger fragments. The transporting power of a stream increases at the rate of the fifth or sixth power of its velocity. Thus, if the normal velocity is trebled, as may be the case after heavy rains, the carrying capacity is increased several hundred times. The result is seen in boulder-strewn torrent tracks in hill country. Large boulders which would not be moved under normal conditions of flow, are shifted with an intermittent motion by the stream in spate, and become partly rounded by the buffeting they receive. Large quantities of smaller boulders, gravel, and sand are also transported at such times, the coarser particles being rolled along on the stream bed and the finer carried in suspension. The principles underlying the transport of small particles by a current of water are utilized in the process of elutriation (see p. 121) for separating particles of different sizes in a sample of sediment.

Transported sediment is dropped by a stream whenever its velocity is checked. A river emerging from a mountain valley on to flatter ground, such as the edge of a plain, builds up a heap of detritus known as an *alluvial cone* where the change of gradient occurs. Since this pile of sediment affects the flow, the river changes its course and so the cone spreads outwards. Deposition at places along a river's course where the flow is locally slackened, as at bends, has been noted above in connection with a meandering stream. The material deposited is mainly sand and gravel, partly rounded during transport, the finer mud particles being carried on down to the sea. Owing to the cushioning effect of the water, particles are only partly rounded by impact ; they are less well-rounded than wind-blown sands.

In the lower course of a mature river the finer alluvium is spread out to form an *alluvial flat* (Fig. 4c) ; this is subject to periodic flooding, and a fresh layer of alluvium is deposited at each flood. The coarser particles are dropped nearest the stream, and gradually build up a bank or *levee* on each side of it, which is only overtopped by the water in time of flood. In some cases the formation of an alluvial flat may involve the burial of the lower slopes of the valley sides, and the alluvium then abuts directly on to the convex upper slopes. Such alluvial deposits may have a small thickness, but may go up to 30 feet or more ; they are very porous, and in excavations the zone of groundwater (p. 258) is met at small depths below the surface of the alluvium. Running sands may occur under these conditions.

The rapid variation in the nature of alluvial deposits is well illustrated by exposures in dock excavations in East London and at other places ; layers of mud, silt, and sometimes peat alternate and thin out in irregular fashion, and may fill hollows (wash-outs) which have been scoured out by floods in earlier deposits.

If a river, after having formed a flood plain of alluvium, is rejuvenated and cuts down its channel to lower levels, remnants of the earlier deposits may be left on the old valley slopes as *terraces* at different levels (Fig. 4c). Thus, in the valley of the River Thames three such terraces are found (see Fig. 102, p. 237), known as the Boyn Hill, Taplow, and Flood Plain terraces respectively the first two being named after localities near Maidenhead. Valuable deposits of gravel and sand which occur in these terraces are excavated on a large scale for supplies of aggregate and sand for concrete and mortar, as for example in Middlesex, around Ashford and Staines.

Alluvial mud may be used as one of the raw materials in the manufacture of cement, as on the River Medway and at Lewes in Sussex, where in both cases river mud is mixed with Chalk in the required proportions.

Drainage of pore-contained water from river-deposited sands and gravels may result when water is taken from wells sunk in the alluvium, and when proper replenishment by rainfall is prevented, as in a built-up area. This removal of the interstitial water causes a slight compaction of the deposit, leading to slow subsidence. In the London area, precise measurements of levels made over a period of 68 years (to 1932) revealed a fairly general subsidence, the maximum amount being nearly 7 inches at the Bank of England. Traverses across the area showed that the subsidence begins where the London Clay gives place at the surface to the gravels and sands which overlie it, and is greatest over the buried channels of old streams such as the Fleet and Walbrook, which were tributaries of the Thames at the time the deposits were laid down.[1] The Bank is built over the old deposits of the Walbrook. The compaction, although small in itself, could cause unequal settlement of large buildings erected on the alluvium and resulting strain on the structures ; this happened in the case of St. Paul's Cathedral, where extensive remedial measures were called for.

Current Bedding. Shallow-water deposits frequently show a structure known as *current-bedding* or " false bedding," which is contemporaneous with their deposition. Successive heaps of gravel or sand deposited by the sudden checking of a current lie one above another, as shown in Fig. 5a. A change in the direction or intensity of the current may wash away the upper part of these layers, and new material is laid down upon their truncated edges (Fig. 5b). Coarse and fine layers may be intercalated and the current-bedding preserved through a considerable thickness of deposit. After the sediment has been consolidated, the structures are seen in the resulting sandstone. The top or bottom of a current-bedded series of sediments is always indicated by the fact that the tops of the layers are truncated, while the bottoms are asymptotic to the floor on which they were deposited. Current-bedding by wind is also found in eolian sands (cf. dune-bedding, Fig. 1A).

Deltas. A river entering a body of still water, such as a lake or the sea, drops much of its load of sediment as its velocity is reduced, and in many cases forms a delta which is gradually built forward into the still water. Where a tidal estuary is present, however, no delta is formed but

---

[1] " The Subsidence of London," by Capt. T. E. Longfield, *Ordnance Survey Prof'l. Paper*, New Series No. 14, 1932.

sand- and mud-flats are laid down where the river's flow is checked by the tidal water ; a fresh-water channel, which may branch into a number of subsidiary channels, is scoured out through the deposits by the discharge of the river at low tide. Not only the coarser sandy sediment in suspension but also much of the finer muddy material settles near a shore-line, though some is carried farther out by weak currents. Settlement of the very fine particles of mud is promoted by flocculation (the aggregation of fine particles into clusters or flocks).

The building of a *delta* proceeds as sediment is deposited at a river's mouth ; the stream then subdivides and flows through the water on either

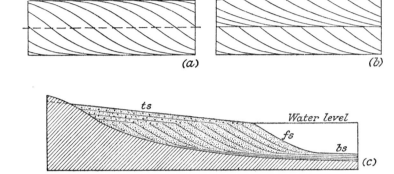

FIG. 5.—CURRENT-BEDDING AND DELTA DEPOSITS.

(*a*) Current-bedded deposits, the upper part of which is later washed away down to the broken line. (*b*) Further material laid down on the truncated edges of the lower deposits. (*c*) Section through a small lake delta ; *ts* = topset beds ; *fs* = foreset beds; *bs* = bottomset beds.

side of the obstacle which it has made. Further deposition of sediment takes place along these distributaries, and after further barriers have been formed the streams branch again. In this way, by repeated bifurcation and sedimentation, the deltaic deposits come to cover a large area which may have a roughly triangular shape (like the Greek letter Δ), as in the case of the Nile delta.

A section through the deposits of a typical small delta is given in Fig. 5*c* ; as each flood brings down its load of sediment the coarser material is dropped on the seaward side of the growing pile and comes to rest at its angle of repose in water, building up the sloping *foreset* beds. Observations show that their slope varies from about 12° to 32°, larger particles standing at the higher and smaller at lower angles. Ahead of the foreset beds and continuous with them, the finer material is deposited as the *bottomset* beds. As the delta is built forward, foreset deposits come to rest on earlier bottomset deposits, as shown in the figure. The upper surface of the delta is composed of gently sloping *topset* beds of coarse material, which are a continuation of the alluvial plain of the river and cover successive foreset deposits.

Large deltas, such as those of the Nile, Ganges, or Indus, which are over 100 miles across and have a large under-water extent beyond the present coast-lines, are thick lenses of sediment in which land-derived materials alternate with marine deposits.

The sediments of an ancient delta can be recognized in the sandstones of the Millstone Grit formation of Yorkshire, which were laid down by a large river discharging in a southerly direction (p. 214).

River Training and Flood Control. Engineering works in connection with rivers (other than impounding reservoirs) are mainly concerned with (a) the improvement of the tidal and non-tidal portions from the point of view of navigation, and (b) the control of floods. This is a large subject, of which the following outline may serve to indicate some of man's activities in modifying and controlling the processes of nature.

Of recent years, many investigations of the behaviour of rivers under varying conditions of discharge and load of sediment have been carried out by means of scale models. Pioneer work was done by Professor Osborne Reynolds at Manchester University where, from 1885 onwards, models of the estuary of the River Mersey were studied and their usefulness in reproducing natural conditions was established. Early models of the Seine and Mersey were also made by L. F. Vernon-Harcourt ; since that time numerous laboratories for similar researches have been established in Europe and America. In Britain, a model of the Severn estuary has been used by Professor A. H. Gibson at Manchester to examine the effects of the proposed tidal-power barrage across the Severn, and, among many others, a model of the Great Ouse and its outlet to the Wash to investigate problems of silting and scour.

Improvement of the lower course of a tidal river for navigation may be carried out in various ways according to the circumstances prevailing ; as, for example, by dredging to remove shoals and deepen the channel, or by the construction of training walls through an estuary to restrict the flow to a given channel, or by the use of low groynes to concentrate the flow in the low-water channel.

Deepening by dredging has been employed in the case of the rivers Clyde and Tyne, both of which were originally very small streams. The Clyde was at one time fordable 12 miles below Glasgow, with a shallow channel and many shoals. From about 1770, stone jetties were built out from the shores in the wider parts of the channel, thereby contracting it and securing greater scour and deeper water. By this means and by constant dredging the Clyde has been given a minimum depth of 24 feet at low water up to Glasgow Harbour, so that it is now navigable by large vessels, and Glasgow has grown from a small town to a great port. Between 1884 and 1890 (after the introduction of steam dredging), 35½ million cubic yards of deposit were removed from the river by dredging.[1] Similarly the Tyne, between Newcastle and the sea, has been deepened by dredging and regulated by groynes and training walls, so that there is now a minimum depth of 30 feet of water up to Northumberland Dock.

A river may be trained to occupy a certain channel either by longitudinal

[1] Quoted from " Tidal Rivers," by W. H. Wheeler (Longmans, 1893).

training walls or by short cross-groynes which keep the main current in the required course. This has the effect, in general, of concentrating the scouring effect of the current and keeping clear the channel. The River Mersey, for example, maintains a deep channel between training walls which run for several miles out into Liverpool Bay. Subsidiary channels can be blocked by walls built across them and the flow thus concentrated in the main stream. In general the height of the training works above low-water level is not more than is necessary to fix the channel, and the works then cause no hindrance to the ebb and flow of the tide.

Flood control, involving the regulation of flood waters so as to prevent large inundations of valuable land or property, is often a matter of considerable importance and no small difficulty. Conditions differ from one river to another, and the various methods employed include (*a*) dredging the channel to increase its cross-section ; (*b*) the building of levees or embankments along the course of the river so as to contain the flood water ;

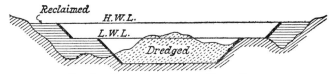

FIG. 6.—CROSS-SECTION OF A TIDAL RIVER.
An example showing training walls (heavy lines) and dredged channel. (After Vernon-Harcourt.)

(*c*) diversion or temporary storage of the flood water ; (*d*) shortening the course of the river to increase the gradient.

The application of some of these methods is illustrated by the works carried out in connection with the Great Ouse river, which are described below. An instance of shortening is provided by the new channel, $\frac{3}{4}$-mile long, which was cut across a loop of the Thames near Walton in 1935, to allow flood water from the River Wey to escape more readily and thus reduce the danger of flooding. Among the many large rivers which have, in the past, given rise to disastrous floods on a large scale is the Mississippi. Artificial banks were formerly constructed along its course and, after being breached and eroded at weak places almost every year, were successively heightened. Following the great inundations of 1927, which affected 18,000 square miles, the responsible authorities initiated a complete change of policy with respect to the river ; instead of seeking to maintain the existing tortuous channel of the Mississippi, it was decided to shorten its course by making artificial cut-offs across some of the bends, thereby providing for a more effective discharge. Twelve cut-off channels of this kind have shortened the river by 116 miles in a distance of 330 miles below its confluence with the Arkansas River, and flood levels have in consequence been lowered ; these works were part of a larger scheme for regulating the river.[1]

Floods of the Great Ouse. The flood problem of the River Ouse

[1] *Engineering News-Record*, Vol. 116, 1936, p. 269. "Straightening the Father of Waters," by G. R. Clemens.

where it flows through the Cambridgeshire and Norfolk fenlands before discharging into the tidal waters of the Wash, had become serious by about 1940. The fens around Ely are a sunken area, and water draining off them is pumped up into a system of artificial channels (drains) maintained at a level high enough to give gravity flow to the sea. The peat, silt, and clay forming the fens were deposited in geologically recent times, and shrinkage of these deposits through drainage and cultivation has resulted in a sinking

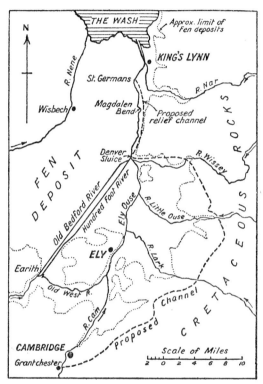

Fig. 7.—Map of Great Ouse Drainage Area (partly after Doran).

of the land surface; this sinking at present amounts to ¾-inch or more per annum. A post driven through 22 feet of peat into underlying clay at Denton Fen, Huntingdonshire, in 1848, with its top then level with the ground, had become exposed over its upper 11 feet by 1932; the depth of peat had thus been halved in the interval. River embankments built on this surface had, of course, sunk with it and have had to be constantly raised, so that in places they are over twice their original height; the necessary width required for further heightening of the banks was not everywhere available and at many points the limit had been reached in this matter.

The water from the upper Ouse catchment above Earith flows north through two artificial channels known as the Old Bedford River and the

New Bedford or Hundred Foot River, down to Denver Sluice, thus short-circuiting the course of the river past Ely (see Fig. 7). Below Denver the river is tidal. The above two channels have high banks on their east and west sides ; the area between them, some 5000 acres, is known as the Washlands and can store flood water when the sluice gates at its northern end are closed by the tide. The drainage from the Fens east of the Hundred Foot River, which is pumped into the high level system already mentioned, can also only be discharged at low tide, and in times of high flood dangerously high water levels occur upstream of Denver.

After the floods of 1937 and 1940, several schemes were put forward for remedying this state of affairs, particularly by reducing the silting in the tidal part of the channel below Denver. The proposal [1] which was adopted by the Great Ouse Catchment Board involved the cutting of a new relief channel about 11 miles long between Denver Sluice and a point downstream near King's Lynn, on the east side of the present river ; this channel would be used only in times of flood and would discharge when the tide was low, intermittent storage of flood water being provided for. The completed channel was opened in October 1959. In another part of the original proposal, tidal water would be impounded by a barrage constructed in the loop of the river known as Magdalen Bend, and used for scouring out the lower channel of the river into the Wash, thus removing silt deposited by incoming tides and preventing a reduction of the capacity of the natural channel. The effect of such a barrage was tested in the model mentioned on p. 19, and the scour was found to extend to the end of the existing training walls at the mouth of the river.

With the Fenland surface continuing to sink at its present rate, a further relief channel is being constructed (Fig. 7, the broken line east of Cambridge). This cut-off channel passes round the margin of the Fens, and will take water from the rivers Cam, Lark, Little Ouse, and Wissey northwards to Denver sluice. It is located on Cretaceous rocks, and is thus independent of the Fen deposits and the compaction of peats in them. The channel was completed as far as the R. Lark in November 1964. The Fenland deposits are discussed on p. 235.

LANDSLIDES

Movements of rock masses known as *landslides* or *landslips* (the two terms are here taken as synonymous), are caused by the direct or indirect action of gravity on unstable material. They are important factors in denudation, and frequently occur near a coast-line and help the sea in breaking down the cliffs. Landslides may be divided into two broad groups [2] according to the nature of the movement involved : (a) *Slides*, in which a surface of sliding is present, separating the moving mass from the stable ground ; and (b) *Flows*, in which there is no surface of sliding,

[1] Due to W. M. Griffith, described by W. E. Doran in *Geogr. Journ.*, April 1941, Vol. xcvii, p. 217.

[2] After the grouping of C. F. S. Sharpe, " Landslides and Related Phenomena ", New York. 1938

but movement takes place by continuous deformation; the motion is generally less rapid than in the case of slides, and may be very slow indeed, but there are transitions from one group to the other.

(a) Included in the first group is the common kind of landslide in which movement takes place on inclined bedding planes (see p. 37 for definition of bedding plane). Beds of rock, or strata, which lie one on another, may, in a line of cliffs, have a slope down to seaward; they are then said to *dip* seaward (Fig. 8a), and are prone to slipping, especially when a bed through which water can percolate rests on a layer of clay, as shown in the figure. The clay, lubricated by rain which has percolated through the overlying strata, or by springs, acts as a surface of sliding when it is wet, and masses of rock break away from the cliff and move down the inclined

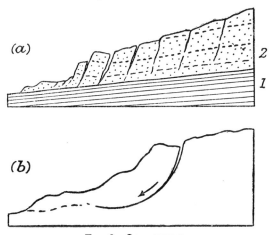

FIG. 8.—LANDSLIDES.

(a) Sketch-section showing a lubricated stratum (1) on which slipping of overlying beds (2 has taken place. (b) Rotational slip in clay.

clay surface under the action of gravity. This is seen, for example, at Ventnor and other localities in the Isle of Wight, where constantly occurring falls of cliff are due to the Chalk slipping over the Gault Clay. At Rousdon, near Seaton, Devon, the Lias Clay has led to similar landslide conditions. Ground which has moved in this manner has a very characteristic tumbled appearance (Plate Ia).

Other examples of slides are the rock-falls from cliffs, where masses break off along joints and bedding planes and fall mainly vertically; and the curved *slips*, as they are usually called, which are very common in clays and unconsolidated materials and are found where banks or cliffs are undercut by a river or the sea, or in railway and road cuttings where excavation has created conditions leading to slipping (Fig. 8b and Plate XVI). Slips of this kind are discussed in connection with cuttings in Chapter 15.

(b) Flows, in the second group, include the type of movement sometimes called "earth-flow," which is a plastic deformation arising in clayey materials with a high water content. Bulging of the sides of clay cuttings is sometimes due to this cause, and is often associated with slipping. Such plastic movements of clay slopes add to the difficulties of maintenance where cuttings are involved ; they are referred to again on p. 305.

Under the same general head come the very slow movements of surface layers on slopes, such as *soil creep* and *rock creep* on hillsides (Plate I<small>B</small>), which continue over a long period until ultimately they may visibly displace trees, fences, and lines of communication. Although not commonly called landslides, they arise from like causes. The cumulative effect of creep in bringing soil and rock fragments within the sphere of action of transporting agents such as rain-wash and rivers is a large contributory factor in the processes of denudation.

THE WORK OF THE SEA

The waves which break on a shore erode the land by the force of their impact and, especially in storms, by the impact of the debris they carry. The debris itself is composed of rock fragments derived either from local cliffs, or brought to the sea by rivers or by currents from a distance. The fragments become rounded and comminuted by the battering they receive from the waves, and make up the familiar pebbly and sandy beach deposits.

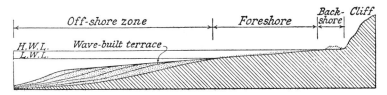

FIG. 9.—NOMENCLATURE OF SHORE ZONES.

The terms used by different writers in describing the parts of a region where land and sea meet vary ; those employed here may be defined as follows. The margin of the land is called the *coast-line*, and the land-zone adjacent to it is the *coast*, which is frequently bounded by a line of cliffs. The *shore* is the zone extending from the base of the cliffs down to low-water mark (Fig. 9) ; it may be sub-divided into the *fore-shore*, which is that part lying between ordinary high and low tide marks, and the *back-shore* or area between high tide level and the foot of the cliffs. When no back-shore is present, high tide then extends up to the cliff base.

In most places around the margins of a land mass there exists a submerged platform of varying width, sloping gently seaward (at about 2 or 3 degrees), which is known as the *continental shelf* (Fig. 10) ; where it ends, the somewhat steeper *continental slope* begins and continues down to the deep ocean floor. A distinction may thus be drawn between relatively shallow seas, such as the North Sea or the Baltic, which lie on the margins of the continents (epicontinental seas), and the deep oceans such as the Atlantic or Pacific.

The shore is a wave-cut platform (p. 28) and on it lie the *beach* deposits,

PLATE 1

(A) LANDSLIP CHASM AT BINDON, SOUTH DEVON, WITH THE CHALK OF BEER HEAD
IN THE DISTANCE

(B) SOIL AND ROCK-CREEP IN FLAGSTONES, RISHTON, LANCS.

PLATE II

(A) WAVE-CUT PLATFORM EAST OF ST. ANDREWS, FIFE.

Photo by H. H. Read.

(B) COAST PROTECTION: GROYNES AND SEA-WALL AT RECULVER, KENT.

which are moved about by waves and covered and uncovered daily by the tides. In the *off-shore zone* beyond low tide level, thicker deposits of land-derived sediment form a terrace whose seaward slope continues that of the wave-cut platform (Fig. 9). The deposits which form this terrace grade from coarser to finer material with progress outwards from the shore, and help to build up the continental shelf.

Tides and Currents. The periodic rise and fall of the sea, or *tide*, is due essentially to the pull exerted by the sun and moon on the water ; the bulge of water thus produced moves round the earth as the latter rotates. The highest ordinary tides are called " spring " tides ; these occur at the times of full and new moon, when the sun and moon and earth are in line. The smallest or " neap " tides occur at the moon's first and third quarters, when its pull is at right angles to that of the sun. At the equinoxes exceptionally high (equinoctial) tides are generated ; when these are accompanied

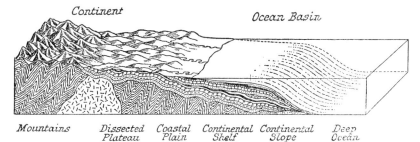

Continent Ocean Basin

| Mountains | Dissected Plateau | Coastal Plain | Continental Shelf | Continental Slope | Deep Ocean |

FIG. 10.—LAND FORMS AND SUBMARINE TOPOGRAPHY (generalized).

by heavy seas in severe storms the coarser deposits of the back-shore, which are normally above the level of spring tides, may be piled up to form a ridge or storm-beach.

With the rise of the tide the water in shallow seas and narrow channels is heaped up so that a *tidal current* is generated ; in the English Channel, for instance, the tidal current flows eastwards at about 2 miles per hour as the tide rises, and westwards on a falling tide. The tidal current in the Mersey estuary reaches 8 miles per hour. In estuaries which shallow and narrow rapidly, the incoming water advances with a steep wave at its front called a *bore*, as in the case of the Severn below Gloucester. In estuaries which are artificially deepened the bore disappears. Tidal currents are in many cases strong enough to move the less coarse sediment in the shore zone, but more rarely to move shingle.

Waves. Wave motion is produced when a water surface is swept by wind. It is an oscillatory motion, and in deep water each particle near the surface moves in a vertical circular orbit, as may be observed by watching the movement of a floating object. Particles below the surface move in phase with the surface particles but in smaller orbits. Waves within an area where they are being driven by wind are known as *forced waves* ; when they move out into water where they are unaccompanied by wind they are called *free waves* or *swell*.

G.E.—C

The height of waves from trough to crest normally varies up to about 30 feet, and is much more than this in heavy seas. The wave-length (distance from crest to crest) of forced waves is from 200 to 600 feet in the open ocean, but the wave-length of a swell may be greater. Wave motion diminishes with depth from the surface, and at a depth equal to the wave-length the movement ceases altogether. At greater depths, even the finest mud on a sea floor is not stirred by water movement. Hence the lower limit of wave action varies, and may be as much as 600 feet, a depth corresponding to the edge of the continental shelf.

As a wave runs into shallow water (i.e. water less deep than a wave-length), friction retards the movement of water in contact with the sea bottom, while the top of the wave runs on. The wave-front thus increases in steepness and ultimately the crest falls over in front of the wave, and the wave is said to break. This forward movement of the water (" wave of translation ") constitutes the means by which a wave becomes an agent of erosion. The breaking of the wave is followed by the *backwash*, which combs down the components of the beach, especially the finer material, towards deeper water where they are temporarily deposited.

With an onshore wind blowing at right angles to the shore-line, water is heaped up against a coast ; this is compensated by a return current away from the land, called the *undertow*, which may be concentrated into narrow channels. The undertow may transport finer sediment out to sea, and in storms a strong undertow can remove large quantities of beach.

Waves meeting a steep coast, such as a line of cliffs fronting relatively deep water, are partly reflected and an up-and-down movement is imparted to the water at the cliff face. On the other hand, where waves run a long distance in very gradually shallowing water, much of their energy is absorbed by friction, and they become reduced in size (and hence in erosive power) before reaching the shore. A flat, sandy fore-shore is therefore to a large extent its own protection against erosion. When the slope of the fore-shore is steeper, low frequency waves may have a constructive effect, resulting in aggradation of the beach deposits.[1]

The pressures exerted by waves were measured by Stevenson,[2] who found that they varied from about 600 up to 2000 pounds per square foot in winter, while in one gale as much as 6000 pounds per square foot was recorded. Recent experiments with models by R. A. Bagnold and C. M. White [3] showed that waves breaking against a wall produced shock pressures ranging from 1440 pounds per square foot to more than three times that amount. The effectiveness of storm waves in breaking up massive stone and concrete structures has been demonstrated many times around the shores of Britain, and it should be noted that storm waves do far more damage in a short time than normal seas acting over longer intervals. Experiments on the action of waves in moving and modifying the form of

[1] W. V. Lewis in *Geogr. Journ.*, August 1931, p. 129.
[2] T. Stevenson, *Trans. Roy. Soc. Edinburgh*, Vol. xvi, p. 25.
[3] *Journ. Inst. Civil Engrs.*, June 1939, Vol. 12, p. 202.

beach deposits have been made both in Britain and the United States with the aid of models.[1]

Littoral Drift. Waves which approach a coast obliquely carry beach material forward up the shore as they advance and break, but the back-wash which flows down the beach as each wave recedes drags back the pebbles and sand along a path nearly at right angles to the shore-line,

thus :   An alongshore movement is therefore imparted to the fragments by the incoming waves, and the cumulative effect is known as *littoral drift* or "long-shore" drifting. It may be supplemented to some extent by coastal currents, but these can carry only the finer sediment, and it is the action of the waves which is the chief cause of the drifting. Transport of coarse material alongshore by wave action in one direction and of fine material by currents in the opposite direction has been observed.

On the east coast of England the prevalent drift of shingle is southward, and along the south coast it is eastward, but there are local exceptions to this general statement. For example, on the Norfolk coast west of Shering-ham the drift is westward towards the Wash. Since a good shingle beach affords the land a considerable measure of protection from the waves, it is generally an advantage to preserve beach deposits and to encourage their accumulation by suitably placed groynes, a matter which is discussed later. On the other hand, interference with the normal process of littoral drift by engineering works may lead to undesired results. To take one example only, the construction of harbour works at Lowestoft arrested the southward travel of beach material there, and much shingle was piled up north of the harbour. Serious erosion resulted at Pakefield, a mile to the south, where the cliffs have been cut back rapidly. The shore lost its protective beach when the normal drift was interrupted, and became open to the attack of the sea.

Spits and Bars. The growth of such coastal features as spits, bars, and other depositional forms is a subject which can only be treated briefly here. Accretion goes on, not without interruption, along some stretches of coast such as that between the Humber estuary and the Wash, while other parts are subject to erosion. A *spit* is a ridge of sand or shingle, ending in open water, which has been built of material drifted alongshore ; it extends out in the direction of the drift from a bend in the coast, as at the mouth of a river or a bay, or from the leeward side of a headland. In the latter case waste derived from the erosion of the headland is contributed to the spit. On the English coasts examples are found at Spurn Head, Blakeney Point, Orfordness, and Great Yarmouth in the east, and at Hurst Castle and Mudeford in the south. The great Orfordness spit on the Suffolk coast deflects the mouth of the River Alde ; this river once entered the sea at Aldeburgh, but now turns southwards there, just before reaching

[1] See R. A. Bagnold, *Journ. Inst. C.E.*, November 1940, Vol. 15, p. 27 ; and U.S. Army Board Report on Sand Movement and Beach Erosion, reviewed in *The Engineer*, Vol. 163, 1937, p. 719.

the sea, and flows parallel to the coast for about another ten miles, being separated from the sea along this part of its course by a bank formed largely of gravel and sand which has drifted southwards. It is estimated that the spit grew 5½ miles in length (from near Orford to its present termination) during the 700 years from the founding of Orford Castle up to 1897 ; since then it has advanced still further but with intervals of recession.[1]

When a spit grows across a bay it forms a *bay-bar*, as at Looe Pool on the south coast of Cornwall. The Dovey estuary in Wales is shut off from the sea, except for a small channel, by a shingle bar. Such a bar protects the bay or estuary from further wave attack, and the coast-line is shortened. The bay also tends to silt up with river-transported sediment, leading to the formation of mud-banks which lie between high- and low-water levels.

Banks of mud or silt formed behind a spit or bar may be converted gradually into dry land by the growth of salt-marsh vegetation, as at Scolt Head Island on the Norfolk coast. In the upward growth of a salt-marsh, the rate of accumulation of sediment has been found by spreading a layer of coloured material on the surface and measuring the amount of silt deposited above it. At Scolt Head Island this varied between about ⅓ and 1 centimetre per year.[2]

Besides the forms described above, other prominences which are in effect compound spits may develop on a coast and are known as *cuspate forelands*. They are gradually built out to sea, as at Dungeness on the Sussex coast. This large shingle structure now extends some 10 miles beyond the old coast-line and its outer part consists of storm shingle ridges which face the dominant waves. Storm waves run in mainly from two directions, south and east, the nearness of the French coast preventing large waves from arriving head-on from the south-east. Seas approaching the coast from the two main directions have built up successive storm beaches, now seen as parallel shingle ridges, in the course of centuries ; a similar explanation would account for other forelands of this type, which are situated where there is a change of exposure of the coast-line. Sea level off Sussex in Roman times was probably 5 or 6 feet lower than at present (cf. p. 160), and the Romney Marshes behind Dungeness were probably drained then.

Types of Shore-line. Many shore-lines are the result of *submergence*, i.e. a sinking of the land relative to the sea. When this happens, water-level rests against the hill and valley slopes of the former land surface ; the hills stand out as headlands and cliffs are then formed around them by erosion, as described below. A shore-line may also result from the *emergence* of a land area from beneath the sea, in which case the coast is straight and featureless, bordering an area of newly exposed sea-floor.[3] Other types of shore-line are formed, for example, by the growth of coral reefs or by volcanic activity.

Coast Erosion. Where a cliff marks the coast-line, a *wave-cut platform*

---

[1] For details see Dr. C. A. M. King's " Beaches & Coasts."

[2] J. A. Steers in *Geogr. Journ.*, May 1939, pp. 399–408.

[3] For a discussion of the evolution of these two types of shore-line the reader is referred to books such as Johnson's " Shore-line Development," 1938.

is usually formed at its base (Plate IIA). The elevation of the platform approximates to low-water level, and it slopes gently seaward. In many instances the rocks of the fore-shore may be seen exposed on this platform, in others they are covered by beach deposits. At the base of the cliffs the sea exerts a " sawing " action, cutting a horizontal notch into and gradually undermining the cliff face. While this goes on, atmospheric denudation is wearing away the upper part of the cliff, tending all the time to reduce its steepness, and debris which falls to the foot of the cliff is broken up by the waves and removed into the off-shore zone, where it is spread as a bank or terrace of sediment (Fig. 9). Thus the cliff recedes as it is under-cut by waves and at the same time worn down by rain, wind, and frost ; the action of the sea is gradually reduced as the wave-cut platform is widened. These combined processes, if left to run their course, would in the end stabilize the position of the coast and reduce the land to a nearly level surface—results rarely achieved because of interruptions which occur in the cycle of erosion. As cliffs are cut back, streams which drain to the coast may be rejuvenated by the steepening of their lower courses ; if the cutting back takes place faster than the streams can achieve a new grade, waterfalls may be formed.

In hard rocks a cliff may stand with a vertical face ; if the rocks are jointed the sea erodes preferentially along the joints, and along other planes of weakness, widening them and removing loosened joint-blocks. In this way caves and tunnels are carved out. The process is assisted by the repeated compression of air in the joints by incoming waves, since the pressure can act at the back and sides of joint-blocks. When the roof of a cave collapses, a long narrow inlet or *geo* is formed. A cave sometimes communicates with the surface by a vertical shaft or *blow-hole* on rocky coasts, as in Cornwall. Erosion along joint planes may in time leave isolated pillars of rock, or *sea-stacks*, sometimes of fanciful shape ; stacks are formed in relatively soft rocks such as the Chalk of the Dorset coast and the Isle of Wight, and notably in harder rocks, as around the northern coasts of Scotland and the Orkney and Shetland Islands (Plate XA).

Where belts of hard and soft rock alternate along a length of coast, the former stand out as headlands and the latter are hollowed out into inter-vening bays in the early stages of shore-line development. The Welsh coast near St. Davids well illustrates the way in which steeply dipping bands of resistant rock, running at an angle to the coast, reinforce the softer strata and project as headlands. In a more mature stage of erosion the headlands themselves are reduced, an effect promoted by wave-deflection. Waves, as they approach the shore, run into shallow water off the headlands before they reach water of similar depth in the bays. Each wave-front thereby becomes deflected, the line of crests being bent so that it is concave towards a headland and convex towards a bay. This results in a concen-tration of wave attack on the headlands from both sides, while the bays are to a considerable extent protected. Erosion of the headlands thus goes on vigorously and at the same time there is comparatively smooth water at the heads of bays, where beaches are accumulated. In course of time the headlands are worn down and the coast-line tends to become more and more nearly a smooth line.

Adjacent hard and soft beds may run parallel to the coast, as at Lulworth Cove, Dorset, where the breaching of a hard outer layer (Portland Beds) on the seaward side has allowed the sea access to the softer rocks (Purbeck and Wealden Beds), and these have been hollowed out into the nearly circular cove behind the barrier of harder strata.

Hard beds lying horizontally over soft ones give rise to overhanging ledges, produced by unequal rates of erosion in the two kinds of rock.

Softer rocks such as sands and clays offer less resistance to erosion and are generally worn back more rapidly by the sea. The Norfolk cliffs between Sheringham and Happisburgh, for example, are made of glacial clays, sands, and gravels, arranged in irregular layers which are often bent and contorted. Where seams of clay occur and slope seawards, rain soaking through overlying gravels or sands saturates the clays, which then become surfaces of sliding (see p. 23). Frequent slips have thus been caused along this coast; the cliffs become more stable when erosion has cut them back to a position in which the folded layers of sediment have a landward dip, i.e. slope away from the sea. Wind erosion of the sandy beds also produces small falls of cliff locally.

Rate of Erosion. The rate of erosion of a coast varies considerably from place to place ; it is greater, in general, on the east and south-east coasts of England than on the west (see also Chapter 8). Exact figures relating to the progress of erosion are difficult to obtain and many more measurements are needed. An estimate of the change that has occurred for a particular locality can sometimes be made by comparing old and new editions of the Ordnance Survey maps of the district. The Sussex coast, for example, just east of Beachy Head is estimated to have receded by 4 to 5 yards per year over a period of 110 years, a high rate of recession. On the Holderness coast of Yorkshire, recent losses by erosion of the relatively soft boulder clay cliffs have probably amounted to some 3 yards in a year, about one acre of land per mile of coast-line being washed away annually ; a strip of coast between two and three miles wide has been lost here since Roman times. Much data relating to changes in the coast-line of Britain were published in the Report of the Royal Commission on Coast Erosion, 1909–11.

The stretch of coast on the east side of Selsey Bill, Sussex, has probably suffered more erosion during the past 50 years than any place in Britain. The mean wave approach here is from the south-south-west, oblique to the shore, giving rise to a north-easterly littoral drift.[1] Old sea defences were smashed in successive storms, and houses and roads at Selsey were being lost to the sea. Erosion along the east side of the promontory had at times reached a rate of 25 feet per year ; the lifeboat station, which was built next to the cliff in 1923, was by 1950 some 750 feet from the shore. (It was replaced in 1960.) Erosion along the west side of the Bill was slower because of better protection from groynes there. With the passing of the Coast Protection Act in 1950, which eased financial difficulties, new

[1] J. Duvivier in *Proc. Inst. Civ. Engrs.*, 20, Dec. 1961, p. 481.

works including articulated groynes were undertaken to secure Selsey Bill against further erosion ; they are referred to on p. 34.

The Horsey Floods.   The disastrous effects of storm waves on a low coast are well exemplified by the breaching of a line of sand dunes at Horsey, Norfolk, in 1938, which resulted in the flooding of 7500 acres of adjoining low-lying land.   Sand-hills extend for some nine miles along this part of the coast, and form a link between cliffs to the north-west and to the south-east. During a strong north-westerly gale on the night of February 12, waves were driven against the dunes with such force that these were demolished over a distance of some 500 yards, and the sea poured through the gap. The waves had overtopped the dunes and cut channels on their landward slopes.   A bed of boulder clay occurs below the dunes on either side of the gap, but at the point where the breach was made this boulder clay appears to be absent ; the dune barrier, therefore, was here less resistant than elsewhere along the coast.   The site of the breach was also opposite the mouth of an old river, the Hundred Stream, which probably entered the sea at this point in the 12th century but has since been silted up, the dunes covering its former mouth.

Subsequent repairs involved the construction of a new wall of concrete-filled bags, held together with steel spikes and surmounted by a parapet wall, along the length of the breach, the top of the parapet being 10 feet above the level of the highest known tide.   The wall is backed by a sand bank planted with marram grass, and at the concrete toe on its seaward side a line of sheet steel piling is driven to prevent undercutting.   This form of construction was used instead of a concrete sea-wall partly on account of the bad foundations which would have been available for the latter ; the sand-hills on either side of the breach were also faced in a similar way.[1]

Tidal Surges in the North Sea.   On the night of January 31, 1953, a severe storm swept south past Scotland [2] into the North Sea, and produced extensive flooding and damage at many places on the east coast of England, from the Humber to Kent.   It also affected the coasts of Holland, with disastrous results.   The spring tides expected at the time were not exceptional, but superimposed on them was a tidal surge, which travelled from north to south and produced high-water levels up to about 8 feet above those predicted (2 feet at Aberdeen, 7 feet at the mouth of the Tees, and over 8 feet at Southend).   A surge is defined, simply, as " a water movement which is quickly generated and whose effects are soon over " ; in this instance it was a rapid rise of sea level which moved down the North Sea with the incoming tide, rather like the bore of a river.

The high-water levels, combined with a northerly gale, resulted in the overtopping of many lines of coastal protection, the sea also breaking through dunes, as between Mablethorpe and Sutton in Lincolnshire, and inundating low-lying areas behind them.   Other wider belts of dunes, e.g.

---

[1] E. G. Mosby in *Geogr. Journ.*, May 1939, pp. 413–18 ; and K. E. Cotton in *Civil Engineering*, January 1940, pp. 6–10.

[2] High northerly winds did great damage to forests in north-east Scotland ; gusts exceeding 120 m.p.h. were recorded in Orkney.

on the north coast of Norfolk, were eroded but often withstood the storm, At Horsey, on the east coast of Norfolk, the wall built in 1938 (and referred to above) helped greatly to maintain that stretch of coast. But at places where the beach was steeper, more severe erosion occurred.

At Lowestoft large areas of the town were flooded by water which came in both behind and over the sea-walls (p. 33), which themselves were unbroken. At Aldeburgh the river Alde kept to its course, but the outer shingle bank at the bend of the river just south of the town, referred to on p. 28, was flattened and much shingle was displaced landwards by the heavy seas. On the Essex coast near Clacton, and at Canvey Island, extensive flooding of areas lying below high-water mark was combined with serious damage to property and loss of life. The railway system of north Kent was seriously disrupted by flooding. The main sea-walls along the Thames estuary held, but water flooded over the lower walls at the Benfleet and other creeks, and once the walls were overtopped they were eroded from inside. Many other details are given in the account by Professor Steers,[1] which has been drawn on here. Much construction of defence works has been put in hand since the events described, and also measures to restore to productivity the agricultural land which was flooded.

A few years earlier, in January 1949, a smaller tidal surge affected the east coasts and had many points in common with that of 1953 ; but water levels in 1949 were somewhat lower. The slow downward movement which has taken place in south-east England, of only 1 to 2 mm. per year but amounting to several feet since Roman times, is discussed on p. 160.

Coast Protection. It is clear that along much of the coast-line the sea is gaining on the land, and cliffs are being worn back, though in other places accretion is taking place as described above (p. 27). Erosive action may be arrested locally by the building of defences such as sea-walls, or by the construction of groynes, the latter being designed to accumulate some of the sand or shingle brought by littoral drift and so build up a protecting beach. A brief discussion follows of protective works of this kind, in so far as they bear on geological factors. On sandy coasts, erosion of dunes may be arrested by the planting of grasses and shrubs to form a stable surface layer which in time becomes grassed over.

Sea-walls are used to protect a coast from wave-action, the shock of which is taken by the wall instead of by the coastal rocks. The form of construction may be a low bank of earth, sand, or other material ; on account of its relatively low cost a bank of this kind is often used for protecting agricultural land. It usually has a gently sloping seaward face covered with a pitching of stone blocks or other resistant material. Another type of construction has been mentioned above in connection with the Horsey breach. At Winchelsea, Sussex, a shingle bank which was broken by the sea in 1930 was successfully repaired by means of a filling of chalk ; the chalk was tipped and consolidated in successive layers, and so built up into a bank closing the gap.

---

[1] J. A. Steers, *Geogr. Journ.*, 119, 1953, p. 280.

Timber stakes driven into the beach in front of a bank have been used to break the force of the waves, as at Walcheren in Holland. At Rye Bay, west of Dungeness, a continuous timber barrier consisting of a double line of piles with a filling of shingle between them, was constructed about 1936 along a length of fore-shore to protect the existing shingle bank; in front of this barrier was placed a single line of closely spaced timber piles to act as a further wave-screen.[1]

Walls of concrete or stone are more durable but more costly; they are usually employed in residential areas, generally in conjunction with a system of groynes. Plate IIb shows an example from Reculver, on the north coast of Kent. In the past, many massive sea-walls of this kind were built with a vertical or nearly vertical face; the breaking of waves against such a wall, however, may sometimes induce scour at the toe of the wall, leading to instability of the structure if the scour is sufficiently deep. An alternative form of wall which has been employed in many situations is of reinforced concrete, having a stepped or gently sloping seaward face. The sloping or stepped face forms a protective apron whose function is to absorb most of the force of the waves as they move up the wall, and to prevent scour. Instances are described in the engineering literature.[2] At Lowestoft, after the breaking of earlier vertical walls by heavy seas, a concrete wall with a wide, nearly horizontal apron and steel piling driven into the beach at the toe was constructed about 1936.[3] This new wall was broken in severe storms early in 1946; the position is an exposed one on the east coast, subject to north-easterly gales, which change the configuration of protective sand-banks off-shore. Subsequently another wall was built behind the line of the previous structure, and withstood the tidal surge of 1953.

Groynes are used to retain or accumulate beach deposits along a shore where there is littoral drift (see p. 27). A good beach is itself a protection against erosion of the land, as it absorbs the impact of the waves which break against it; but it may be considerably modified by storms and sometimes changed rapidly, as witnessed by the recorded lowering of one beach by 14 feet in a single storm. In general, groynes are placed normal to a coast-line or to the prevailing longshore current, and at a distance apart approximately equal to their length, though there is much difference of opinion as to their dimensions and spacing, and conditions vary at each locality. Groynes are commonly made of timber, but may be of stonework or concrete. They should be founded sufficiently deep to provide against scour at low tides. Drifting beach deposits accumulate on the weather side of the groynes, which can be made high enough to produce a uniform accumulation of beach, but not so high as to give rise to a large drop in level on their leeward sides. As the profile of a beach changes, it may be necessary to adjust the height of the groynes, for example, by adding longitudinal planks between the posts in the case of timber structures; adjustable screw-piles

---

[1] *Engineering*, Jan. 10, 1936, pp. 27–30 and 81–3.

[2] See, for example, F. M. G. Du-Plat Taylor in *Journ. Inst. Civ. Engrs.*, Nov. 1940.

[3] H. J. Deane and E. Latham, in *Engineering*, Sept. 25, 1936, pp. 329 and 377.

which can be raised or lowered by turning, to suit the prevailing beach level, have also been used instead of fixed posts.

Efforts to stabilize the seriously eroded coast at Selsey Bill (p. 30) began in 1950 with the construction of *articulated groynes*. These consisted of massive concrete blocks weighing $15\frac{1}{2}$ tons each, linked transversely in pairs by hinged steel bars, and pinned to the underlying gravel by vertical steel rails. Successive pairs of blocks formed the first of two groynes, 190 feet long and 16 feet wide, which was built on the west side of the debris at Selsey village. This groyne functioned well for several years, taking the impact of heavy seas from the south-south-west; a second articulated groyne was then built to the east of it, and the original groyne converted into a rigid breakwater, in 1960. These structures, together with a new sea-wall and groyne system along the east side of the promontory, have succeeded in controlling erosion. (Further details are given in the paper quoted on p. 30.)

By analogy with natural conditions, from which it is seen that erosion proceeds most rapidly at points where rocks of one kind give place to others of different hardness (and therefore different resistance), it will be evident that defence works such as a length of sea-wall along a stretch of coast may be only of local or temporary value. The effect of a wall is like that of a hard stratum of rock : where it ends erosion still goes on rapidly, possibly cutting back behind the end of the wall, so that one part of the coast is protected at the expense of adjacent parts. A comprehensive plan dealing with a whole coast-line is therefore needed. In default of this ideal, provision can sometimes be made for suitable terminations to coastal works. Thus at the leeward end of a series of groynes, serious erosion may develop to the lee of the last groyne ; where new works do not join on to existing works, it may be possible to carry on the groyning along the coast into a region where there is greater stability of beach deposits, or to deal with the matter in some other way. The problem of erosion is aggravated when shingle is removed in large quantities from beaches, as for local construction, and in places it has been necessary to regulate or prohibit this.

Marine Deposits. Much material derived by denudation from land areas is deposited near a coast, in a stable environment (p. 120). After sorting by waves and currents, the products of denudation are built up into new deposits, mainly in shallow water. The fragments are distributed according to size, ranging from the coarse shingle of the beach through sands and muds to the finest particles which are carried by feeble currents out to sea and slowly accumulated. When compacted and hardened, such deposits become sedimentary rocks like conglomerate, sandstone, and shale. These marine sediments are described as littoral, shallow-water, or deep-sea deposits according to the areas in which they have been laid down. In the shore zone are formed the *littoral deposits*, which include boulders, pebbles, and coarse sands which lie between high and low tide-marks. *Shallow-water deposits* are those laid down below low-tide level, to depths of about 100 fathoms (the lower limit of wave action). They comprise sands, fine sands, silts, and muds, which are deposited over wider areas than the coarser accumulations of the beaches. In them are embedded marine shells and other organic remains which ultimately are preserved as fossils in the sediment. In some environments calcareous organic matter (e.g. shell sands) may predominate, or fine calcareous muds are laid down, eventually to become beds of limestone. All these shallow-water sediments are deposited on the continental shelf which in most places surrounds a land mass. Other environments are discussed on p. 120.

Beyond the 100-fathom line, where the continental slope forms a transition from the shelf to the ocean depths (Fig. 10), lie the *deep-sea deposits*, which are subdivided into land-derived muds on the continental slope (*bathyal deposits*) and, at still greater depths, the oozes and the Red Clay

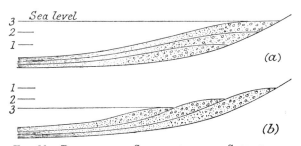

FIG. 11.—DEPOSITION OF SEDIMENTS NEAR A SHORE-LINE.
a) Land sinking, (*b*) rising, relative to sea. 1, 2, 3 denote successive water-levels. Vertical scale exaggerated.

(*abyssal deposits*). The latter accumulate very slowly but cover large areas of the ocean floor, and extend down to the greatest known depths (about 32,000 feet).

The order in which shallow-water sediments are deposited, i.e. from coarse to fine material with increasing distance from a coast, is shown in Fig. 11. They form lens-shaped masses, thicker at the coarser end and thinning out seawards. If sediments are laid down on a sinking sea-floor, as must often have been the case in past geological times, the different lenses of material over-lap successively (Fig. 11*a*), and finer grades come to be deposited above coarser. Thus sands may grade into silts and muds in a vertical as well as a horizontal direction. A large thickness of deposit may accumulate under these conditions, the sedimentation keeping pace with the sinking area and the depth of water remaining much the same.

When deposits are laid down on a slowly rising sea-floor, successive lenses of sediment are related as shown in Fig. 11*b*, and coarser grades may then come to lie on the finer parts of older layers. If the area of sedimentation is intermittently raised and lowered, giving varying depths of water at different times, then the deposits oscillate from one kind to another ; for example, coarser layers may be intercalated between finer or vice versa.

It is evident that, at any given time, different kinds of deposit may be forming in different environments. The term *facies* is used to express this conception, and is applied to the sediments or to the rocks resulting from their consolidation. Thus, there is a transition from a sandy facies near a shore to a contemporaneous muddy facies in deeper water. Not only the nature of the sediments, but other features such as colour and the different kinds of fossils preserved in them are also understood in the term facies, which includes all the characters which go to distinguish a deposit. Sediments formed on land, such as wind-blown sands, constitute a continental facies as distinct from a marine facies.

Deep-sea Deposits. The muds and oozes of the deep sea, which are being formed today, are less easily investigated than the more accessible sediments, but are interesting because of their wide extent and distinctive characters : they usually contain no large fragments, no remains of shallow-water animals, and no features due to current or wave action. They are spread in horizontal layers over great distances and connected with shallower water sediments by a gradual transition. Our knowledge of these deposits in the past was due to the *Challenger* Expedition of 1872–6, which obtained many hundreds of samples dredged from the ocean floors of the world. More recently, new methods of obtaining core samples of deep-sea deposits have been introduced and are being developed, and the results of the new *Challenger* expedition, which ended in 1952, are yielding much new information. Exploration of the ocean floors by echo-sounding apparatus has also given important results. The mid-Atlantic ridge, for instance, which runs from north to south, is now known to be a submerged mountain range comparable in size to the Rockies, and separating ocean basins to the east and west in which deep-sea deposits are found.

The *muds* are named according to their colour—green, red, and blue (in increasing order of depth)—and represent very finely divided land-derived material ; they lie mainly between depths of 500 and 1500 fathoms. At still greater depths are found the *oozes*, made of the calcareous and siliceous skeletons of minute floating sea organisms, which fall to the bottom and accumulate there at a slow rate. The most extensive among them is the *Globigerina Ooze*, a calcareous deposit composed largely of the minute globular shells of the foraminifer known as *Globigerina*, and estimated to cover nearly 50 million square miles of the ocean floor at an average depth of 2000 fathoms. It is found in the Atlantic, Indian, and Pacific Oceans. The siliceous *Radiolarian Ooze* has a smaller extent (between 2 and 3 million square miles), chiefly in the South Pacific Ocean ; it lies at greater depths than those reached by calcareous particles, which are slowly dissolved as they sink through deep water.

From about 2200 fathoms down to the greatest known depths occurs the deposit named the *Red Clay*, which is estimated to cover 52 million square miles of submarine surface. This soft, plastic material is derived from fine volcanic dust which has fallen from the atmosphere and slowly settled through great depths of water. Hard parts of fishes, such as sharks' teeth, are found embedded in samples of the Red Clay which have been dredged up. Spherules of meteoric iron were found in the deposit at depths of 3000 fathoms in the North Atlantic ; and many manganese nodules ("sea potatoes") lie in places on the ocean floors.

Bedding-planes and other Structures. Sedimentary rocks occur in beds or layers which are bounded by more or less regular and parallel surfaces called *bedding-planes*. The development of these structures was initiated at the time the sediment was deposited. Bedding-planes generally represent interruptions or breaks in the course of sedimentation, which are revealed by differences of composition, size of particles, colour, or hardness, which are inherent in successive parts of the deposit. In the fully-formed rocks they appear as a series of parting planes, and they divide a formation into the familiar beds or *strata*, which may vary in thickness from a fraction of an inch to many feet. Bedding is also known as stratification; a group of beds deposited one above another and forming a lithological unit is called a *formation*. Weathering helps to show up the presence of bedding-planes in rocks exposed at the surface; they are sometimes difficult to observe in unweathered rocks. Thin bands of differing colour or texture sometimes alternate within a stratum, and are described as *banding*; they are usually less than an inch wide. (For lamination see p. 131.)

Littoral or shallow-water deposits sometimes show features such as *ripple-marks*, *rain-prints*, or *sun-cracks*, which were developed in the newly laid sediment when it was exposed between tide-marks, and were preserved by a quickly deposited cover of further sediment. Ripple-marks are found on the bedding-planes of certain sandstones, and are due to wave-action which impressed small undulations on the surface of the sand; they are a sign of shallow-water conditions, and may occur throughout great thicknesses of rock, as in the sandstones of Table Mountain, Cape Town. Worm-tracks and the footprints of animals, and even the impressions of rain-drops, are also sometimes preserved in this way.

Rocks of all kinds are traversed by fractures known as *joints*, along which there has been little or no relative movement of the two sides. In sedimentary rocks there are commonly two sets of joints nearly at right angles to one another and to the bedding-planes, the joints of each set being parallel; the rock therefore breaks naturally into rectangular blocks. If the bedding is horizontal the joints are vertical or nearly so (Plate XA). Other joints oblique to the two main sets are often present (p. 196). Igneous rocks (p. 88) are also generally traversed by more or less regular systems of joints (Plates VB, VIA, VIIIB).

THE WORK OF ICE

A land surface whose topographical features have been fashioned by the action of rivers and atmospheric agents is considerably modified when it becomes covered by an ice-sheet or by glaciers. Valleys are deepened and straightened, and rock surfaces smoothed by erosion, and when the ice melts away it leaves behind a variety of deposits which mark its former extent. The main features of these processes are discussed in the following pages; the deposits formed during the Great Ice Age, when large parts of the British Isles and north-west Europe, and of North America, were under a load of ice in a geologically recent period (the Pleistocene), are further discussed in Chapter 11 (p. 233 *et seq.*).

Ice is formed by the compaction of snow in cold regions and at high altitudes, where the supply of snow exceeds the wastage by melting. In an intermediate stage between snow and ice the partly compacted granular mass is called *névé*. Ice of sufficient thickness will begin to move down a slope, and such a moving mass is called a *glacier*. It may occupy a valley, as a *valley glacier*, of which many examples are found in the Alps, the Rockies, and other mountain regions ; they are the relics of larger ice-caps. Where several valley glaciers meet on low ground in front of a mountain range, a stagnant accumulation of ice, or *piedmont glacier*, is formed, e.g. the Malaspina Glacier of Alaska. The much larger accumulations of thick ice constitute the *ice-sheets*, and cover great areas. The Greenland ice-sheet extends over about half a million square miles at the present day, and the Antarctica ice-sheet is six times greater. " Islands " of rock standing up through an ice-sheet are called *nunataks*.

When a glacier meets the sea it begins to float and break up into ice-bergs, a process known as " calving." Any land-derived debris in the ice is then carried by the bergs, and dropped as they become reduced by melting.

Motion of Glaciers. Valley glaciers have been extensively studied in Switzerland and in other countries where they are accessible. The ice breaks away from the parent snow-field by a big crevasse known as the *bergschrund*, and in moving over the ground it behaves rather like a very viscous body, flowing over the irregularities of its course. It has a granular texture similar to the crystalline structure of metals. Movement occurs by melting and re-freezing at the surfaces of crystals, along gliding-planes within the crystals, and also along shear planes in the mass, the ice breaking as it rises over an obstruction, on its way down to lower levels ; tension crevasses with complicated patterns are also formed (Plate IIIA), especially near the ice margin. An average rate of movement of an Alpine glacier is 2 feet per day, but this figure varies considerably. It depends on the steepness of the slope over which the ice is moving, on the thickness of ice, and on the air temperature. Rates up to 60 feet per day have been measured in Greenland. At lower levels, where melting balances the supply of ice descending a valley, the size of a glacier is gradually reduced until it ends in a " snout," from which issues a stream fed by the melting ice. Such glacial streams may supply reservoirs which store water for hydro-electric power generation ; the glacier is in effect a frozen reservoir.

Transport by Ice. A glacier carries along boulders and stones of all sizes which fall on to its surface from the valley walls on either side, and superficial debris of this kind is called *moraine*. It frequently lies in two marginal bands, or *lateral moraines*, parallel to the sides of the glacier ; in some places the ice is completely covered by stones and dirt. The confluence of two glaciers, as when a tributary enters the main valley, results in the formation of a *medial moraine* from the two laterals which become adjacent where the ice-streams meet. The united glaciers below the point of junction thus possess one more line of moraine than the number of tributaries.

Rock debris which falls into crevasses is carried forward within the ice, and blocks under these conditions may penetrate by their own weight to the sole of the glacier. Other fragments are " plucked " from rocks over which the ice moves, and are held in the lower part of the mass, which becomes packed with dirt and fragments. This assorted material, much of which is protected from wear as it is surrounded by ice during transport, is known as *englacial material*; fragments may become partly rounded at a subsequent stage by the action of glacial streams. Later, when the ice has melted, large transported blocks are left stranded wherever they happen to be. They are called indicator boulders, or *erratics*, since they are generally different from the local rock on which they come to rest. A study of the distribution of erratics has made it possible to draw conclusions as to the extent and direction of travel of the ice which, during the Pleistocene glaciation of the British Isles, moved out from the higher mountain regions in the north. Blocks of the distinctive microgranite from Ailsa Craig in the Firth of Clyde, for example, are found as far south as North Wales ; and boulders of laurvikite (*q.v.*), a Norwegian rock, are found along the Yorkshire coast, indicating ice-transport across what is now the North Sea.

Glacial Erosion. Ice moving over a land surface removes soil and loose material, exposing the bed-rock below, and acts as a soft abrasive. The surface debris, together with material which has worked its way down through the ice, is held in the lower part of the glacier as explained above. It is rubbed over the rock floor, which becomes smoothed in the process and lubricated by the melting of the ice under pressure ; thus a *glaciated surface* is formed. Blocks held in the sole of the glacier may cut and scratch the surfaces over which they are carried, producing grooves or *striae* which point in the direction of motion ; the blocks themselves may become striated. Hollows ground out by the ice form *rock basins* and are often occupied by lakes or tarns at the present day.

At the head of a valley glacier, the " plucking " action of the ice at the bergschrund forms an armchair-shaped hollow called a *corrie* or *cirque* (the Welsh *cwm*), which is sometimes occupied by a lake as at Glaslyn, Snowdon. Rock obstructions in the path of a glacier are smoothed on their iceward slopes and " plucked " on the leeward side ; when exposed to view after the removal of the ice, they show the rounded forms known as *roches moutonnées* (Fig. 12*a*), which are typical of glaciated mountain regions. The profile of a valley down which a glacier has flowed is changed from a **V**- to a **U**-shaped form. Such a valley presents a rougher, rocky aspect when viewed upstream than when looking down the valley, since in the latter case it is the ice-smoothed slopes that are seen. The valley is deepened by the passage of the ice, and spurs which formerly projected into it are truncated so that sharp bends have been removed. Tributary valleys which were once graded to the main valley are left cut off at some height above the new floor ; they are known as *hanging valleys,* and the streams from them form water-falls as they drop down to the new level (Fig. 12*c*). Alluvium subsequently deposited on the floor of the main valley may level up the bottom of the **U**-shaped profile.

Glacial Deposits. When a glacier or ice-sheet has retreated, it leaves behind it characteristic deposits of sediment to which the term *glacial* *drift* is given. This is irregularly distributed, generally thickest in valleys, and shows a lack of sorting and arrangement which distinguishes it from water-borne sediment. Reference has already been made to erratics. The phenomenon known as *crag and tail* (Fig. 12*b*) is found in low lying drift-covered country, and consists of any upstanding mass of hard rock (the "crag") behind which a gently sloping "tail" of drift has been preserved during the passage of the ice. A well-known example is provided by the

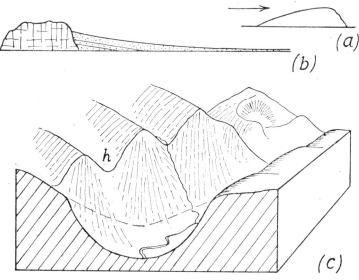

FIG. 12.—ICE EROSION FORMS.

(*a*) Roche moutonnée. (*b*) Crag and tail (to smaller scale), ice movement from left to right. (*c*) U-shaped profile of glaciated valley, with hanging valleys (*h*) and truncated spurs between tributaries to main valley. Corrie in distance. Original valley profile shown by broken line.

Castle Rock, Edinburgh, and the High Street which runs eastward from it on the tail of drift.

Debris dropped at the end of a glacier as the ice melts forms a hummocky ridge called a *terminal moraine* ; successive heaps of this kind mark stages in the recession of the ice as seen, e.g., in some Yorkshire dales and in North Wales. Streams of melt-water flow in tunnels in the base of the ice and move much material, which becomes partly rounded in the process. When these streams emerge along the ice-front their speed is checked and the transported debris is spread out on land as an *outwash fan* of gravel and sand. If the debris is discharged into still water it builds up a delta. Ridges and mounds of gravel deposited by such sub-glacial streams, with their length roughly at right angles to the ice-front, are termed *eskers* ; other ridges or sheets of sand and gravel which were derived from the ice along its margins during pauses in its retreat, and lie parallel to the ice-margin, are called *kames*. Good examples of these glacial gravels can be seen near Carstairs in Lanarkshire, and in the Clyde valley to the south, and at many

PLATE III

Photo by Gilbert Wilson.

(B) ROCK FOLD OUTLINED IN SNOW, THE BIFERTENSTOCK, SWITZERLAND.

Photo by G. Van Praagh.

(A) CREVASSES IN GLACIER, OETZ THAL, TYROL.

PLATE IV

(A) PARALLEL ROADS OF GLEN ROY IN SCOTLAND : THE SHORE LINES OF A
GLACIAL LAKE.

Photo by H.M. Geological Survey.

(B) IRREGULAR SOLUTION-SURFACE OF CHALK, COVERED BY BOULDER CLAY.
NEAR CLAYDON, SUFFOLK.

places in the north of England. Fine laminated clays known as *varves* may also be deposited in still water impounded in front of a glacier, or in glacial lakes (p. 42) ; they show alternate coarser (silty) and finer (muddy) layers. The mud particles, which settle slowly in water, lie on the more quickly sedimented silt, and each pair of layers (coarse and fine) represents a season's melting of the ice. Varved clays thus provide a time scale, in which a pair of layers counts as one year (see also p. 236).

The deposit known as *boulder clay* is formed underneath an ice-sheet ; it is a more or less stiff clay composed of the ground-up debris (fine rock-flour) contributed by the melting out of englacial material and by the abrasion of the rocks over which the ice has passed, and embedded in this clay are boulders and stony fragments of all sizes. It is deposited as an irregular layer over the surface of the ground, and is unstratified except where modified by water. The colour of the clay depends on that of the rocks from which the ice obtained the raw materials during its passage. Thus a red boulder clay is formed when the ice has passed over red rocks, as for the Irish Sea ice which crossed the red Triassic rocks of Cheshire on its way into the Midlands, carrying also far-travelled boulders from the Lake District and southern Scotland (see Fig. 101, p. 234). An old name for hardened boulder clay is *till*.

A *drumlin* is a smooth oval-shaped mound, commonly 100 to 150 feet in height, which is built of boulder clay or englacial debris, sometimes moulded over a roche moutonnée. The long axis of the oval is parallel to the direction taken by the ice. Drumlins are well developed in the country bordering the Lake District, as in the Vale of Eden, Westmorland.

From the point of view of the engineer, boulder clay is one of the most difficult and treacherous deposits with which he may have to deal. It is widely distributed in the north of England, East Anglia, and the Midlands (see Chapter 11), and is extremely variable in character. It may be sandy, or may contain many stones and boulders, or pockets consisting mainly of gravel with a clay matrix ; or it may be almost without stones and nearly all clay. Very large boulders are sometimes present. Excavation in this material is often difficult : large boulders hinder the use of mechanical appliances and may have to be broken by blasting, and the frequent varia-tion in the deposit adds uncertainty to the work. Boulder clay also masks the true nature of the underlying rock surface, concealing hollows and even deep valleys ; such buried glacial channels may lead to complications if their presence is not suspected. The extent of a drift-filled valley (not seen at the surface) at Drumry, near Glasgow, was tested by means of a torsion balance survey ; this method was possible because of the considerable difference in density between the drift (1·72) and the underlying solid rocks (2·38), and it may prove a useful preliminary to borehole data. Boring through boulder clay, for example to find the depth of the rock floor, presents its own problems ; the bore may strike a large boulder, and in the past occur-rences of this kind have been mistaken for the penetration of solid rock below the drift. In such circumstances the bore should be continued for 15 or 20 feet ; few boulders are likely to exceed these dimensions.

On the other hand, boulder clay may form a useful impermeable layer at a reservoir site, but careful inspection and analysis of the material is necessary to ensure that it is, in fact, water-tight (see p. 282). Some Scottish and other boulder clays are used locally for brick-making, and burnt boulder clay has been used as ballast on light railways in Suffolk.

Glacial Lakes. When glaciers descending from high ground encroach upon an area, the streams normally flowing through the valleys may be dammed up by the ice, and a lake thus formed. A famous example is provided by the Parallel Roads of Glen Roy. These three terraces, the beaches of a former lake at successive times, run along the sides of the glen one above the other (Plate IVA). The waters from the glen drain into Glen Spean and, when the latter was occupied by ice, were ponded up, eventually finding outlet by a col at the head of Glen Roy. This level was maintained long enough for a well-marked beach to be formed ; then as the ice in the main valley diminished, a lower outlet for the glacial lake was established, and the second terrace was formed, the third being made later at a still lower level.

A modern example of a glacial lake is to be found high up in the Himalayas, about 30 miles south of the Karakoram Pass. In recent years the River Shyok, a tributary of the Indus, has been periodically blocked by the advance of the Khumdan glacier across its gorge. The ice dam in 1932 formed a barrier 500 feet high and over 1000 feet thick. A lake slowly forms behind the ice over a length of 10 miles, and the bursting of the dam, which occurred three times between 1928 and 1933, releases a flood of water which does great damage to villages and cultivation lower downstream. July and August are danger months, and a close watch is kept on the ice at that time. Difficulties of construction in roadless country at high altitudes, and prohibitive costs, have hitherto prevented the making of a by-pass channel to release the impounded water.

The Grand Coulee, a canyon over 40 miles long and two to three miles wide, in the State of Washington, U.S.A., provides an instance of an old glacial channel being utilized for engineering works of considerable size. The canyon was cut by the overflow waters of a glacial lake which was impounded by ice blocking the gorge of the Columbia River. The waters overflowed past the margin of the ice at a high level, for a long enough time to cut a large natural spillway (the Grand Coulee). This spillway was eroded in basaltic lavas, and is in places over 600 feet deep, with a large waterfall (now dry) at one point. After the recession of the ice the river recovered its old channel. The Grand Coulee has now been made the site of a reservoir, water for irrigation purposes being impounded between two low dams built across it. The reservoir was filled and began to deliver water in 1952. The geology of the main dam on the Columbia River, adjacent to the Coulee, is discussed on p. 296.

SELECTED REFERENCES

CHARLESWORTH, J. K. " The Quaternary Era " (Vol. 1). 1958. Arnold, London.

COTTON, C. A. " Geomorphology." 7th edition, 1958. Whitcombe and Tombs, New Zealand.

FLINT, R. F. " Glacial and Pleistocene Geology." 1957. Wiley & Sons, New York.

HOLMES, A. " Principles of Physical Geology." 2nd edition, 1965. Nelson, Edinburgh.

KING, C. A. M. " Beaches and Coasts." 1959. Edward Arnold, London.

KUENEN, P. H. " Marine Geology." 1950. Wiley. (Chapman & Hall, London.)

SPARKS, B. W. " Geomorphology." 1960. Longmans Green, London.

WRIGHT, W. B. " The Quaternary Ice Age." 2nd edition. Macmillan.

Chapter 2

THE STUDY OF MINERALS

After tracing, in the preceding pages, the course of geological processes acting at the earth's surface, we now examine the rocks and minerals which are subject to their activities.

Minerals are the units which make up a rock, just as bricks put together make a building. A *rock* may therefore be defined as an assemblage of minerals; the term includes soft and loose materials such as clays and sands, as well as the harder substances which would popularly be called "rock." Three broad groups are distinguished:

1. *Igneous Rocks.* These have originated below the earth's surface, and have solidified from a hot, molten condition. E.g. basalt, granite.
2. *Sedimentary Rocks,* made of the breakdown products of older rocks, fragments of which have been brought together and sorted by the action of water or wind at the earth's surface, and built up into sedimentary deposits. E.g. sandstone, clay.
3. *Metamorphic Rocks,* derived from either igneous or sedimentary rocks, but recrystallized from their original condition by the action of heat and pressure. E.g. marble, slate.

Rocks of all these kinds go to form the earth's *crust*, i.e., the outer rigid shell of our planet, accessible at the surface and in quarries, cuttings, mines, and deep borings. Igneous rocks compose by far the greater part of the crust (see p. 165). As is well known from the evidence of deep mining operations, temperature increases downwards from the surface at an average rate of 1° C. for approximately every 110 feet. The rate is higher near an active volcanic centre. The pressure under which the rocks exist also increases with depth, due to the weight of superincumbent material. Assuming that the temperature gradient persists through the crust, it is readily calculated that at depths of 15 to 20 miles temperatures would be such that most known rocks would melt. But owing to the effect of the high pressures which must prevail at such depths, it is unlikely that matter there is in a molten condition. A small increase in temperature or decrease of pressure, however, might result in the formation of local bodies of mobile rock-material.

The average composition of the earth's crust has been estimated to be as follows:

SiO_2	59·1%	Na_2O	3·7%		
Al_2O_3	15·2	K_2O	3·1		
Fe_2O_3	3·1	H_2O	1·3		
FeO	3·7	TiO_2	1·0		
MgO	3·5	P_2O_5	0·3		
CaO	5·1	rest	0·9	Total:	100·0

The last item includes the oxides of manganese, barium, zirconium, lithium, strontium, and other metals including useful ones such as copper, zinc, and nickel; and also gases such as carbon dioxide, sulphur dioxide, chlorine, fluorine, and many others.

From these figures it can be shown that eight elements together form 98 per cent. of the crust. In order of abundance they are: oxygen (47%), silicon (27%), aluminium (8%), iron (5%), calcium ($3\frac{1}{2}$%), sodium ($2\frac{1}{2}$%), potassium ($2\frac{1}{2}$%), and magnesium (2%). These elements, combined in various ways as metallic silicates and oxides, make up most of the *rock-forming minerals*. The other minerals, which account for the remaining 2 per cent of the crust, include carbonates, phosphates, sulphates, sulphides, chlorides, and fluorides. Some metals, for example gold and silver, occur in small quantities " native," i.e. in an uncombined state.

Before beginning the study of rocks it is necessary to know something of the chief minerals which compose them. A *mineral* is defined as a natural inorganic substance having a definite chemical composition or range of composition, and a regular atomic structure to which its crystalline form is related.

The chief rock-forming minerals are silicates, since silicon and oxygen are the chief constituents of the earth's crust. Although over a thousand different minerals are known to the mineralogist, the common silicates are relatively few. They are described, together with the main non-silicate minerals, in the next chapter. For a complete classification the student is referred to text-books on Mineralogy such as those mentioned on page 60.

Minerals are studied and identified by means of their *physical* and *optical characters*, their *crystalline form*, and their *chemical composition*; these properties are discussed in the following pages.

PHYSICAL CHARACTERS

Included under this head are properties such as *colour, lustre, form, hardness, cleavage, fracture*, and *specific gravity*. Not all of these properties would necessarily be needed to identify any one mineral; two or three of them taken together may be sufficient, apart from optical properties (p. 52). Other characters such as *fusibility, magnetism*, and *electrical conductivity* are also useful in some cases as means of identification, and will be referred to as they arise in the descriptions of mineral species. In a few instances *taste* (e.g. rock-salt) and *touch* (e.g. talc, feels soapy) are valuable indicators

Colour. Some minerals have a distinctive colour, for example the green colour of chlorite. On the other hand, most naturally occurring minerals contain traces of substances which modify their colour. Thus quartz, which is colourless when pure, may be white, grey, pink or yellow, when certain chemical impurities or included particles are present.

Much more constant is the colour of a mineral in the powdered condition, known as the *streak*. This may be produced by rubbing the mineral on a piece of unglazed porcelain, called a streak-plate, or other rough surface. Streak is useful, for example, in distinguishing the various oxides of iron :

hematite (Fe_2O_3) gives a red streak, limonite (hydrated Fe_2O_3) a brown, and magnetite (Fe_3O_4) a grey streak.

Lustre. Lustre is the appearance of a mineral surface in reflected light ; it depends upon the amount of reflection that occurs at the surface. It may be described as *metallic*, as in pyrite or galena ; glassy or *vitreous*, as in quartz ; *resinous* or greasy, as in opal ; *pearly*, as in talc ; or *silky*, as in fibrous minerals such as asbestos and satin-spar (fibrous gypsum). Minerals with no lustre are described as *dull*.

Form. Under this heading come a number of terms which are commonly used to describe the various forms assumed by minerals in groups or clusters ; the crystalline form of minerals is discussed on page 48.

Acicular—in fine needle-like crystals, e.g. schorl, natrolite.

Botryoidal—consisting of spheroidal aggregations, somewhat resembling a bunch of grapes ; e.g. chalcedony. The curved surfaces are boundaries of the ends of many crystal fibres arranged in radiating clusters.

Concretionary or nodular—terms applied to minerals found in detached masses of spherical, ellipsoidal, or irregular shape ; e.g. the flint nodules of the Chalk.

Dendritic—moss-like or tree-like forms, generally produced by the deposition of a mineral in thin veneers on joint planes or in crevices ; e.g. dendritic deposits of manganese oxide.

Fibrous—consisting of fine thread-like strands ; e.g. asbestos and satin-spar.

Granular—in grains, either coarse or fine ; the rock marble is an even, granular aggregate of calcite crystals.

Reniform—kidney-shaped, the rounded surfaces of the mineral resembling those of kidneys ; e.g. kidney iron-ore, a variety of hematite.

Scaly—in small plates ; e.g. tridymite.

Tabular—showing broad flat surfaces ; e.g. the 6-sided crystals of mica.

Hardness, or resistance to abrasion, is measured relative to a standard scale of ten minerals, known as Mohs' Scale of Hardness:

1. Talc.	6. Orthoclase Felspar.
2. Gypsum.	7. Quartz.
3. Calcite.	8. Topaz.
4. Fluorspar.	9. Corundum.
5. Apatite.	10. Diamond.

These minerals are chosen so that their hardness increases in the order 1 to 10. Hardness is tested by attempting to scratch the minerals of the scale with the specimen under examination. A mineral which scratches calcite, for example, but not fluorspar, is said to have a hardness between 3 and 4, or H = 3–4. Talc and gypsum can be scratched with a finger-nail, and a steel knife will cut apatite (5) and perhaps felspar (6), but not quartz (7). Soft glass can be scratched by quartz. The hardness test, in various forms, is simple and easily made and extremely useful ; it is a ready means for distinguishing, for example, between quartz and calcite.

Cleavage. Many minerals possess a tendency to split easily in certain regular directions, and yield smooth plane surfaces called *cleavage planes* when thus broken. These directions depend on the **arrangement** of the atoms in a mineral (p. 62), and are parallel to definite crystal faces. *Perfect, good, distinct* and *imperfect* are terms used to describe the quality of mineral cleavage. Mica, for example, has a perfect cleavage by means of which it can be split into very thin flakes ; felspars have two sets of good cleavage planes. Calcite has three directions of cleavage.

Fracture. The nature of a broken surface of a mineral is known as *fracture*, the break being irregular and independent of cleavage. It is sometimes characteristic of a mineral and, also, a fresh fracture shows the true colour of a mineral. Fracture is described as *conchoidal*, when the mineral breaks with a curved surface, e.g. in quartz and flint ; as *even*, when it is nearly flat ; as *uneven*, when it is rough ; and as *hackly* when the surface carries small sharp irregularities. Most minerals show uneven fracture.

Specific Gravity. Minerals range from 1 to over 20 in specific gravity (e.g. Platinum = 21·46), but most lie between 2 and 7. For determining this property a steelyard apparatus, such as the Walker Balance, is used ; the mineral (or rock) is weighed in air and in water and the specific gravity, G, computed from the usual formula :

$$G = W_1/(W_1 - W_2),$$

where $W_1 =$ the weight in air, and $W_2 =$ the weight in water. For determinations on smaller fragments a delicate type of spring balance, or other apparatus, may be used (for descriptions of apparatus, see textbooks on Mineralogy).

The specific gravity of small mineral *grains* is estimated by the use of heavy liquids, of which the chief are :

Bromoform ($CHBr_3$), $\qquad$ G = 2·80 $\Big\}$ (dilute with benzene).
Methylene Iodide (CH_2I_2), G = 3·33

Clerici's solution,[1] $\qquad\qquad$ G = 4·25 (dilute with water).

In one method, a series of liquids (e.g. bromoform in various stages of dilution) is placed carefully in a tube, one liquid resting upon another in the order of their densities, with the heaviest at the bottom. After a time they merge and give a gradation in density which increases downwards. Grains will sink in this column to the level where their density corresponds to that of the liquid ; the tube is calibrated by means of grains whose specific gravity is known.

Heavy liquids are also used for the separation of light and heavy grains in sands (see page 127).

CHEMICAL COMPOSITION

The elements present in a mineral can be detected by means of a blowpipe analysis.[2] The composition of a mineral is also obtained by chemical analysis ; the compositions of the common rock-forming minerals are included in their descriptions in the next chapter. Rare elements may be present as small traces in certain minerals ; and of recent years various geochemical methods of testing rocks for " trace elements " have been introduced.

---

[1] A mixture of thallium formate and thallium malonate.
[2] Details of blow-pipe tests are given in " Rutley's Mineralogy " (see p. 60).

CRYSTALLINE FORM

The science of Crystallography is important in the wider study of minerals, but can only be treated in summary form here. Minerals occur as *crystals*, i.e. bodies of geometric form, bounded by *faces* arranged in a regular manner and related to the internal atomic structure. When a mineral substance grows out of a fused, liquid state (or out of solution or by sublimation), it tends to assume its own characteristic crystal shape; the angles between adjacent crystal faces are always constant for similar crystals of any particular mineral. Faces are conveniently defined by reference to *crystallographic axes*, three or four in number, which intersect in a common origin within the crystal and form, as it were, a scaffolding on which the crystal faces are erected. The arrangements of faces in crystals possess varying degrees of symmetry; according to their type of symmetry, crystals can be arranged in seven Systems of crystallization, which are summarized below and illustrated in Fig. 13. A *plane of symmetry* divides a crystal into exactly similar halves, each of which is the mirror image of the other; it contains one or more of the crystallographic axes. The

System	Axes	Planes of Symmetry	Mineral Examples
CUBIC (or Isometric)	3 equal axes at right angles to one another	9	Garnet, leucite, fluorite, rocksalt, zinc-blende, pyrite
HEXAGONAL AND TRIGONAL	4 axes: three equal and horizontal, and spaced at equal intervals; one vertical axis	7	Beryl, nepheline, apatite Tourmaline, calcite, quartz
TETRAGONAL	3 axes at right angles: two equal and horizontal, one vertical axis longer or shorter than the others	5	Zircon, cassiterite (tin-stone), idocrase
ORTHORHOMBIC	3 axes at right angles, all unequal	3	Olivine, enstatite, topaz, barytes
MONOCLINIC	3 unequal axes: the vertical axis (c) and one horizontal axis (b) at right angles, the third axis (a) inclined in the plane normal to b	1	Orthoclase felspar, hornblende, augite, biotite, gypsum
TRICLINIC	3 unequal axes, no two at right angles	none	Plagioclase felspars, axinite

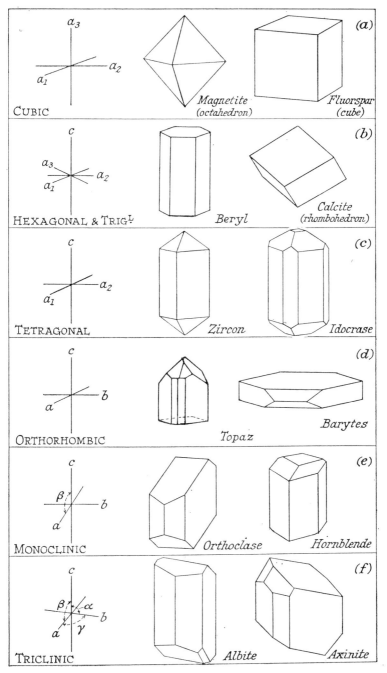

CUBIC

a_3
a_2
a_1

Magnetite
(octahedron)

Fluorspar
(cube)

(a)

HEXAGONAL & TRIG^L

c
a_3
a_2
a_1

Beryl

Calcite
(rhombohedron)

(b)

TETRAGONAL

c
a_2
a_1

Zircon

Idocrase

(c)

ORTHORHOMBIC

c
b
a

Topaz

Barytes

(d)

MONOCLINIC

c
β
b
a

Orthoclase

Hornblende

(e)

TRICLINIC

c
β
α
b
a
γ

Albite

Axinite

(f)

FIG. 13.—CRYSTAL SYSTEMS.

number of planes of symmetry stated in the table is that for the highest class of symmetry in each of the Systems.[1]

Crystal Faces. In the Cubic system, the common forms [2] are the cube (six faces, Fig. 13a), the octahedron (eight faces, Fig. 13a), the dodecahedron (twelve diamond-shaped faces, Fig. 32b), the trapezohedron (twenty-four faces, Fig. 32c); and with lower symmetry the pyritohedron (twelve pentagonal faces, Fig. 34), and the tetrahedron (four triangular faces, the smallest number possible for a regular solid), among others. Crystals may grow as one form only, or as a combination of two or more forms ; for example, Garnet (Fig. 32) occurs as the dodecahedron, as the trapezohedron, or as a combination of the two.

In the Orthorhombic, Monoclinic, and Triclinic systems, where the axes are all unequal, faces are named as follows : A face which (when produced) cuts all three axes is called a *pyramid* ; there are eight such faces in a complete form, one in each octant formed by the axes. Faces which cut two lateral axes and are parallel to the vertical axis are known as *prisms*, and make groups of four, symmetrically placed about the axes. A *pinacoid* is a face which cuts any one axis and is parallel to the other two. A *dome* cuts one lateral and the vertical axis, and is parallel to the other lateral axis. These faces are illustrated by a crystal of Olivine (Fig. 14). In the Tetragonal system the terms pyramid and prism are used as above ; but since the two horizontal axes are equal, the term *2nd order prism* is used instead of pinacoid, and *2nd order pyramid* instead of dome.

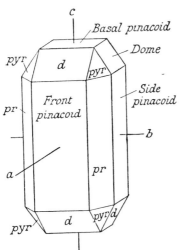

FIG. 14.—OLIVINE CRYSTAL.

To show crystal axes and faces in the orthorhombic system. *pr* = prism. *d* = dome. *pyr* = pyramid.

Lastly, in the Hexagonal and Trigonal systems the names pyramid and prism are used as before for faces which cut more than one lateral axis ; but since there are now three lateral axes instead of two, six prism faces (parallel to the *c*-axis) are found in the Hexagonal system (see Beryl, Fig. 13b), and 12 pyramid faces. In Trigonal crystals, some faces are arranged in groups of three, equally spaced around the *c*-axis. This is seen, for example, in a rhombohedron of calcite (Fig. 13b), a form having six equal diamond-shaped faces. Calcite also occurs as " nail-head " crystals, bounded by the faces of the rhombohedron combined with the hexagonal prism (Fig. 15a) ; and in " dog-tooth " crystals (Fig. 15b) where the

[1] There are 32 classes of symmetry, which are subdivisions of the seven Systems of crystallization.

[2] A *form* in crystallography is made up of faces all of one kind.

pointed terminations are bounded by six faces of the scalenohedron. In quartz crystals, the apparently symmetrical 6-sided terminations are not pyramid faces but a combination of two rhombohedra whose faces alternate, as shown by shading in Fig. 15c. This fact is shown by etching a quartz crystal with hydrofluoric acid, when two different sets of etch-marks appear

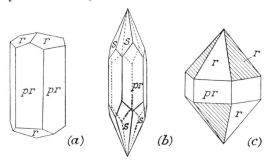

FIG. 15.—CALCITE AND QUARTZ.

(a) Nail-head spar. (b) Dog-tooth spar. (c) Quartz, with negative rhombohedron shaded. *r* = faces of rhombohedron. *pr* = prism. *s* = scalenohedron.

on the alternate triangular faces. The trigonal symmetry of quartz is also shown by extra faces which are sometimes present.

Symbols are given to crystal faces and are based on the lengths of the intercepts which the faces make on the crystallographic axes, or the reciprocals of the intercepts (Miller symbols). The subject of notation cannot be further discussed here, but is treated fully in works listed at the end of this chapter.

Twin Crystals and Crystal Aggregates. When two closely adjacent crystals have grown together with a crystallographic plane or direction common to both, but one reversed relative to the other, a *twin crystal* results.

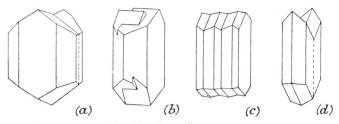

FIG. 16.—TWIN CRYSTALS.

(a) Augite, showing re-entrant angle ; twin plane parallel to front pinacoid. (b) Carlsbad twin of Orthoclase. (c) Multiple twin of plagioclase (Albite twinning). (d) Arrow-head twin of Gypsum.

It is convenient in many cases to think of a twin as a single crystal sectioned by a plane (the twin plane), one-half of the twin being rotated relative to the other half on this plane. If the rotation is 180°, points at opposite ends of a crystal are thus brought to the same end as a result of the twinning and re-entrant angles between crystal faces are then frequently produced and are characteristic of many twins. Examples are shown in Fig. 16.

The felspar twins are important ; in orthoclase the plane on which the two halves of the twin are united may be parallel to the side pinacoid (Carlsbad twin, Fig. 16b), or to a diagonal plane (Baveno twin), or to the basal pinacoid (Manebach twin). These are all *simple twins.* The plagioclase felspars develop repeated or *multiple twinning* on planes parallel to the side pinacoid (Fig. 16c) ; the twin lamellæ are generally narrow and are seen as regular parallel stripes on certain faces of a plagioclase crystal (such as the basal plane ; see also p. 74).

Twin crystals are a special case of *crystal aggregates* ; the latter range from irregular groups of crystals to perfectly parallel growths. A crystal aggregate is made up of two or more individuals, and may contain crystals of different kinds or all of one kind.

The foregoing short account of crystals is necessarily incomplete, but the features which have been indicated form a background to the further study of minerals in thin section.

OPTICAL PROPERTIES OF MINERALS

Rock Slices. The use of the petrological microscope in the study of minerals was made possible by a device due by H. C. Sorby of Sheffield, in 1850. Sorby, applying the method used earlier by W. Nicol for sectioning fossil wood, prepared slices of minerals and rocks so thin that light could be transmitted through them and their contents studied under the microscope.

In making a rock slice, a chip of rock (or slice cut by a rotating steel disc armed with diamond dust) is smoothed on one side and mounted

FIG. 17.—THIN SECTION OF ROCK PREPARED FOR THE MICROSCOPE.

on a strip of glass 3 inches by 1 inch. Continental slides are $1\frac{3}{4} \times 1$ inch. The specimen is cemented to the glass strip by means of Canada balsam, a gum which sets hard after being heated. The mounted chip of rock is then ground down with carborundum and emery abrasives to the required thinness, generally 30 microns (1 micron = $\frac{1}{1000}$ millimetre). It is now a transparent slice, and is completed by being covered with a thin glass strip fixed with balsam. Surplus balsam is washed off with methylated spirit. The surfaces of the specimen have been smoothed in making the slice, and they are free from all but very small irregularities. The effects observable when light is transmitted through such a slice of crystalline material are described in the following pages.

Refraction and Refractive Index. A ray of light travelling through one medium is bent or *refracted* when it enters another medium of different density. Fig. 18 shows the path of such a ray (RR), which makes angles *i* and *r* with the normal (NN) to the surface separating the two media. The angle between the ray and the normal to the surface is smaller in the optically denser medium, i.e. a ray is bent towards the normal on entering a denser medium, and conversely.

If the angle of incidence is measured for air, as is usual, then the ratio $\dfrac{\sin i}{\sin r}$ is called the *refractive index*, n, for the other medium, and is constant whatever the angle of incidence. It can be shown that $\sin i$ and $\sin r$ are proportional to the velocities of light (v_1, v_2) in the two media, i.e. $n = \dfrac{\sin i}{\sin r} = \dfrac{v_1}{v_2}$. The refractive index of a substance is therefore inversely proportional to the velocity of light through the substance.

When a ray (R'R', Fig. 18) passes from one medium (n_1) into another of lower refractive index (n_2), at an angle of incidence known as the *critical angle* (i_c), it is refracted along the interface between the two media. If the

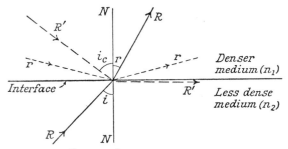

FIG. 18.—REFRACTION OF RAYS OF LIGHT AT THE INTERFACE BETWEEN TWO MEDIA.

angle of incidence exceeds the critical angle, the ray will not cross the interface but will be totally reflected from it, as shown for the ray *rr* in the figure. This property is made use of in the Nicol prisms which form an important part of the petrological microscope.

For Canada balsam, the gum in which rock slices are mounted, $n = 1.54$. Minerals with a much higher or lower refractive index than this appear in stronger outline, in a thin section under the microscope, than those which are nearer in value to balsam (this is illustrated by some of the minerals shown in Fig. 30); garnet ($n = 1.83$) is an example of a mineral which shows a very strong outline. Minerals whose refractive index is near to 1.54 appear in weak relief, as in the case of quartz ($n = 1.553$ to 1.544). Some minerals have an index less than that of balsam, e.g. fluorspar ($n = 1.43$).

Becke's Test. The refractive index of a crystal can be compared with that of an adjacent crystal or of Canada balsam by means of this test. In the case of a mineral in contact with balsam at the edge of a slice, a bright line of light appears along the margin of the mineral. This is best seen with a high-power objective, and is due to the concentration of light rays refracted at the boundaries of the mineral. On racking *up* the focussing screw of the microscope a short distance, the bright Becke line moves into the substance with the *higher* refractive index. Conversely, on racking *down*, the bright line moves into the medium of *lower* refractive index. It is thus possible to determine whether the refractive index of a mineral is above or below 1·54, or, in the case of two adjacent minerals, which of them has the higher value. Best results are obtained from crystal margins which are approximately vertical in the slice, i.e. not overlapping obliquely.

Polarized Light. According to the Wave Theory of Light, a ray is represented as a wave motion, propagated by vibrations in directions at right angles to the path of the ray. In ordinary light these vibrations take

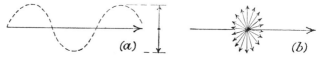

(a) *(b)*

FIG. 19.—(*a*) POLARIZED LIGHT, consisting of vibrations in one plane.
(*b*) ORDINARY LIGHT (diagrammatic), composed of many vibrations in planes containing
the direction of the ray.
Double-headed arrows represent double amplitude of vibrations.

place in all planes containing the direction of propagation ; in plane polarized light the vibrations are confined to one plane (Fig. 19*a*). Light which passes through a crystal is, in general, polarized. While much can be learned from a microscopic examination of minerals in ordinary transmitted light, polarized light enables minerals to be identified with certainty, reveals twin crystals, and shows the nature of mineral alterations.

Double Refraction. Crystals other than those in the Cubic system have the property of splitting a ray of light which enters them into two rays, one of which is refracted more than the other. A cleavage rhomb of clear calcite does this effectively, as is shown if it is placed over a dot on a piece of paper ; two dots are then seen on looking down through the crystal, i.e. two images are produced (1 and 2 in Fig. 20). On turning the crystal, one dot appears to move round the other. The light passing through the calcite is split into two rays, called the ordinary ray (O) and the extraordinary ray (E). The two rays travel at different velocities in the crystal, the E-ray being the faster, and both rays are plane polarized.

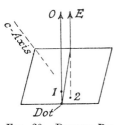

FIG. 20.—DOUBLE RE-
FRACTION OF CALCITE.
O = ordinary ray. E =
extraordinary ray. 1,
ordinary image. 2, extra-
ordinary image.

A mineral which has this property of dividing a ray of light into two is said to be *doubly refractive* or *birefringent*. Since the two rays within the mineral travel at different velocities, there are two values of refractive index, one for each ray. The difference between these two values is known as the *birefringence* of the mineral ; it is spoken of as " strong " or " weak " birefringence according as its amount is great or small. Calcite is an example of a strongly birefringent mineral ; its maximum and minimum indexes of refraction are 1·658 and 1·486, and its birefringence is therefore 0·172. Quartz is an example of a mineral with a weak birefringence, 0·009.

Minerals which have the same refractive index for light which enters in any direction are called *isotropic* ; they do not divide a ray entering them and are therefore *singly refracting*. All Cubic crystals are isotropic, and also all basal sections of Hexagonal and Tetragonal crystals.[1]

The Nicol Prism. It is possible to isolate one of the two rays passing through a doubly refracting calcite crystal by means of an invention due to W. Nicol (1828). A long rhomb of clear calcite, the variety known as Iceland Spar, is taken and cut diagonally (along AC, Fig. 21) ; the two halves are re-cemented by Canada balsam. The ends of the crystal are ground down to a position AB, so that they make an angle of 68° with the long edge of the rhomb. A ray of light (R) entering the prism is divided into ordinary and extraordinary rays as described above. The film of balsam is at such an angle to the path of the O-ray that the latter is totally reflected from it, and absorbed in the black mount of the prism. Only the E-ray passes through the balsam and emerges from the opposite face of the calcite ; the vibrations of this ray are parallel to the short diagonal of the end face of the prism, and the plane in which they occur is called the vibration plane of the nicol.

Petrological Microscope. Two Nicol prisms, called *nicols* for short, are mounted in the petrological microscope ; one (the *polarizer*) is below the stage, the other (the *analyser*) above the stage, Fig. 22. The lower nicol or polarizer is capable of rotation against a spring-loaded catch which normally holds it in one position. The analyser cannot be rotated (except in some special instruments) but can be slid into and out of the tube of the microscope. When the polarizer is held in position by its catch, the two nicols are so set that the vibration directions for their E-rays are at right angles. This setting is known as " crossed nicols." The stage of the microscope can be rotated and is graduated in degrees. In many modern microscopes, discs of polaroid are used instead of nicol prisms. Polaroid is a synthetic material which polarizes light passing through it, and gives similar results to the nicol.

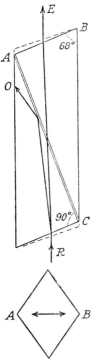

FIG. 21. — NICOL'S PRISM.

AC = film of balsam.
R = incident ray.
O = ordinary ray.
E = extraordinary ray.

Passage of Light through the Microscope. Light is reflected

---

[1] There is one direction in a calcite crystal along which light entering it is not split into two rays, but passes through the crystal undivided and unpolarized. This direction is known as the *optic axis* of the crystal, and in calcite it coincides with the *c*-axis (crystallographic). Such a mineral is called *uniaxial* ; all Hexagonal and Tetragonal minerals are uniaxial. Orthorhombic, Monoclinic, and Triclinic crystals all have *two* optic axes, i.e. two directions along which light can pass without being doubly refracted. They are therefore called *biaxial*.

from the mirror (Fig. 22) up through the polarizer, where it is plane polarized. If no mineral or rock section is placed on the stage, the light from the polarizer passes up through the objective and so enters the analyser, vibrating as it left the polariser. Since the analyser only transmits vibrations at right angles to those from the polarizer, the nicols being " crossed," no light emerges from the eyepiece of the microscope. This fact should be tested as follows : With polarizer in, analyser out, look through the eye-piece and adjust the mirror so that the light is reflected

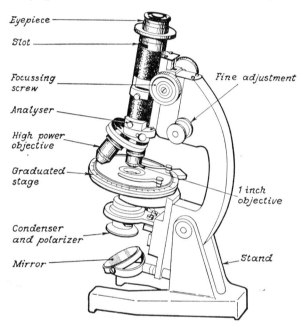

FIG. 22.—A PETROLOGICAL MICROSCOPE.

up the tube. Slide in the analyser; a completely dark field of view should result if the nicols are in adjustment and of good quality.

But with a slice of a doubly refracting mineral placed on the stage of the microscope, and nicols crossed, a coloured image of the mineral is usually seen. A thicker or thinner slice of the same mineral produces a different colour. These effects are explained as follows :

The ray of light which leaves the polarizer vibrating in one plane enters the thin section of the mineral on the stage of the microscope, and in general becomes resolved into two rays (since the mineral is birefringent), an O-ray and an E-ray. One of these travels faster than the other through the mineral slice; they can therefore be called the " fast " ray and the " slow " ray. They emerge from the slice vibrating in two planes at right angles (Fig. 23), and there is a phase difference between them, since they have travelled at different speeds and by different paths through the mineral slice.

The two rays enter the upper nicol (analyser), where each is again resolved into two by the doubly refracting calcite.   Of these *four* rays now

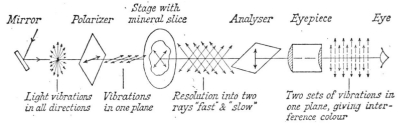

FIG. 23.—PASSAGE OF LIGHT THROUGH MICROSCOPE (diagrammatic).

travelling through the analyser, the two O-rays are totally reflected inside the prism, while the two E-rays emerge from it *vibrating in the same plane* but out of phase with one another.   This results in interference between the emergent vibrations, and the eye sees an interference colour, also called the *polarization colour*, which is of diagnostic value.

Polarization Colours.   White light is made up of waves of coloured light, from red at one end of the spectrum to violet at the other.   Each colour has a different wave-length;   that of red light, for example, is 0·00076 mm., and of violet light 0·00040 mm.   These lengths are also expressed as 760 and 400 millimicrons respectively.   (1 millimetre = 1000 microns = 10^6 millimicrons, or $\mu\mu$).

The interference of the two rays leaving the analyser of the microscope results in the suppression of some colours and the enhancement of others. A colour is intensified when its two waves are additive ;   another is eliminated when the two waves for that colour cancel one another.   Whether the two waves for any particular colour are additive or the reverse depend on the amount of the phase difference (acquired in the mineral slice) in relation to the wave-length for the colour in question.   The complete or partial suppression of some components of the white light leaves a balance which is the interference or polarization colour.

The polarization tints shown by minerals between crossed nicols form the series known as Newton's Scale of Interference Colours ;   a familiar example of Newton's Scale is provided by the colours seen in a thin film of oil resting on water.   They can be demonstrated by means of a tapering slice of a single mineral ;   a *quartz wedge* is such a slice, cut from a quartz crystal parallel to its *c*-axis and ground so that it increases in thickness from zero at one end to about 0·25 mm. at the other.   It is mounted in Canada balsam between glass strips, and can be inserted in a slot in the tube of the microscope in a direction at 45° to the plane of the nicols. The wedge when viewed between crossed nicols shows a series of colour bands across its length (Fig. 24).   At the thin end come greys, which pass into paler grey, then white, yellow, orange, and red as the thickness increases. This red marks the end of the 1*st Order* of colours.   Next come violet, blue, green, yellow, orange, and a second and brighter red which marks the end

G E —E

of the *2nd Order*. The colours of the spectrum are repeated in the 3rd and 4th Orders, but these contain progressively more delicate tints, and in the 5th and higher orders (at the thick end of the wedge) the colours become so

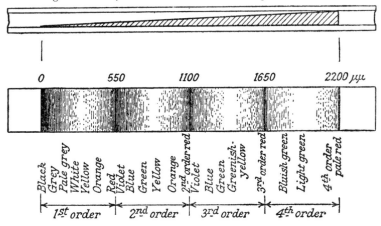

FIG. 24.—QUARTZ WEDGE and (below) NEWTON'S SCALE OF COLOURS.

pale that they ultimately merge into white. The phase difference between two waves of white light which gives a rise to a 1st Order red is 550 $\mu\mu$, that for the 2nd Order red 1100 $\mu\mu$, and so on, a red colour appearing at intervals of 550 $\mu\mu$.

The polarization colour obtained with a particular mineral slice depends on (1) the birefringence of the slice, which in turn depends on the refractive indexes of the mineral and the direction in which it has been cut; and (2) the thickness of the slice.[1] These facts are illustrated by the quartz wedge and are discussed further in the next paragraph.

Polarization of Quartz. A crystal of quartz has a maximum refractive index of 1·553, for light vibrating parallel to the *c*-axis of the crystal, and a minimum value of 1·544 for light vibrating in a direction perpendicular to the *c*-axis, (Fig. 25). The difference in these two values is 0·009, which is the maximum birefringence for the mineral. This birefringence holds only for a longitudinal slice of a quartz crystal; the polarization colour of such a slice is a pale yellow (if the slice is of standard thickness). As explained above, the polarization colour is produced by the interference of two rays which have acquired a phase difference in traversing the mineral; the birefringence of 0·009 represents a phase difference of 0·009 microns, or 9 millimicrons, per micron thickness of slice. Since the usual thickness is 30 microns, the full phase difference between the two rays after passing

[1] For let v_1 and v_2 be the velocities of the fast and slow rays in the mineral slice' and t the time in which the fast ray traverses the slice of thickness l. Then $l = v_1 t$.

In the same time the slow ray has gone a distance $l' = v_2 t$. The phase difference, or lag of one ray behind the other, is given by

$$l - l' = v_1 t - v_2 t, = t\left(\frac{1}{v_2} - \frac{1}{v_1}\right).v_1 v_2, = l\left(\frac{1}{v_2} - \frac{1}{v_1}\right).v_2,$$

i.e. phase difference is proportional to the thickness of the slice and to the birefringence.

through the slice of quartz is 30 × 9 = 270 millimicrons, which corresponds to a pale yellow in the 1st Order of Newton's Scale (Fig. 24).

Consider now a basal section of quartz, i.e. one cut perpendicular to the c-axis (the direction *aa* in Fig. 25). Such a slice has only one value of refractive index for light vibrations traversing it. It has therefore no birefringence, i.e. it is isotropic and appears completely black between crossed nicols.

Between the above extremes, the pale yellow colour (maximum) and black (or nil), a slice of quartz cut obliquely to the c-axis will show a white or grey polarization colour, the tint passing from dark grey to pale grey and white as the orientation of the slice approaches parallelism with c-axis.

Thus, in general, a crystal slice gives a characteristic colour between crossed nicols according to the direction in which it has been cut from the

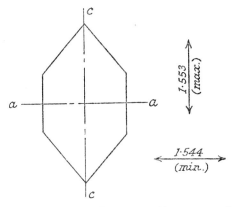

FIG. 25.—VIBRATION DIRECTIONS AND REFRACTIVE INDICES IN A VERTICAL SECTION
OF QUARTZ.
(*cc* = direction of c-axis   *aa* = direction of a lateral axis.)

mineral. The maximum birefringence and polarization colour of some common minerals, for a 30-micron thickness of slice, are given below :

Mineral	Max. Biref.		Colour.
Muscovite	0·043	1290 $\mu\mu$ =	3rd order delicate green.
Olivine	0·035	1050 ,, =	bright 2nd order red.
Augite	0·025	750 ,, =	2nd order blue.
Quartz	0·009	270 ,, =	1st order pale yellow.
Orthoclase	0·007	210 ,, =	1st order grey.

Extinction. When a birefringent mineral slice is rotated on the microscope stage between crossed nicols, one or other vibration direction in the mineral can be brought parallel to the vibration plane of the polarizer. This occurs four times in each complete rotation. In such positions the light vibrations from the polarizer pass directly through the mineral slice to the analyser, where they are cut out, so that no light emerges ; the mineral thus appears completely dark at intervals of 90° during rotation. This effect is known as *extinction*. Half-way between successive extinction positions the mineral appears brightest.

The nicols of the microscope are so set that their vibration planes are parallel to the cross-wires of the diaphragm, one " east-west," the other " north-south." If now a mineral is found to be in extinction when some crystallographic direction such as its length or a prominent cleavage is brought parallel to a cross-wire, the mineral is said to have *straight extinction* with regard to that length or cleavage. If extinction occurs when the length of the mineral makes an angle with the cross-wire, it is said to have *oblique extinction* ; the extinction angle can be measured by means of the graduations around the edge of the stage.

Pleochroism. This is the name given to the change of colour seen in some minerals when only *one nicol*, the polarizer, is used and the mineral is rotated on the stage of the microscope. Pleochroism is due to the fact that the mineral absorbs the components of white light differently in different directions, well seen in the mica biotite. When this mineral is oriented with its cleavage direction parallel to the vibration plane of the polarizer it appears a much darker brown than when at 90° to that position. Hornblende and tourmaline are two other strongly pleochroic minerals.

Twinkling. Certain minerals have one value of refractive index much higher than, and the other nearer to, that of Canada balsam (1·54). The values for calcite, for example, are 1·66 and 1·49. When a slice containing crystals of calcite is viewed through the microscope and the polarizer rotated below it (the analyser not being used), the crystals show a change in relief and strength of outline as the vibrations from the polarizer coincide alternately with the directions of maximum and minimum refractive index in the mineral. The result is a characteristic *twinkling* effect. It is also seen in the mineral dolomite.

Summary of Observations with a thin slice of mineral or rock:

1. Ordinary Light. Look for form, cleavage, colour, inclusions, and alteration products. Estimate refractive index (Becke's Test).
2. Polarized Light. (*a*) One nicol : Test for pleochroism, twinkling. (*b*) Crossed nicols : Cubic minerals are isotropic. In other (anisotropic) minerals observe the polarization colour, extinction, twinning. Examine opaque minerals by reflected light (or " top light," i.e. light reflected from the surface of the mineral).
3. The magnification of the microscope, for the combination of lenses used, may be estimated by observing a scale with small graduations: the apparent diameter of the microscope field divided by the intercept seen on the scale gives the approximate magnification.

BOOKS FOR FURTHER REFERENCE

" Rutley's Mineralogy," by H. H. READ. 25th edition, 1957. Murby & Co.
" Introduction to Geology " (Chap. 3, Mineralogy), by H. H. READ and J. WATSON. 1962. Macmillan.

Chapter 3

THE ROCK-FORMING MINERALS

The silicate minerals, as already indicated, are the most important rock formers ; they are described first in this chapter, and are followed by the chief non-silicate minerals. The order adopted for the silicate groups is based on the results of X-ray analysis, of which a brief statement is given below. For the purpose of this book, only the commonly occurring members of each group are described in detail. Less common species are referred to in small-type notes which can be omitted on a first reading. While the nomenclature may perhaps seem formidable at the start, the student should not be discouraged by the necessity for remembering a comparatively small number of new names. A working knowledge of the common rock-forming minerals is essential to any further study of the rocks.

It is convenient to distinguish between minerals which are *essential* constituents of the rocks in which they occur, their presence being implied by the rock name, and others which are *accessory*. The latter are commonly found in small amount in a rock but their presence or absence does not affect the naming of it. *Secondary* minerals are those which result from the decomposition of earlier minerals, often promoted by the action of water in some form, with the addition or subtraction of other material, and with the formation of by-products.

Atomic Structures. In recent years the atomic structure of crystals has been investigated by methods of X-ray analysis.[1] The arrangement and spacing of the atoms of which a crystal is composed control its regular form and properties. For example, the atoms of sodium and chlorine in a crystal of common salt (NaCl) are arranged alternately at the corners of a cubic pattern (Fig. 26), which is repeated indefinitely in all directions. Salt crystals grown from solution are cubes, a shape which echoes the internal structure.

When the silicate minerals were investigated it was found that they could be placed in a very few groups, according to the arrangement of the silicon and oxygen atoms. These groups corresponded broadly to the existing

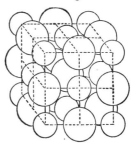

FIG. 26.—ARRANGEMENT OF ATOMS IN NaCl (small circles, Na ; large circles, Cl).

mineral families which had long before been worked out from a study of their shape and symmetry. A silicon atom is tetravalent, and is always surrounded by four oxygen atoms which are spaced at the corners of a regular tetrahedron (Fig. 27a). This SiO_4-tetrahedron is the unit of silicate structure, and is built into the different structures as follows :

[1] See, for example, " Crystal Structures of Minerals," by W. L. Bragg and G. F. Claringbull. 1965. Bell, London ; and W. L. Bragg, " Atomic Structure of Minerals." 1937.

61

1. *Separate SiO_4-groups* are found in some minerals, e.g. olivine, garnet. In olivine the tetrahedra are closely packed in regularly spaced rows and columns throughout the crystal structure, and are linked together by metal atoms (Mg, Fe, Ca, etc.) situated between the tetrahedra. Since each oxygen has two negative valencies and silicon four positive valencies, the SiO_4-group has an excess of four negative valencies ; these are balanced when it is linked to metal atoms contributing four positive valencies, as in olivine, Mg_2SiO_4. Some Mg atoms may be replaced by Fe. (*Note :* In this account the word atom is used throughout instead of ion, which is more strictly correct.)

2. *Single Chain Structures* (Si_2O_6) are formed by SiO_4-groups linked together in linear chains, each group sharing two oxygens with its neighbours (Fig. 27c). This structure is characteristic of the Pyroxenes, e.g. diopside, $CaMg(Si_2O_6)$. Similar considerations to those mentioned above as regards valencies hold good here. The chains lie parallel to the c-axis of the mineral, and are bonded together by Mg, Fe, Ca or other atoms, which lie between them. The vertical cleavages in the mineral run between the chains, as shown in Fig. 27h, and intersect at an angle of 87°. Aluminium atoms, since they have nearly the same size as silicon, may replace silicon in the structure to a limited extent, and may also occur among the atoms which lie between the chains ; in this way aluminous pyroxenes such as augite are formed.

Ring structures are built up by groups of three, four, or six tetrahedra, each of which shares two oxygens with its neighbours. Fig. 27b shows a ring of six linked tetrahedra, which is found in the mineral beryl, $Be_3Al_2Si_6O_{18}$.

3. *Double Chain Structures* (Si_4O_{11}), in which two single chains are joined together side by side (Fig. 27e), are found in the Amphiboles, e.g. tremolite, $Ca_2Mg_5(Si_4O_{11})_2(OH)_2$. The double chains run parallel to the c-axis of the minerals, and are linked laterally by metal atoms lying between the chains. The cleavage directions are as shown in Fig. 27i, and intersect at an angle of 124°. In hornblende, aluminium replaces part of the silicon (cf. augite above). Hydroxyl groups, (OH), are always present in the Amphiboles to the extent of about one to every eleven oxygens.

4. *Sheet Structures* (Si_4O_{10}) are formed when the SiO_4-tetrahedra are linked by three oxygens each, and lie with their bases in a common plane (Fig. 27g). Sheets of this kind are found in the Micas and other flaky minerals (e.g. chlorite, talc, the clay minerals), whose perfect cleavage is parallel to the silicon-oxygen sheets. In the mica muscovite, $KAl_2(AlSi_3)O_{10}(OH)_2$, aluminium replaces about one quarter of the silicon, and hydroxyl is always present. The Si_4O_{10}-sheets are arranged in pairs, with aluminium atoms between them, and each pair is separated from the next pair by a layer of potassium atoms. Other structures involving silicon-oxygen layers are discussed under Clay Minerals, p. 132.

5. *Three-dimensional Frameworks* (SiO_2) are formed when each tetrahedron is linked by all four corners, each group sharing its four oxygens with adjacent groups. The mineral quartz, SiO_2, has a framework in which the SiO_4-groups form a series of linked spirals. In the Felspars another type of framework is found, and Al replaces part of the Si. Thus in orthoclase felspar, one silicon in four is replaced by Al ; the substitution of trivalent aluminium for a tetravalent silicon releases one negative (oxygen) valency, which is satisfied by the attachment of a univalent sodium or potassium atom, thus :

Orthoclase $= KAlSi_3O_8$; Albite $= NaAlSi_3O_8$; and Anorthite $= CaAl_2Si_2O_8$. The K, Na, or Ca atoms are accommodated in spaces within the frameworks.

The above results are summarized in the table on page 64.

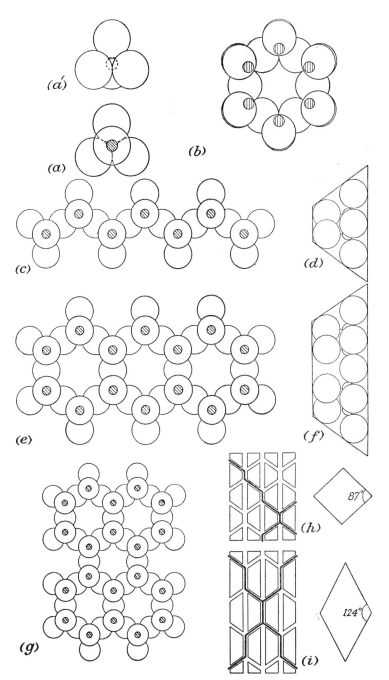

Fig. 27.—Silicate Structures.

Small shaded circles represent silicon, open circles oxygen atoms, in approximate relative sizes. (*a, a′*) SiO₄-tetrahedron in plan and elevation. (*b*) Si₆O₁₈ ring. (*c*) Single chain, Si₂O₆. (*d*) Single chain, end view. (*e*) Double chain, Si₄O₁₁. (*f*) Double chain, end view. (*g*) Si₄O₁₀ sheet. (*h* and *i*) Stacking of single and double chains respectively, (viewed along *c*-axis), and resulting cleavage directions.

Type of Structure	Repeated Pattern	Example of Mineral
Separate SiO_4-groups	SiO_4	Olivine
Single Chain	Si_2O_6	Pyroxenes
Double Chain	Si_4O_{11}	Amphiboles
Sheet	Si_4O_{10}	Micas
Framework	$\begin{cases}(Al, Si)_n O_{2n} \\ SiO_2\end{cases}$	Felspars Quartz

Progress from the simple structure of separate tetrahedra to the three-dimensional framework involves increasing complexity of atomic structure; this is related in a general way to physical properties such as density and refractive index, which decrease as the atomic structures become more complex. Also, those minerals of simple structure (e.g. olivine) crystallize out early from magma, at a high temperature, whereas those of more complex structure tend to form at successively lower temperatures. The descriptions which follow are given in the order of the groups above.

Identification of Minerals in the Hand Specimen. Many minerals can be identified in a rock specimen with some degree of certainty, but it is not always possible to do this, for two reasons: (i) the mineral may be too small to be identifiable easily; (ii) only one or two characteristic features may be seen, and these together may be insufficient to determine the mineral. In such cases, low magnification (six or eight diameters) with a pocket lens may be enough, but failing that recourse must be had to the microscope for identification.

It should be possible to identify the common rock-forming minerals in the hand specimen with a pocket lens where one dimension of the mineral grain is not less than about 1 mm. With practice much smaller grains can be determined. The most useful characteristics for this purpose are:

1. General shape of grains, depending on the crystallization of the mineral; the faces of well-formed crystals can often be observed, but where grains have been modified (e.g. by rounding) other properties must be used.
2. Colour and transparency.
3. Presence or absence of cleavage.
4. Presence or absence of twinning, and type of twinning.
5. Hardness.

In the following descriptions of minerals, notes are included to aid identification in the hand specimen on the above lines. They are followed by notes on the simpler optical properties of the mineral; the abbreviations *R.I.* (refractive index) and *Biref.* (birefringence) are used throughout, and in stating the polarization colours of minerals it is assumed that sections are of normal thickness (30 microns).

SILICATE MINERALS

THE OLIVINE GROUP

Olivine.

Common olivine has the composition $(MgFe)_2SiO_4$, in which Fe replaces part of the Mg. The name Forsterite is given to pure Mg_2SiO_4, a mineral found in some metamorphosed limestones (p. 149); the corresponding iron silicate Fayalite, Fe_2SiO_4, is rare in nature.

Crystals : Orthorhombic (Fig. 14); pale olive-green or yellow; vitreous lustre; conchoidal fracture. $H = 6\frac{1}{2}$. $G = 3\cdot2$ to $3\cdot6$.

Olivine occurs chiefly in basic and ultrabasic rocks. Since it crystallizes at a high temperature, over 1000° C., it is one of the first minerals to form from many basic magmas [1]; the crystals thus grow in a largely fluid medium and develop their own characteristic shape. Decomposition to green serpentine (p. 80) is common.

PROPERTIES IN THIN SECTION. Porphyritic crystals [2] commonly show 6- or 8-sided sections, the outline generally somewhat rounded. Cleavage rarely seen; irregular cracks common (Fig. 30*A*).

Colour : None when fresh. Alteration to greenish serpentine is very characteristic, this mineral being often developed along cracks and around the margins of olivine crystals. Some olivines have been entirely converted to serpentine; or relics of original olivine may be preserved as isolated colourless areas in the serpentine. Magnetite (Fe_3O_4) may be formed, during the alteration, from iron in the original olivine, and appears as small black specks in the serpentine.

Mean R.I. = $1\cdot66$ to $1\cdot68$, giving a bold outline in Canada Balsam.

Biref : Strong (max. = $0\cdot04$), giving bright 2nd and 3rd order polarization colours. Twinning is usually absent.

THE PYROXENE GROUP

The pyroxenes belong to two systems of crystallization :

1. Orthorhombic, e.g. *Enstatite, Hypersthene.*
2. Monoclinic, e.g. *Diopside, Augite, Aegirite.*

They possess two good cleavage directions parallel to the prism faces of the crystals (*prismatic cleavage*); the intersection angle of the cleavages is nearly 90°, a characteristic feature of the group (see Fig. 27*h*). They form 8-sided crystals, and being silicates of Fe and Mg they are dark in colour (except diopside).

ORTHORHOMBIC PYROXENES

Enstatite, $MgSiO_3$. **Hypersthene,** $(MgFe)SiO_3$.

Enstatite generally contains a small amount of Fe which replaces part of the Mg; when the proportion of $FeSiO_3$ exceeds 15 per cent of

---

[1] *Magma* is the name given to molten rock material from which igneous rocks have consolidated (see. p. 88).

[2] Porphyritic crystals are large compared with the grain size of the matrix in which they are set; they are generally well-formed crystals.

the whole, certain optical properties are changed and the mineral is called hypersthene.[1]

Crystals : Usually dark brown or green (hypersthene nearly black), 8-sided and prismatic. In addition to the prismatic cleavages mentioned above there are poorer partings parallel to the front and side pinacoids ; lustre, vitreous to metallic. H = 5 to 6. G = 3·2 (enstatite), increasing with the iron content to 3·5 (hypersthene).

The minerals occur in some ultrabasic rocks and in basic rocks such as norite (*q.v.*), as black lustrous grains interlocked with the other constituent minerals ; also in some andesites, usually as small black porphyritic crystals.

PROPERTIES IN THIN SECTION. 8-sided cross-sections are shown when crystals are idiomorphic,[2] with two good cleavages nearly at right angles ; traces of a third cleavage are sometimes seen, parallel to the side pinacoid.

Colour : Enstatite is nearly colourless and not pleochroic ; hypersthene shows pleochroism from pale green to pink.

Mean R.I. = 1·65 (enstatite) to 1·73 (hypersthene) ; cf. augite.

Biref : Weak ; max. = 0·008 (enstatite) rising to 0·016 (hypersthene), giving grey, white, or yellow 1st order polarization colours.

Extinction : Straight with reference to the cleavage in longitudinal sections parallel to the *c*-axis. Twinning rare.

Enstatite and hypersthene are distinguished from augite by their weaker birefringence and straight extinction, and relative scarcity of twinning.

MONOCLINIC PYROXENES

Augite, $(CaMgFeAl)_2(SiAl)_2O_6$.

A complex aluminous silicate whose formula can be written as above in conformity with the Si_2O_6 pattern of the atomic chain structure. The relative proportions of the metal atoms (Ca, Mg, Fe, Al) are variable within limits, giving a range of composition and therefore different varieties of the mineral.

Crystals : Commonly 8-sided and prismatic, terminated by two pyramid faces at each end ; brown to black in colour, vitreous to resinous lustre. Twin crystals (Fig. 16a) show a re-entrant angle. H = 5 to 6. G = 3·3 to 3·5.

Augite occurs chiefly in basic and ultrabasic rocks ; e.g. in gabbro, where it appears as dark areas intermingled with the paler felspar. In fine-grained basic rocks it is not distinguishable in the hand specimen unless it is porphyritic. Augite is also a constituent of some andesites and diorites, and occasionally of granites.

PROPERTIES IN THIN SECTION. Idiomorphic crystals show characteristic 8-sided transverse sections, bounded by prism and pinacoid faces, with the two prismatic cleavages intersecting at nearly 90°. Longitudinal sections show only one cleavage direction (Fig. 30B).

---

[1] The names " enstatite " and " hypersthene " have Greek derivations which refer to the colour change in pleochroism : *enstates,* weak ; *sthene,* strong.

[2] *idiomorphic* = having its own form, i.e. well-developed.

Colour : Pale brown to nil ; except a purplish variety containing titanium (titaniferous augite). Zoning (see p. 75) and " hour-glass structure " are shown by colour variations. Pleochroism generally absent.

Mean R.I. = about 1·70, giving strong relief in balsam.

Biref : Strong (max. = 0·025). Polarization in bright 1st and 2nd order colours, in sections of normal thickness. Weak biref. shown by some sections.

Extinction : Oblique, up to 45° in longitudinal sections, except those parallel to the front pinacoid, which show straight extinction. In transverse sections extinction is symmetrical with the intersecting cleavages. Simple and " strip " twins are frequent.

Alteration : Augite may change to chlorite (p. 80) by hydration, with the loss of some constituents ; epidote and calcite may form as by-products.

Diallage. A variety of augite possessing an extra parting parallel to the front pinacoid, which gives the mineral a laminated structure. Colour, green or greenish-brown ; lustre, metallic. In thin section the prominent parting appears as closely spaced parallel lines, and the mineral is easily recognized by this feature. Found in gabbros.

Diopside, $CaMg(Si_2O_6)$. A non-aluminous pyroxene forming 8-sided crystals, usually pale green in colour. It occurs in some basic rocks and

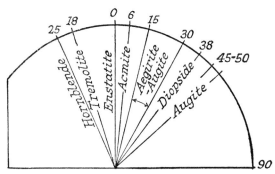

FIG. 28.—EXTINCTION ANGLES OF PYROXENES AND AMPHIBOLES, ON SIDE PINACOID SECTIONS (010).

in metamorphic rocks such as contact-altered impure limestones. In thin section it is colourless or very pale green, but similar in polarization colour to augite. It differs from augite in having a smaller extinction angle (38°) and somewhat lower R.I.

Aegirite, $NaFe'''(Si_2O_6)$, usually with some Ca, Mg, and Al in small amounts. (The name *acmite* is used for the pure silicate.) Crystals are usually green or brown in colour, 6-sided and prismatic ; vitreous lustre. H = 6. G = 3·5. Occurs chiefly in Na-rich rocks, such as nepheline-syenite and phonolite, where (like augite) its dark colour is in contrast with the other constituents. It is not always identifiable without an examination in thin section. The name *aegirite-augite* is used for minerals intermediate between augite and aegirite (i.e. with some content of NaFe'''').

PROPERTIES IN THIN SECTION. Cross-sections often 6-sided, longitudinal sections elongated ; cleavages as in augite.

Colour : Green ; pleochroism marked, in shades of green and greenish-brown.
Mean R.I. = about 1·77.

Biref : Strong (max. = 0·04), giving 3rd order polarization colours which are largely masked by the green body-colour of the mineral.

Extinction : Oblique in most longitudinal sections, at a small angle (about 6° for acmite) : this and the colour and pleochroism are means of distinction from augite. Aegirite-augite has a larger extinction angle, from 15 to 30° in side pinacoid sections (see Fig. 28).

THE AMPHIBOLE GROUP

This large family of minerals crystallizes in the Orthorhombic, Monoclinic and Triclinic systems, but only the Monoclinic amphiboles [1] are of importance here. They have a tendency to form long, prismatic crystals, and have two good cleavage directions parallel to the prism faces, meeting at 124°, an angle which is determined by the lateral spacing of the atomic chains in the crystal structure (Fig. 27*i*). The most common amphibole is *hornblende*, of which there are numerous varieties.

Hornblende, $(CaMgFeNaAl)_{3-4}(AlSi)_4O_{11}(OH)$.

A complex aluminous silicate whose formula can be written as above. The relative proportions of the metal atoms vary within the limits shown, giving a range of composition ; the (OH)-radicle is found in all amphiboles (cf. " water of crystallization ").

Crystals : Monoclinic, dark brown or nearly black ; usually 6-sided, of longer habit than augite, with three dome faces at each end (Fig. 13*e*). Twinning on the front pinacoid results in a crystal of similar appearance, but having four faces at one end and two at the other. Vitreous lustre. H = 5 to 6. G = 3 to 3·4.

Hornblende commonly occurs in diorites and andesites as the dark constituent ; in andesite it is porphyritic and may be recognized by its elongated shape, the length of the crystals being often several times their breadth. It is also found in syenites and in some granites, and in metamorphic rocks such as hornblende-schist.

PROPERTIES IN THIN SECTION. 6-sided transverse sections, bounded by four prism and two pinacoid faces, are very characteristic (Fig. 30*C*), and show the prismatic cleavages intersecting at 124°. Longitudinal sections are elongated and show one direction of cleavage parallel with the crystal's length.

Colour : Green to brown ; pleochroism strong in shades of green, yellow and brown. A brown variety, often with a dark border, is called " basaltic hornblende " and contains ferric iron.

Mean R.I. varies from 1·63 to 1·72 in different hornblendes.

Biref : Strong (max. = 0·024), giving 2nd order polarization colours which are somewhat masked by the body-colour of the mineral.

Extinction : Oblique in most longitudinal sections, at angles up to 25° with the cleavage ; sections parallel to the front pinacoid show straight extinction. Twinning is common.

Alteration to chlorite, with the formation of by-products, is often seen.

[1] From the Greek *amphibolos*, doubtful (superficially resembling pyroxene).

Hornblende is to be distinguished from augite by its colour and lower maximum angle of extinction; and from biotite, which it may resemble in sections showing one cleavage direction, by the fact that biotite always gives straight extinction.

Tremolite, $Ca_2Mg_5(Si_4O_{11})_2(OH)_2$ ⎫
Actinolite, $Ca_2(MgFe)_5(Si_4O_{11})_2(OH)_2$ ⎬ Non-aluminous amphiboles.
⎭

Crystals : Elongated, often in bladed aggregates; colour white (tremolite) or green (actinolite), sometimes translucent; vitreous lustre. H = 5 to 6. G = about 3.

These minerals occur mainly in metamorphic rocks, e.g. tremolite in impure contact-altered limestones, actinolite in metamorphosed basic rocks such as actinolite-schist.

PROPERTIES IN THIN SECTION. Elongated crystals, sometimes in radiating clusters; diamond-shaped cross-sections with two good cleavages intersecting at 124°.
Colour : Tremolite is colourless; actinolite, pale green and weakly pleochroic.
Mean R.I. = 1·62 to 1·64.
Biref : = 0·027 (max.), giving bright 2nd order polarization colours.
Extinction : Oblique in longitudinal sections, up to 18°.

Asbestos. The fibrous form of tremolite, in which crystals grow very long and are flexible. In commerce the term " asbestos " also includes other fibrous minerals such as *chrysotile* (a form of serpentine, *q.v.*) and *crocidolite* (a soda-amphibole). These minerals are useful because of their resistance to heat and because of their fibrous nature, which enables them to be woven into fireproof fabrics, cord, and brake-linings, and made into boards, tiles, and felt.

THE MICAS

Probably the most prominent feature of the micas is their property of splitting into very thin flakes, due to their perfect basal cleavage. The reason for this cleavage lies in the atomic sheet-structure possessed by these minerals (see p. 62). They are conveniently grouped as: (1) LIGHT MICAS, which include *muscovite* [1] (potash mica), the rarer *paragonite* (sodium mica), and *lepidolite* (lithium mica); and (2) DARK MICAS, which range from *phlogopite* (magnesium mica), through *biotite* [2] (ferromagnesian mica), to the iron-rich *lepidomelane*. Biotite and muscovite are the two commonest species. Muscovite and phlogopite have important uses as insulators in electrical apparatus, because of their high dielectric strength.

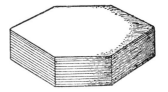

FIG. 29.—MICA CRYSTAL.

Crystals are Monoclinic, with a pseudo-hexagonal symmetry which yields 6-sided tablets or " books " of mica; the perfect cleavage is parallel to the basal plane (Fig. 29). Cleavage flakes are flexible, elastic, and generally

---

[1] Named after Muscovy, Russia, where it was first found.
[2] Named after its French discoverer, M. Biot.

transparent. A 6-rayed percussion figure is seen when a flake is struck with a pointed instrument, and one of the three cracks thus produced is parallel to the plane of symmetry of the crystal.

Muscovite, $KAl_2(Si_3Al)O_{10}(OH)_2$.

Form and cleavage as stated above. White in colour, unless impurities are present to tint the mineral; pearly lustre. $H = 2$ to $2\frac{1}{2}$ (easily cut with a knife). $G =$ about 2·9 (variable).

Muscovite occurs in granites and other acid rocks as silvery crystals, from which flakes can be readily detached by the point of a penknife. Also in some gneisses and schists. It is a very stable mineral, and persists as minute flakes in sedimentary rocks such as micaceous sandstones. The name *sericite* is given to secondary muscovite; it may be produced by the alteration of orthoclase (see p. 73). The mica of commerce comes from large crystals found in pegmatite veins (p. 111).

PROPERTIES IN THIN SECTION. Longitudinal sections (i.e. across the cleavage) are often parallel-sided and show the perfect cleavage (Fig. 30D); basal sections appear as 6-sided or irregular colourless plates. Alteration uncommon.

Mean R.I. = 1·59.

Biref: Strong (max. = 0·04), giving bright 3rd order pinks and greens in longitudinal sections. Basal sections have a weak double refraction.

Extinction: Straight, with reference to the cleavage.

Biotite, $K(MgFe)_3(Si_3Al)O_{10}(OH)_2$.

Crystals are brown to nearly black in hand specimen; single flakes are pale brown and have a sub-metallic or pearly lustre. Form and cleavage as stated above. $H = 2\frac{1}{2}$ to 3. $G = 2\cdot8$ to $3\cdot1$.

Biotite occurs in many igneous rocks, e.g. granites, syenites, diorites, and their lavas and dyke rocks, as dark shiny crystals, distinguished from muscovite by their colour. Also a common constituent of certain gneisses and schists.

PROPERTIES IN THIN SECTION. Sections showing the cleavage often have two parallel sides and ragged ends (Fig. 30D). In some biotites, small crystals of zircon enclosed in the mica have developed spheres of alteration around themselves by radioactivity. These spheres in section appear as small dark areas or " haloes " around the zircon and are pleochroic.

Colour: Shades of brown and yellow in sections across the cleavage, which are strongly pleochroic; the mineral is darkest (i.e. light absorption is a maximum) when the cleavage is parallel to the vibration direction of the polarizer. Basal sections have a deeper tint and are only feebly pleochroic.

Mean R.I. = about 1·64.

Biref: Strong, about 0·05 (max.) in sections perpendicular to the cleavage, but the 3rd order polarization colours are obscured by the body-colour of the mineral. Basal sections are almost isotropic.

Extinction: Parallel to the cleavage. Alteration to green chlorite is common, when the mineral loses its strong birefringence and polarizes in 1st order greys (see under Chlorite).

Phlogopite, $KMg_3(Si_3Al)O_{10}(OH)_2$. Less deeply coloured than biotite,

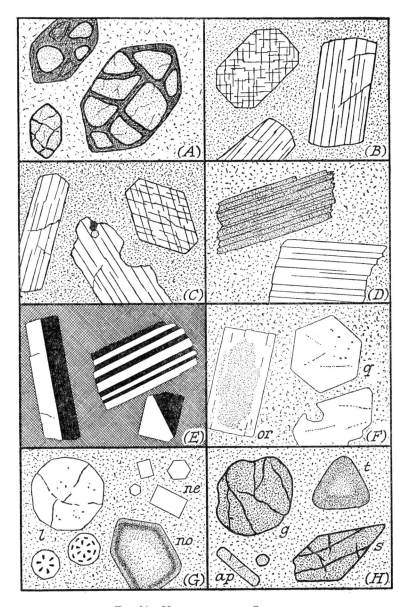

FIG. 30.—MINERALS IN THIN SECTION.

(A) Olivine, with serpentine-filled cracks. (B) Augite. (C) Hornblende. (D) Mica (biotite, dark ; muscovite, light). (E) Felspars (crossed nicols) : simple twins of ortho-clase, multiple twin of plagioclase. (F) Quartz (q) and kaolinized orthoclase (or). (G) Felspathoids : leucite (l) ; nepheline (ne), nosean (no). (H) Garnet (g), sphene (s), apatite (ap), and tourmaline (t).

sometimes a coppery red ; often shows a 6-rayed star pattern (asterism) when a cleavage flake is held up to the light. Found in certain igneous rocks and in metamorphosed impure limestones. *R.I.* and birefringence are similar to those of biotite.

THE FELSPAR GROUP

The felspars [1] are the most abundant of all the silicate minerals and are essential constituents of most igneous rocks. They have framework structures (p. 62), and form monoclinic and triclinic crystals ; they are aluminous silicates of potassium, sodium, and calcium, the chief members of the group being :

Orthoclase, $KAlSi_3O_8$.
Albite, $NaAlSi_3O_8$.
Anorthite, $CaAl_2Si_2O_8$.

There is also the rare barium-felspar, *Celsian,* $BaAl_2Si_2O_8$.

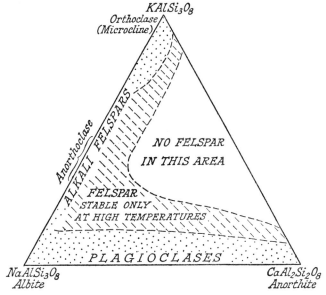

FIG. 31.—FELSPAR COMPOSITION DIAGRAM (after Chudoba).

For a felspar represented by a point within the triangle, the proportions of the three quantities Orthoclase, Albite, Anorthite are given by the lengths of the perpendiculars from the point on to the sides of the triangle.

Mixtures of orthoclase and albite occur over a somewhat limited range (see Fig. 31) and are known as the *alkali felspars* ; they commonly contain a large amount of one member (orthoclase or albite) with a smaller amount of

---

[1] Also spelt " feldspar."

the other. They include orthoclase, soda-orthoclase (containing some Na), and anorthoclase (in which the proportion of Na is greater than K, see below). Mixtures of albite and anorthite, however, occur in all proportions [1] and constitute the *plagioclase felspars*, an important series which is used for purposes of rock classification. The subdivisions of this series are given on p. 74.

Orthoclase, KAlSi$_3$O$_8$. " Potash-felspar."

Crystals : Monoclinic ; white or pink in colour, vitreous lustre ; bounded by prism faces, basal and side pinacoids, and domes (Fig. 13e). Simple twins are frequent : Carlsbad twins unite on the side pinacoid (Fig. 16b), Manebach twins on the basal plane, and Baveno twins on a diagonal plane (dome) parallel to the a-axis (Fig. 30E). Two good cleavages, parallel to the side and basal pinacoids, intersect at 90° ; the name of the mineral is due to this property (from the Greek *orthos*, straight or rectangular, and *klasis*, breaking). H = 6. G = 2·56. A colourless glassy variety is known as *sanidine*, a high temperature form found in quickly-cooled lavas.

Orthoclase occurs in granites and syenites as hard, cleaved white or pink crystals, generally constituting the greater part of the rock. In the dyke rocks related to granites and syenites, orthoclase may occur as porphyritic crystals (see p. 98). Found also in some gneisses and felspathic sandstones.

PROPERTIES IN THIN SECTION. Shape often nearly rectangular if crystals are idiomorphic, irregular if interlocked with other minerals. Cleavage not always seen.

Colour : None when fresh, but shows frequent alteration to kaolin (p. 151), when the mineral appears " cloudy " and looks white by top light.

Mean R.I. = 1·52 ; this is below that of Balsam, and may provide a useful means of confirming identification, using Becke's test.

Biref : Weak (max. = 0·008), giving 1st order grey and white polarization colours, in sections of normal thickness.

Extinction : Usually oblique, up to 21° on the side pinacoid ; sections perpendicular to the side pinacoid show straight extinction. Simple twins common ; distinguished from plagioclase by the absence of multiple twinning. *Alteration* to kaolin (p. 81) is common ; sometimes alters to an aggregate of small secondary white mica flakes (*sericite*), revealed by their bright polarization colours.

Microcline, KAlSi$_3$O$_8$. Triclinic potash-felspar.

Crystal form is similar to that of orthoclase, but the two cleavages (parallel to the basal and side pinacoids) meet at 89½° instead of exactly 90°.

Colour : White, pink, or green.

R.I. and *Biref :* Similar to orthoclase. Multiple twinning, with two intersecting sets of gently tapering twin-lamellæ ; in thin sections this is seen as a characteristic " cross-hatching " effect between crossed nicols, and distinguishes microcline from other felspars. Found, for example, in granites subjected to stress.

Anorthoclase. Triclinic alkali-felspar (Fig. 31), with more Na than K. One specimen analysed had the composition : albite 65 per cent, orthoclase

---

[1] The complete range of mixtures in the plagioclases is possible because the atoms of Na and Ca are nearly the same size, and either can enter the same atomic framework without distorting it. But the K-atom is larger, and cannot be built so readily into one crystal structure with the smaller Na and Ca atoms.

35 per cent, with mean R.I. = 1·525, and G = 2·58. Properties in thin section similar to those of microcline. Anorthoclase is the beautiful grey schillerized [1] felspar which occurs in *laurvikite* (a Norwegian syenite, p. 110); it is also found as rhomb-shaped crystals in *rhomb-porphyry* in the Oslo district.

The Plagioclases.

Felspars of this series are formed of mixtures (solid solutions) of albite, $NaAlSi_3O_8$, and anorthite, $CaAl_2Si_2O_8$, in all proportions. The range of composition is divided into six parts, each of which is given a specific name, as follows :

From 100 to 90% Albite, and	0 to	10% Anorthite .	.	*Albite*
„	90 „ 70	„	„	10 „	30	„	.	*Oligoclase*
„	70 „ 50	„	„	30 „	50	„	.	*Andesine*
„	50 „ 30	„	„	50 „	70	„	.	*Labradorite*
„	30 „ 10	„	„	70 „	90	„	.	*Bytownite*
„	10 „ 0	„	„	90 „	100	„	.	*Anorthite*

A plagioclase, for example, containing 40 per cent albite and 60 per cent anorthite would be called labradorite.

Crystals : Triclinic ; white or colourless (albite) to grey (labradorite), bounded by prisms, basal and side pinacoids, and domes (Fig. 13*f*). Vitreous lustre. Cleavages are parallel to the basal and side pinacoids, and meet at an angle of about 86° (hence the name, from the Greek *plagios*, oblique ; *klasis*, breaking). Multiple twins parallel to the side pinacoid (Albite twinning, Fig. 16*c*) are characteristic of the plagioclases ; the closely spaced twin-lamellæ can often be seen with a lens as stripes on the basal cleavage and other surfaces. Another set of twins is sometimes developed on planes, parallel to the *b*-axis, which usually make a small angle with the basal pinacoid (Pericline twinning). H = 6 to 6½. G = 2·60 (albite), rising to 2·76 (anorthite).

Plagioclase felspars occur in most igneous rocks, and in some sedimentary and metamorphic types. In the coarser grained igneous rocks the plagioclase appears as white or grey cleaved crystals, and is often distinguishable by its multiple twinning.

PROPERTIES IN THIN SECTION. Idiomorphic crystals (e.g. in lavas) commonly show rectangular sections ; parallel-sided " laths," with their length several times as great as their breadth, are seen when the crystals sectioned are tabular (i.e. flat and thin) parallel to the side pinacoid (see Fig. 38 (4)). Cleavage not often visible. The minerals are normally colourless but may be clouded with alteration products.

The characteristic multiple twinning appears as light and dark grey parallel stripes between crossed nicols (Fig. 30*E*), and sets of alternate stripes extinguish obliquely in different positions.

---

[1] *Schiller* is the play of colours seen by reflected light in some minerals, in which minute platy inclusions are arranged in parallel planes ; the schiller effect is produced by the interference of light reflected from these included plates.

Mean R.I. and other optical properties are as follows:

	Mean R.I.	Maximum Biref.	Max. Symmetrical Extinction Angles for twin-lamellæ, in sections perpendicular to side pinacoid (see below).
Albite	1·53	0·011	from 18° to 12°
Oligoclase	1·54	0·008	„ 12 „ 0, 0 to 13
Andesine	1·55	0·007	„ 13 „ 27
Labradorite	1·56	0·009	„ 27 „ 39
Bytownite	1·57	0·010 ⎫ over 39°	
Anorthite	1·58	0·012 ⎭	

Albite and andesine, which may have the same angle of extinction, have values of R.I. which are respectively below and above 1·54 (the R.I. of Balsam), and Becke's test may be used to decide a particular case.

The values of extinction angle given above apply only to those sections in which the twin planes are perpendicular to the plane of the slice. This condition is fulfilled, (1) if a crystal shows even illumination when the twin-lamellæ are parallel to one of the cross-wires, and (2) if the sets of alternate twin-lamellæ extinguish symmetrically on either side of a cross-wire. To test this, select a likely crystal and note the angles of extinction of alternate lamellæ by turning the stage of the microscope to the left and to the right, starting each time from the mid-position where the twin-lamellæ are parallel to a cross-wire. The two angles thus obtained should be equal, or very nearly so. Measure a number of suitable crystals in the slice and take the *maximum* value as the criterion. It is important to follow this rule closely.

As a first approximation, it should be noted that a symmetrical extinction angle of a few degrees (or straight extinction in a microlith) indicates an oligoclase, and a wide angle one of the basic plagioclases such as labradorite.

A description of other methods of distinguishing the different plagioclases in thin section is beyond the scope of this book.

Zoning : (1) A plagioclase crystal may contain numerous inclusions which became locked up in it at some period during its growth ; these inclusions are often arranged in zones parallel to the crystal faces. The core of a crystal, for instance, may contain many inclusions while the marginal zone is clear. This is known as zoning by inclusions.

(2) Zoning also results from differences in the composition of successive layers of material acquired during a crystal's growth. For example, a plagioclase may have begun to grow as anorthite ; but because of changes in the relative concentrations of constituents in the melt which was breeding the crystal, further growth may have made use of material containing progressively less anorthite and more albite. A slice of such a crystal seen between crossed nicols does not show sharp extinction in one position, but the zones of different composition extinguish successively at slightly different angles as the slice is rotated.

Zoning is also shown by minerals other than plagioclase, e.g. augite, tourmaline.

THE FELSPATHOID GROUP

Minerals of this group resemble the felspars chemically, and have 3-dimensional framework structures (p. 62) ; they differ from the felspars in their lower content of silicon. Stated in another way, the Al : Si ratio is higher in the felspathoids than in the corresponding felspars. The two chief felspathoids, which are only briefly discussed here because their occurrence is somewhat limited in nature, are :

Leucite, $K(AlSi_2)O_6$ (cf. Orthoclase).
Nepheline, $Na(AlSi)O_4$ (cf. Albite).

Nepheline generally contains some $KAlSiO_4$, a substance which is named *kaliophilite*. Derivatives from nepheline by the addition of a sulphate, chloride, or carbonate, are :

Sodalite, $3(NaAlSiO_4).NaCl$.
Nosean, $6(NaAlSiO_4).Na_2SO_4$.
Hauyne, $3(NaAlSiO_4).CaSO_4$.
Cancrinite, $4(NaAlSiO_4).CaCO_3.H_2O$ (approx.).

Leucite, $K(AlSi_2)O_6$.

Crystals : Cubic, commonly in the form of the trapezohedron (Fig. 32c), with an imperfect cleavage. Colour, dull white (hence the name, from the Greek *leucos*, white). H = 5 to 6. G = 2·5.

Leucite occurs in certain undersaturated lavas which have a low silica- and high alkali-content, such as leucite-basalt (e.g. Vesuvian types) and leucitophyre.

In thin section, 8-sided or rounded colourless sections, often much cracked, are common. The small " sago grain " variety found in some lavas generally has symmetrically arranged inclusions (Fig. 30G).

R.I. = 1·51 (i.e. below balsam). Crystals may be isotropic, or may show anomalous double refraction in patchy 1st order greys, due to lamellar twin structures which develop as the crystals cool.

Nepheline, $Na(AlSi)O_4$.

Crystals : Hexagonal ; short 6-sided prisms when idiomorphic (as in lavas). Colourless or white. The variety *elæolite*, which occurs in plutonic rocks, has no regular form, and is grey with greasy lustre. The latter, together with its lower hardness, distinguish it from quartz. H = $5\frac{1}{2}$ to 6 (can just be cut with knife). G = 2·6.

Nepheline occurs in undersaturated rocks such as phonolite (*q.v.*) and nepheline-syenite ; weathered surfaces of the latter may be pitted where the nepheline crystals have been worn down below the level of the more resistant felspars.

In thin section, hexagonal (basal) and rectangular (longitudinal) sections are shown in lavas (Fig. 30G). Colourless when fresh, the mineral is frequently altered and then appears clouded (hence the name, from the Greek *nephele*, a cloud). Yellow cancrinite is also an alteration product.

R.I. = 1·54 (mean), slightly higher than for orthoclase.

Biref : Weak (0·004), giving low grey polarization tints. Basal sections are isotropic.

Extinction : Straight in longitudinal sections. Nepheline does not twin ; this and its usual lack of cleavage, help to distinguish it from orthoclase.

FORMS OF SILICA

Silica is found uncombined with other elements in a number of crystalline forms, of which *Quartz* is specially important and of widespread occurrence as a rock-forming mineral. Since quartz has a 3-dimensional framework type of structure (p. 62), with a Si : O ratio of 1 : 2, it is placed here with the silicate minerals. There are also high-temperature forms of silica, such as *tridymite* (see below) ; aggregates of quartz fibres give *chalcedony* (p. 80) ; the cryptocrystalline forms *flint, opal,* are described under Secondary Minerals.

Quartz, SiO_2.

Crystals: Trigonal (p. 50) ; 6-sided prisms with rhombohedral terminations (Fig. 13b), sometimes with other small faces belonging to additional forms. Vitreous lustre ; conchoidal fracture. Colourless when pure (e.g. " *rock crystal* "), but many coloured varieties occur, the colour being due to traces of impurities, e.g. *rose quartz* (pink), *smoky quartz* (grey), *milky quartz* (white), *amethyst* (violet). Some quartz contains minute inclusions or liquid-filled cavities. $H = 7$; cannot be scratched with a knife. $G = 2.66$.

Quartz occurs as an essential constituent of granites, and can be easily recognized as hard, glassy grains of irregular shape and without cleavage. Also as porphyritic crystals in acid dyke-rocks and lavas. *Vein quartz* is an aggregate of shapeless crystals, and can be recognized by its glassy or milky appearance and by its hardness ; it is often stained brown by iron oxides. Well-formed crystals are found in cavities (*druses*), occurring both in veins and in granitic rocks. Sands and sandstones are largely composed of grains of quartz, owing to its resistance to abrasion (see p. 124) ; the mineral is also found in gneisses and schists.

PROPERTIES IN THIN SECTION. Basal sections are regular hexagons (Fig. 30F) when the crystals are well-formed ; see Fig. 25 for longitudinal section. When the mineral has crystallized among others, as in granite, its shape is irregular.

Colourless. Never shows alteration, but crystals in lavas sometimes have corroded and embayed margins.

R.I. = 1·553 (max.), 1·544 (min.) ; weak outline in Canada balsam.

Biref : = 0·009 (max.) in sections parallel to the c-axis, giving pale yellow polarization colour (see p. 59); basal sections are isotropic. Oblique sections give 1st order greys or whites. *Extinction :* Straight in longitudinal sections.

Twinning occurs, but is rarely seen in thin sections. Quartz is distinguished from orthoclase by the absence of twinning and by its entire lack of alteration ; it always appears fresh, although inclusions may be present.

Tridymite. This form of silica crystallizes at temperatures above 850° C., in small hexagonal plates, and appears in thin sections as a series of minute scales. It is found in some acid lavas, and also in artificial furnace linings such as silica bricks, where its presence is an index to the temperature reached during the burning of the brick.

ACCESSORY MINERALS

Silicates included under this head are tourmaline, garnet, sphene, zircon, and, for convenience, the metamorphic minerals andalusite and cordierite. Other accessory minerals, such as apatite and magnetite, are described under Non-silicate Minerals (p. 83).

Tourmaline. Complex boro-silicate of Na, Mg, Fe, and Al, with a structure having Si_6O_{18} rings (Fig. 27b). There are many varieties, according to the relative proportions of the metal atoms ; boron makes up nearly 2 per cent of the whole, and is an essential part of the mineral.

Crystals : Trigonal ; commonly long black prismatic forms (Fig. 32*a*), which show striations parallel to their length. Vitreous lustre. Red, green and blue transparent varieties, sometimes zoned, are cut for gems.

Schorl is an iron-rich tourmaline which commonly grows in radiating clusters of needle-like crystals, e.g. in pneumatolysed granites (p. 150). H = 7. G = 3 to 3·2.

Tourmaline occurs as an accessory in some granites ; also in vein rocks such as pegmatites, which fill fissures where steam and vapours containing boron and fluorine have been active. It is frequently idiomorphic and black in colour, and is then easily recognized.

In thin section, colour is yellow to greenish-grey (Fig. 30*H*) ; frequently shows colour zoning ; strongly pleochroic, maximum absorption occurring when the length of a longitudinal section is at right angles to the vibration direction of the polarizer, and the mineral then appears darkest.

R.I. = 1·65 (max.), 1·62 (min.).

Biref : Moderately strong, but polarization colours are often masked by the body-colour. Basal sections are isotropic. Extinction parallel to length.

Garnet. The garnets form a group having the general composition $R_3''R_2'''(SiO_4)_3$, where $R'' = $ Ca, Mg, Fe, or Mn, and $R''' = $ Al, Fe''', or Cr. Common garnet is the claret-red *almandine*, $Fe_3Al_2(SiO_4)_3$, or the dark brown *andradite*, $Ca_3Fe_2(SiO_4)_3$. Among the other species may be mentioned *pyrope*, $Mg_2Al_2(SiO_4)_3$, precious garnet ; and *grossular*, $Ca_3Al_2(SiO_4)_3$ in some metamorphosed limestones.

Crystals : Cubic, in the form of the trapezohedron (Fig. 32*c*), the rhomb-dodecahedron (Fig. 32*b*) or combinations of the two. H $= 6\frac{1}{2}$ to $7\frac{1}{2}$. G $= 3·5$ to 4·2, for the different species.

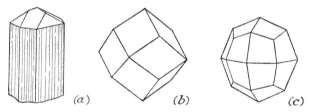

(*a*)　　　　　(*b*)　　　　　(*c*)

Fig. 32.—(*a*) CRYSTAL OF TOURMALINE. (*b*) GARNET, rhomb-dodecahedron (12 faces). (*c*) GARNET, trapezohedron (24 faces).

Garnet commonly occurs in metamorphic rocks such as mica-schist, as well-formed crystals (porphyroblasts, p. 146) ; also as an accessory mineral in granites and other igneous rocks.

In thin section, garnet stands out in bold relief by reason of its high R.I. (1·7 or more), and often presents a somewhat rounded outline (Fig. 30*H*) ; no cleavage ; generally broken by irregular cracks. Colourless or pale pink. Garnet is isotropic (i.e. transmits no light between crossed nicols).

Sphene (Titanite), $CaTiSiO_5$.

Crystals : Monoclinic ; flat and wedge-shaped (named from the Greek *sphene*, a wedge). Colour : Generally yellow, brown, or grey. Prismatic cleavage. Frequently twinned. H = 5. G = 3·5. Sphene occurs as small well-formed crystals in many granites, diorites, and syenites.

In thin section, sphene stands out in strong relief on account of its high *R.I.* (1·9 to 2·0), and surface irregularities are emphasized. Pleochroism is often marked. *Biref:* Strong, giving delicate polarization tints which are usually masked by the body colour. The wedge shape is characteristic (Fig. 30*H*).

Zircon, $ZrSiO_4$.

The tetragonal crystals, usually very small, are bounded by prism and pyramid faces (Fig. 13*c*). Some zircons are colourless, other varieties yellow or reddish-brown. H = 7·5. G = 4·7.

Zircon contains traces of radio-active elements which give rise to pleochroic haloes, as in mica enclosing zircon (see p. 70). It occurs in granites and syenites as an original constituent (of early crystallization and therefore often enclosed in other minerals); it is very resistant to abrasion and hence frequently found as water-worn grains in the heavy residues of sands derived from the weathering of granite areas (p. 127).

In thin section, zircon appears as small colourless grains. *R.I.* = 1·93, giving a very strong outline in Balsam. *Biref:* Very strong; polarization is in high order colours. Recognized chiefly by its shape and occurrence.

Andalusite, Al_2SiO_5, or $Al_2O_3SiO_2$.

Crystals: Orthorhombic, bounded by four long prism faces and two basal pinacoids; a transverse section is nearly square. Colour: Pink or

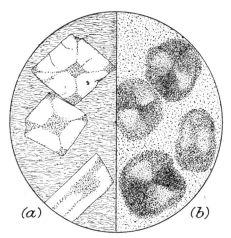

FIG. 33.—(*a*) CHIASTOLITE in chiastolite-slate. (*b*) CORDIERITE in spotted rock (crossed nicols to show sector twinning).

grey. The variety *Chiastolite* contains inclusions of carbon which are clustered mainly along the edges where two prism faces meet and down the centre of the crystal (see cross-section, Fig. 33*a*). H = 7·5. G = 3·2.

In thin section, andalusite is distinguished by its patchy pink pleochroism, the coloured areas not extending to the boundary of the mineral.

Mean R.I. = 1·64. *Biref :* Weak (0·009 max.). Chiastolite is distinguished by its carbon inclusions and shape of cross-sections.

Andalusite is found in contact-metamorphosed shales and slates (e.g. andalusite-hornfels, see p. 147), and sometimes as an accessory in granite.

Cordierite, $Mg_2Al_3(AlSi_5)O_{18}$.

Crystals : Orthorhombic; nearly hexagonal shape; groups of three crystals often grow together as sector twins (Fig. 33b). Occurs in metamorphic rocks such as spotted-rock and hornfels (p. 147) and occasionally in granites near a contact zone.

In thin section : Colourless, resembles quartz in *R.I.* and birefringence. May be distinguished from quartz by the sector twinning, by the presence of alteration products, and by its manner of growth (p. 147), which results in imperfectly formed crystals containing many inclusions; yellow pleochroic haloes are sometimes present.

SECONDARY MINERALS

Described under this head are the minerals *chlorite, serpentine, talc, kaolin, epidote, zeolite,* and *chalcedony,* all of which result from the alteration of pre-existent minerals.

Chlorite, $(MgFe)_5Al(Si_3Al)O_{10}(OH)_8$, variable.

The chlorites [1] form a family of green flaky minerals which are hydrous silicates of magnesium and aluminium. Some Fe replaces Mg and gives colour to the chlorite. Like the micas, they have a perfect cleavage, due to the " sheet " type of atomic structure (p. 62); they differ from the micas in containing no alkalies, and in other properties noted below. Different kinds of chlorite are given distinctive names (e.g. penninite, clinochlore); these are not distinguished in the following general description.

Crystals : Monoclinic, frequently 6-sided in shape, with a perfect cleavage parallel to the basal plane; the mineral splits into hexagonal flakes which are flexible but not elastic (cf. mica). H = 2 to $2\frac{1}{2}$ (often soft enough to be scratched by the finger-nail). G = 2·65 to 3·0.

Chlorite is found in igneous rocks, as described below, and in metamorphic rocks such as chlorite-schist.

PROPERTIES IN THIN SECTION. Chlorite occurs as an alteration product of biotite, augite, or hornblende; it may replace them completely, forming a *pseudomorph* (= " false form ") in which the aggregate of chlorite flakes and fibres retains the shape of the original mineral. Together with other minerals such as calcite, chlorite also forms an infilling to cavities in basalts (*q.v.*); the variety called *vermicular chlorite* appears as small rounded and " worm-like " areas.

Colour : Shades of bluish-green and yellowish-green, sometimes very pale; noticeably pleochroic; cleavage often seen.

Mean R.I. = about 1·58.

Biref : Weak; grey polarization tints, but abnormal interference colours known as ultra-blue and ultra-brown are shown by some chlorites (penninite).

Serpentine, $Mg_6Si_4O_{10}(OH)_8$. Some Fe replaces Mg.

Serpentine is an alteration product of olivine, of orthorhombic pyroxene,

[1] From the Greek *chloros,* green.

or of hornblende. One possible equation of the change from olivine to
serpentine may be written thus :

$$4(Mg_2SiO_4) + 4(H.OH) + 2CO_2 \rightarrow Mg_6Si_4O_{10}(OH)_8 + 2MgCO_3.$$
$$\text{Olivine} \qquad \text{Water} \qquad\qquad\qquad \text{Serpentine}$$

This reaction takes place in an igneous rock while it is still moderately
hot (*hydrothermal action*), the source of the hot water being magmatic ;
it is thought that the change from olivine to serpentine may also be brought
about by the action of water and silica.

Serpentine grows as a mass of green fibres or plates, which replace
the original mineral as a pseudomorph. The fibrous variety is called
chrysotile, and is worked in veins for commercial asbestos (see p. 69) ;
the name *bastite* is given to fibrous pseudomorphs after orthorhombic
pyroxene, and a platy variety of serpentine is called *antigorite*. In the
mass, serpentine is rather soapy to the touch, and may be coloured red
if iron oxide is present. H = 3 to 4. G = 2·6. Serpentine is found in
basic and ultrabasic rocks (p. 103), and in serpentine-marble.

PROPERTIES IN THIN SECTION. As a pseudomorph after olivine, serpentine appears
as a matte of green fibres, weakly birefringent, and having a low R.I. (1·57).
Specks of black magnetite, the oxidized by-product from iron in the original
olivine, are often present. The change to serpentine involves an increase in
volume, and this expansion may fracture the surrounding minerals in the rock,
fine threads of serpentine being developed in the cracks so formed.

Talc, $Mg_3Si_4O_{10}(OH)_2$. A soft, flaky mineral, white or greenish in colour,
which occurs as a secondary product in basic and ultra-basic rocks, and in talc-
schist (p. 155). It is often associated with serpentine. Flakes are flexible but
not elastic, and are easily scratched by the finger-nail. H = 1. Talc is used as
a filler for paints and rubber, as an absorbent, toilet powder, etc. *Steatite* (*soap-
stone*) is a massive form. In thin section, talc resembles muscovite in its polarization, but the rocks in which it occurs are not those which would contain muscovite,
a feature which enables the distinction to be made.

Kaolin (China Clay).

This substance is largely made up of the mineral *kaolinite*, $Al_4Si_4O_{10}(OH)_8$,
one of the group of Clay Minerals (see p. 132) ; the latter, like the micas,
are built up of silicon–oxygen sheets (p. 62).

Kaolin is derived from the breakdown of felspar by the action of water
and carbon dioxide ; the chemical equation for the change is given and
the kaolinization of granite masses is described on p. 151. It is white
or grey, soft and floury to the touch, with a clayey smell when damp.
G = 2·6. In thin section it is seen as a decomposition product of felspar,
which when altered appears clouded and looks white by top light (i.e. by
light reflected from the surface of the slice and not transmitted through it).

Epidote, $Ca_2(AlFe)_3(SiO_4)_3(OH)$.

The monoclinic crystals of this mineral are typically of a yellowish-
green colour, and are elongated parallel to the *b*-axis. Often in radiating
clusters ; vitreous lustre. H = 6 to 7. G = 3·4.

Epidote occurs as an alteration product of calcic plagioclases or of augite; also as infillings to vesicles in basalts, and as pale green veins traversing igneous and metamorphic rocks.

In thin section, grains of epidote are pale yellow and pleochroic; the basal cleavage is sometimes seen. *Mean R.I.* = about 1·75, giving a strong outline in Balsam; polarization is in bright 2nd and 3rd order colours, a distinctive feature of the mineral.

The Zeolites.

These form a group of hydrated aluminous silicates of calcium, sodium, or potassium; they contain molecular water which is readily driven off on heating, a property to which the name refers (Greek *zein*, to boil). They occur as white or glassy crystal clusters, filling or lining the cavities left by escaping gases (amygdales, p. 98) in basic lavas, and are derived from felspars or felspathoids by hydration. Artificial zeolites are manufactured and used in water-softening processes, which depend on the *base-exchange* properties of the minerals: a sodium zeolite takes up calcium ions from the calcium bicarbonate in the water being treated, in exchange for its sodium ions, which go into solution as sodium bicarbonate. The mineral is restored or " regenerated " by treating with brine, from which it again acquires sodium ions in exchange for calcium ions, and is then ready for further use.

Two commonly occurring natural zeolites are:

Analcite, $NaAlSi_2O_6H_2O$.
Crystallizes in the Cubic system and is white in colour. $G = 2.25$. Occurs as a primary mineral in undersaturated rocks such as analcite-dolerite (p. 102), as well as in the amygdales of basalts. In thin section, analcite appears as colourless isotropic plates, with R.I. = 1·487, i.e. well below that of Balsam.

Natrolite, $Na_2Al_2Si_3O_{10}2H_2O$.
Forms white, acicular orthorhombic crystals, generally in radiating clusters. $G = 2.2$. In thin section, crystals show straight extinction and weak birefringence. R.I. = 1·48.

Chalcedony, SiO_2.

Radiating aggregates of quartz fibres, having a white or brownish colour and waxy appearance in the mass. Chiefly found in layers lining the vesicles of igneous rocks. In thin section, such layers show a radiating structure, of which the crystal fibres have straight extinction and give an extinction " brush " which remains in position as the stage is rotated. *R.I.* = 1·54; polarization colours are 1st order greys.

Flint. Cryptocrystalline[1] silica, possibly with an admixture of opal, representing a dried-up gel; occurs in nodules in the Chalk (see p. 139). Often black in colour on a freshly broken surface, with conchoidal fracture. Split flints were much used in the past as a decorative facing to buildings, but the flint industry which once flourished in East Anglia is now nearly extinct.

Opal. Hydrated silica, SiO_2nH_2O; amorphous. White, grey, or yellow in colour, with a pearly appearance (opalescence), and often displaying coloured internal reflections. Conchoidal fracture. H = about 6. $G = 2.2$. Occurs as a filling to cracks and cavities in igneous rocks. When it replaces woody tissues

---

[1] *Cryptocrystalline:* made of a large number of minute crystals which are too small to be distinguished separately except under very high magnification.

it preserves the original textures and is known as *wood opal*. Opal is an undesirable constituent in rocks used for concrete aggregates, owing to the possibility of reaction occurring between it and alkalis in the cement.

In thin section, colourless and isotropic, with low *R.I.* (1·44).

NON-SILICATE MINERALS

Only the more commonly occurring non-silicate minerals have been selected for description, fuller treatment being beyond the scope of this book ; they are here listed in the order in which they are described :

Oxides : Magnetite, Hematite, Limonite, Ilmenite, Cassiterite.
Carbonates : Calcite, Dolomite, Siderite.
Phosphate : Apatite.
Sulphates : Gypsum, Barytes.
Sulphides : Pyrite, Marcasite, Pyrrhotite, Galena, Zinc-blende.
Fluoride : Fluorspar.
Chloride : Rock-salt.

Magnetite, Fe_3O_4. Magnetic oxide of iron.

Crystallizes in black octahedra (Fig. 13a, Cubic system) ; also occurs massive. Metallic lustre ; opaque. Black streak. $H = 5\frac{1}{2}$ to $6\frac{1}{2}$. $G = 5·18$. Occurs in small amount in many igneous rocks, not usually visible in hand specimen ; when segregated into large masses it forms a very valuable ore of iron, as in North Sweden and the Urals. Grains of magnetite are commonly found in the heavy residues obtained from sands.

In thin section, black and opaque when viewed by transmitted light ; by reflected light, steely grey.

Hematite, Fe_2O_3.

Crystals are rhombohedral (Trigonal), black and opaque, with steely metallic lustre ; this variety of hematite is called *specular iron ore*. *Kidney ore* is a massive, reniform variety with a radiating structure. Earthy hematite is called *reddle*. Red streak. $H = 5\frac{1}{2}$ to $6\frac{1}{2}$. $G = $ about 5·2. When it occurs in large deposits, as in Cumberland, hematite is an important ore of iron ; the great Lake Superior deposits contain 50–60 per cent of iron. Hematite is a cementing material in sandstones (*q.v.*), is soluble in dilute acids, and gives the red staining seen in many rocks (see p. 143).

In thin section, hematite appears red by " top light " or, if sufficiently thin, by transmitted light.

Limonite. $2Fe_2O_3 3H_2O$. Hydrated iron oxide.

Amorphous ; occurs in masses having a radiating fibrous structure (similar to that of hematite), in concretions, and in an earthy state. Colour, brown to yellow ; brown streak. $H = 5$. $G = 3·8$. Limonite is a very common colouring medium in rocks, and results from the hydration of other iron oxides and from the alteration of other minerals containing iron (e.g. pyrite). The mineral *Goethite*, $FeO(OH)$, is often associated with limonite ; it occurs as yellow-brown orthorhombic crystals, often tabular, and is pleochroic.

Ilmenite. FeOTiO$_2$.

Forms platy Trigonal crystals which are black and opaque. Moderately magnetic ; black streak. H = 5 to 6. G = 4·5. Found in basic igneous rocks in small grains ; also occurs massive, and may form large segregations, as in Norway and Canada. Ilmenite is the chief ore of titanium, which is used in the manufacture of white paint.

In thin section ilmenite is black and opaque when unaltered ; but it changes by hydration to a whitish substance called *leucoxene*, which can be detected by its white appearance when viewed by reflected light. The presence of the alteration product therefore helps to distinguish ilmenite from magnetite.

Cassiterite (Tin-Stone), SnO$_2$.

Crystals are tetragonal, dark brown to black in colour, opaque and heavy. Knee-shaped twins often seen. H = 6 to 7. G = 6·8. Found in veins of quartz, often associated with tourmaline and fluorspar, in granite areas (e.g. Cornwall). Water-worn grains of cassiterite can be recovered from many stream sands ("placer" deposits) in granite areas ; this type of deposit is worked extensively for commercial supplies of tin in Malaya.

Calcite, CaCO$_3$.

Crystals : Trigonal (p. 50) ; a cleavage rhombohedron is shown in Fig. 13b. "Dog-tooth spar" and "nail-head spar" (Fig. 15) are varieties formerly named from their resemblance to those objects. Generally colourless or white, but may have various tints. Cleavage is perfect, parallel to the rhombohedral faces, and twinning is common on rhombohedral planes. H = 3 ; the ease with which the mineral can be scratched with a knife affords a useful index to identification. G = 2·71. Calcite dissolves in dilute acids, with effervescence.

Limestones are essentially composed of calcium carbonate, of which the crystalline form,[1] calcite, may constitute a large part. Calcite also occurs as a secondary mineral in igneous rocks, e.g. in the amygdales of basalts. Veins of calcite often fill fractures in many rocks. Calcite is commonly associated with sulphide ores such as blende and galena in mineral veins. Vein calcite may be recognized by its white or pink colour, and is distinguished from quartz by its lower hardness.

PROPERTIES IN THIN SECTION. Crystals generally irregular in shape, colourless, the cleavage apparent in some sections.

R.I. = 1·658 (max.), 1·486 (min.) ; these values are respectively above and below the R.I. of Balsam. In consequence, a *twinkling* effect is seen when the polarizer is rotated below the slice (the analyser not being used) : the mineral shows changes in relief and strength of outline as the plane of the nicol coincides alternately with each of the two vibration directions of the calcite, with their different refractive indexes. Sections transverse to the c-axis do not show twinkling.

Biref : = 0·172 (max.) ; polarization colours are whites of the higher orders,

---

[1] Another crystalline form of calcium carbonate is *aragonite*, orthorhombic ; it is ess common, and less stable, than calcite, and is often associated with gypsum.

or delicate pinks and greens for sections whose birefringence is less than the maximum. Lamellar twinning appears as bands of colour along the diagonals of rhomb-shaped sections.

Dolomite, $CaCO_3MgCO_3$.

Crystals : Trigonal; crystals occur as rhombohedra, sometimes with curved faces. Cleavage perfect as in calcite. Colour: White, yellow or brown. Vitreous to pearly lustre. $H = 3\frac{1}{2}$ to 4 (cf. calcite). $G = 2\cdot85$. Dolomite is not readily dissolved by *cold* dilute HCl; this provides a useful test for the mineral, which may otherwise be difficult to distinguish from calcite in a rock specimen. Occurs chiefly in dolomitic limestones (see p. 137).

PROPERTIES IN THIN SECTION. Similar to those of calcite, but dolomite develops more prominent rhomb-shaped crystals and is thereby recognizable (Fig. 43 (3)). Crystals are sometimes zoned by inclusions near their borders.

Siderite (Chalybite), $FeCO_3$.

Found as brown rhombohedral crystals, and also massive. White streak, pearly to vitreous lustre. $H = 3\frac{1}{2}$ to $4\frac{1}{2}$. $G = 3\cdot8$. Siderite is important in ironstone deposits as a source of iron, e.g. the Cleveland iron ore, Yorks. It may replace calcium carbonate in a limestone and may also be precipitated direct from solution to form a sedimentary deposit (p. 143).

Apatite, $Ca_5F(PO_4)_3$ (fluor-apatite ; in chlor-apatite, Cl is present instead of F).

Crystals: Hexagonal, pyramids and prisms terminated by basal plane (Fig. 34a). Colour: Usually a brown or greenish tint, but varies greatly. $H = 5$. $G = 3\cdot2$. Apatite occurs as a common accessory mineral in many

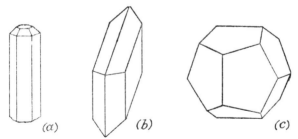

FIG. 34.—(a) APATITE. (b) GYPSUM. (c) PYRITE (pyritohedron).

igneous rocks, the crystals being usually visible only with the microscope ; large crystals occur in coarse-grained veins (pegmatites), which yield commercial supplies, from which phosphate is obtained for use as fertilizer.

PROPERTIES IN THIN SECTION. Small, colourless elongated prisms and hexagonal cross-sections are typical (Fig. 30H); sometimes in long, needle-like crystals. *R.I.* $= 1\cdot63$; the mineral shows moderately strong relief in Balsam. *Biref:* Very weak, giving low grey polarization colours. Straight extinction.

Gypsum, $CaSO_4 2H_2O$.

Forms colourless or white monoclinic crystals, diamond-shaped and flat parallel to the side pinacoid (Fig. 34b); also "arrow-head" twins (Fig. 16d). Cleavage is perfect parallel to the side pinacoid. Pearly lustre. H = 1½ to 2 (easily scratched by the finger-nail). G = 2·3. *Selenite* is the crystalline variety. *Alabaster* is a white or pink massive variety, and the form known as *satin-spar* is made of silky fibres occurring in veins.

Gypsum is formed chiefly by the evaporation of salt water in shallow inland seas, the calcium sulphate in solution being precipitated, as at the southern end of the Dead Sea; extensive deposits of Permian age, hundreds of feet thick, are worked at Stassfurt, Germany (p. 140). Gypsum is also formed by the decomposition of pyrite (FeS_2) in the presence of calcium carbonate, e.g. crystals of selenite found in the London Clay are due to this reaction. Gypsum is much used in the building industry in the manufacture of plasters and plaster board, and as a retarder of cement. *Anhydrite*, $CaSO_4$, is frequently associated with gypsum (see p. 140).

Barytes, $BaSO_4$.

Forms colourless, white, or brown orthorhombic crystals which are elongated parallel to the b-axis (Fig. 13d). Perfect cleavages are developed parallel to the prism faces and to the basal plane, so that when broken the mineral yields flat diamond-shaped cleavage fragments. Also occurs massive and in other forms. Vitreous lustre. H = 3 to 3½. G = 4·5 (hence known as "heavy spar"). Barytes, generally associated with calcite (and sometimes with the barium carbonate, *witherite*), occurs chiefly in ore-veins carrying zinc-blende and galena, e.g. in the north of England. It is used in the manufacture of paint and paper.

Pyrite, FeS_2.

Occurs as Cubic crystals, commonly in the form of the cube or the pyritohedron (a form with twelve pentagonal faces, Fig. 34c), pale brassy-yellow in colour, with metallic lustre. The faces of the cube are often striated. Pyrite strikes fire with steel (a point of distinction from marcasite), and was formerly used instead of flint in fire-arms; it is not readily soluble in hydrochloric acid. H = 6 to 6½. G = about 4·8.

Pyrite occurs in ore-veins, in shales and slaty rocks, and as an accessory mineral in some igneous rocks. It sometimes contains small quantities of copper and gold; large deposits of pyrite are worked for sulphur, as at Rio Tinto, Spain, and copper is also obtained from them.

Marcasite, FeS_2.

The orthorhombic iron sulphide, paler and slightly softer than pyrite, and decomposed readily by acids. H = 6. G = 4·9. Found in concretions in sedimentary rocks, such as the Chalk; nodules of pyrite with a radial crystalline structure are also found in the Chalk.

Pyrrhotite (Magnetic Pyrites), Fe_nS_{n+1} (where n = 6 to 11).

Forms tabular hexagonal crystals with a brownish or coppery colour. Magnetic (a distinction from pyrites). H = 4. G = 4·5. Pyrrhotite often contains a small amount of nickel (up to 5 per cent), and is then worked as a source of that metal. The extensive nickel deposits at Sudbury,

Canada, which yield the greater part of the world's nickel supply, contain a large proportion of pyrrhotite.

Galena. PbS; generally with some content of silver sulphide (" argentiferous galena "). Forms Cubic crystals, with faces of the cube and octahedra, lead-grey in colour; perfect cleavage parallel to cube faces. Also occurs massive. Metallic lustre, even fracture. $H = 2\frac{1}{2}$. $G = 7\cdot5$. Galena occurs in lodes associated with blende, calcite, quartz, and other minerals, often filling fracture zones, as at Broken Hill, New South Wales. It is also deposited in joints and fissures in limestones, as in the Derbyshire occurrences. It is the chief ore of lead and an important source of silver.

Blende. (Zinc-blende ; sphalerite), ZnS.

Forms Cubic crystals of tetrahedral type, usually brown or black in colour, with perfect cleavage parallel to crystal faces. Some varieties are transparent. Resinous lustre ; brittle, conchoidal fracture. $H = 3\frac{1}{2}$ to 4. $G = $ about 4. Blende is the principal ore of zinc, and occurs in association with galena (q.v.), e.g. in Derbyshire and Cumberland.

Fluorspar (Fluorite), CaF_2.

Cubic crystals are commonly cubes, occasionally octahedra, and may be colourless, white, green, yellow, or purple. Perfect cleavage parallel to octahedron faces ; vitreous lustre ; often transparent. $H = 4$. $G = 3\cdot2$. Sometimes zoned, from green (at centre) through white to purple (outermost zone), the latter being probably formed at a lower temperature than the white and green varieties. Fluorspar occurs in veins and is frequently associated with blende and galena, or with tinstone (see p. 84). It is used in enamels, as a flux in steel-making, and in the manufacture of certain kinds of glass. A massive purple or blue variety from Derbyshire is called " blue john " and is used for ornaments.

Rock Salt (Halite), NaCl.

Forms cubic crystals which may be colourless, white, or yellow cubes, soluble in water and having a characteristic taste. Perfect cubic cleavage. $H = 2$. $G = 2\cdot2$. Rock salt occurs, with gypsum and other salts, as a deposit from the evaporation of enclosed bodies of salt water (see p. 140). Deposits are worked in the Triassic beds of Cheshire, at Stassfurt, Germany, in Ontario and Michigan, and in other countries. The salt is extracted either as brine pumped up from the salt-beds and then evaporated, or by mining by means of shafts and galleries. It is used in many chemical manufacturing processes, and for preserving and domestic purposes.

CHAPTER 4

VOLCANOES AND IGNEOUS INTRUSION

Physical Geology, as we have seen, is concerned with the activity of natural agents which operate at the earth's surface. There are other geological processes, however, which originate *below* the surface, and these give rise to the phenomena which are the subject of the present chapter. Molten rock material, which is generated within or below the earth's crust, reaches the surface from time to time and flows out from volcanic orifices as streams of lava. Similar material which does not reach the surface may, on the other hand, be injected into the rocks of the crust, giving rise to a great variety of igneous intrusions which slowly cool and solidify. These are the *igneous rocks* (see p. 44) ; many of them, which were formed during past geological ages, are now exposed to view through the removal of their covering rocks by denudation.

The molten rock material from which igneous rocks have consolidated is called *magma*. As far back as 1785 a Scottish geologist, James Hutton, demonstrated the igneous origin of certain rocks, at a time when this was much disputed, and later a basalt-like rock with crystals of olivine and felspar was made synthetically by Sir James Hall, by cooling an artificial melt under pressure. Much modern work has been done on melts.

Natural magmas are hot, viscous, siliceous melts containing gases. The chief elements present in magma are silicon and oxygen, and the metals potassium, sodium, calcium, magnesium, aluminium, and iron (in the order of their chemical activity) ; together with these are small quantities of many other metals, and gases such as carbon dioxide, sulphur dioxide, and steam. Magmas are thus very complex bodies, and the rocks derived from them have a wide variety of composition. Cooled quickly, a magma solidifies as a rock-glass (without crystals) ; cooled slowly, rock-forming minerals crystallize out from it.

The content of silica [1] in igneous rocks varies from over 80 per cent to less than 40 per cent ; as silica is an acid-forming oxide, magmas and rocks containing much of it were originally called *acid*, and those with less silica and correspondingly more of the basic oxides were called *basic* (see analyses, p. 99). This broad distinction is a useful one. Basic magmas are also less viscous than acid magmas. The temperatures at which they exist are not known completely, but measurements at volcanoes indicate values in the neighbourhood of 1000° C. for basic lavas (p. 90) ; this figure may be considerably lowered if fluxes are present. (A flux is a substance which lowers the melting point of substances with which it is mixed ; the gases in magma, for example, act as fluxes.)

---

[1] The amount of silicon in a rock is expressed as the oxide *silica*, SiO_2, in a chemical analysis.

PLATE V

Photo by H.H. Read.

(A) AGGLOMERATE AT CHARNWOOD FOREST, LEICESTERSHIRE.

(B) WHIN SILL (DOLERITE) WITH COLUMNAR JOINTING, OVERLYING SAND-
STONE. CASTLE POINT, NEAR EMBLETON, NORTHUMBERLAND.

PLATE VI

Photo by H.M. Geological Survey.

(A) DOLERITE DYKE CUTTING TRIASSIC SANDSTONES ON SHORE NEAR KILDONAN CASTLE, ARRAN.

(B) GRANITE AT HAYTOR, DARTMOOR : THE CURVED LINE WITH SHADOW AT BOTTOM LEFT OF THE TOR MASS IS AN INTRUSIVE CONTACT BETWEEN TWO GRANITES.

VOLCANOES

Volcanoes are conduits between the earth's surface and hot bodies of magma situated within the crust at no great depth. In the upper parts of a magma chamber gases accumulate, and when a line of weakness exists in the overlying rocks, a volcanic *pipe* or conduit may be formed, up which the magma is forced under pressure. The chief gas concerned in this activity is steam, though many other gases are present, such as CO_2, nitrogen, and SO_2. In some instances magma is quietly extruded from a vent as lava; in others, where the accumulated gas pressure is sufficiently high, it may be discharged upwards at intervals with explosive violence. The expanding gases burst the lava into countless small fragments which ultimately fall around the vent, or are blown to a distance by the wind. Thus deposits of *volcanic dust* or *ash* are formed; larger fragments, termed *lapilli*, and still larger lumps of ejected magma, known as *bombs*, may also be ejected. With these magmatic products may be mingled fragments and blocks of rock torn by the force of the eruption from the walls of the volcanic vent, or from the rocks underlying the volcano.

An eruption is frequently spectacular and often disastrous to life and property, so that it is an event that attracts much attention; descriptions of past volcanic outbursts date back to Pliny's account of the violent eruption of Vesuvius which overwhelmed Pompeii and Herculaneum in A.D. 79. Modern studies have been made from observatories situated on volcanoes, as at Vesuvius by Perret, and at Kilauea. More recently the aeroplane has allowed greater accessibility; the building of the new island of Surtsey, for instance, around a volcanic vent off the south coast of Iceland in 1963, was observed and photographed from the air.

The distribution of volcanoes is related to lines of weakness in the earth's crust; thus the coastal areas of the Pacific, which follow the trend of great lines of folding and faulting, are studded with many volcanoes. Vents in the central Mediterranean area are also probably related to fractures. There are very few active vents in the interior of the continents; those in East Africa are aligned along the Rift Valley system.

Volcanic activity can be classified as follows :—

(1) Fissure Eruptions. (2) Shield Volcanoes, with little explosive action (Hawaiian Type). (3) Volcanoes of the Central Vent type, with cones built largely of fragmental material ejected from the vent (e.g. Vesuvius). (4) Paroxysmal Eruptions, with the emission of large quantities of deadly gases but little or no lava (Peléean Type). (5) Fumaroles, Geysers, and Hot Springs, the waning stages of volcanism. The main features of each of these types are discussed briefly in the following paragraphs.

(1) **Fissure Eruptions.** These represent the simplest form of extrusion, in which lavas issue quietly from linear cracks in the ground. The lavas are generally basic and mobile; they have a low viscosity and spread rapidly over large areas. In past geological times vast floods of basalt (a basic rock) have been poured out over different regions, and are attributed to eruptions from fissures. Among the extensive remains of

these basalts at the present day are the Deccan Traps,[1] which cover an area of some 400,000 square miles in Peninsular India and reach a thickness which in places exceeds 6000 feet, being built up of flow upon flow of lava. The plateau-basalts of the Snake River area in North America cover 200,000 square miles ; and the basalts of Antrim and the Western Isles of Scotland, including the hexagonally-jointed rocks of the Giant's Causeway and of Staffa, are the remnants of a much larger lava-field which may originally have extended to Greenland. The basalt flows of the world are estimated to cover in all 964,000 square miles (2,500,000 sq. km.). Professor Joly (1925) postulated that the source of these widespread lava flows was a layer of basaltic composition situated beneath the earth's outer crust ; other evidence for the existence of such a layer is discussed on p. 165.

Fissure eruptions have occurred in historic times in Iceland, some of the fissures reaching a length of 10 miles (15 km.) or more. The Laki fissure was active in 1783, and extruded a very mobile basalt which flowed for over 50 miles. Often small craters due to subordinate explosive activity are built at intervals along the course of a fissure. The Laki fissure carries a line of such cones and was opened twice. Recently active fissures in which the rock was still hot have been observed in East Iceland. In general, rapid extrusion of very fluid lava and little explosive activity are characteristic of fissure eruptions.

(2) **Shield Volcanoes.** Shield volcanoes are characterized by large flat cones of lava with gentle slopes ; they are built up of many lava flows, mainly basaltic in nature, which are emitted from a caldera or from fissures on the slopes of the cone. It has been suggested that they represent volcanic activity localized at points along original fissures. The lavas are emitted quietly, with little explosive activity, and in great volume.

Mauna Loa, the world's largest volcano, is a shield volcano situated in Hawaii in the South Pacific. The island of Hawaii is composed almost entirely of lava, and rises 30,000 feet from the ocean-bed. The summit is 14,580 feet above sea level (Fig. 35a). The caldera at the summit of Mauna Loa is a great elliptical pit $3\frac{1}{2}$ miles in length and $1\frac{3}{4}$ miles across ; fountains of lava play within it, the jets of molten rock sometimes reaching a height of hundreds of feet. Spray from these fountains is blown by the wind to form glassy threads known as *Pélé's hair* (so called after Pélé, the goddess of Hawaii). Eruptions from fissures on the slopes of the volcano occur at intervals of a few years.

A more accessible crater is that of Kilauea, situated on the eastern slope of the main mountain of Hawaii, about 4000 feet above sea-level. Within it is a lava lake, the top of the volcanic conduit, a vertically sided pit in which the level of the molten rock at times rises and falls with great rapidity. At intervals the lake becomes crusted over, and at other times lava fountains are ejected, due to the discharge of gases. The temperature of the lava at the surface has been measured and found to be 1050° C. or more ; but 100° less at 20 feet below it, since burning gases keep the basic lava hotter at the surface.

[1] *Trap* is an old field term for a fine-grained igneous rock.

Shield volcanoes are found on other islands of the Sandwich group, in Java, and in Iceland, where they were active in geologically recent (Pleistocene) times.

(3) **Central Vent Volcanoes.** With their stratified cones and central funnel-shaped orifices, these approach more closely to the popular conception of a volcano. Vesuvius, Etna, and Stromboli in the Mediterranean region, Popocatepetl in the Andes, and many others active at the present day belong to this type. Where the dissected cones of volcanoes which

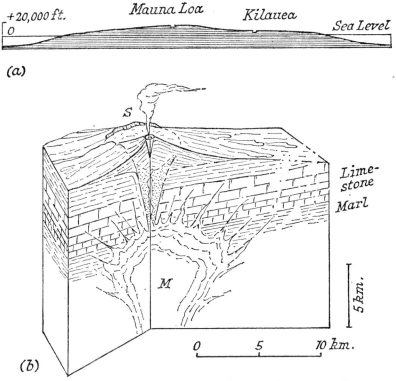

(a)

(b)

Fig. 35.—(*a*) Flat Lava-Cone of Hawaii; (*b*) Block Diagram of Vesuvius; *S* = Somma (old crater), *M* = magma below volcanic pipe (after Umbgrove).

were active in past geological ages are now exposed to view by the processes of denudation, their structure can be studied in detail; Arthur's Seat, Edinburgh, and Largo Law in Fife, are good examples of such "fossil volcanoes."

Vesuvius is perhaps the best known of all volcanoes, since for a long time observations of its activity have been made and recorded at the observatory on the mountain itself. A volcanic cone such as that of Vesuvius is built up mainly of layers of ejected material—ash, lapilli, bombs, and blocks; the layers dip radially outwards on the outer slopes of the cone, and inwards near the central pipe or neck (Fig. 35*b*). The latter forms the main conduit for the emission of gases and lava, but during an eruption the sides of the cone may be breached by fissures connected with the volcanic pipe, and lava streams flow down the slopes of the volcano from these orifices. As the eruption progresses, the gases which have accumulated under pressure in the magma chamber beneath the volcano are released, and magma is blown out in fragments by their sudden expansion. These ejected fragments fall on and around the volcano as a rain of dust and ash ; if they become mixed with rainfall they form a fluid mud which flows down the slopes as a mud-stream, and may overwhelm buildings and crops, as in the case of Herculaneum (A.D. 79). The volcanic pipe itself is cleared by the tremendous uprush of gas, but after the eruption has subsided the vent ultimately becomes choked again with debris or filled with a solid plug of lava.

The debris in and around the vent contains the largest ejected masses of lava, bombs (p. 89), which are embedded in dust and ash ; a deposit of this kind is known as *agglomerate* (Plate VA). The layers of ash and dust which are formed for some distance around the volcano, and which build its cone, become hardened into rocks which are called *tuffs*.[1] When eruptions take place on the sea floor, as may happen if a submarine vent is opened, the ejected dust, ash, and lapilli may form deposits interbedded with normal aqueous sediments.   This is the case with many of the ancient rocks of North Wales, Shropshire, and the Scottish Lowlands, where considerable thicknesses of bedded tuffs are found, pointing to extensive volcanic activity in the past. All these deposits comprise the *pyroclastic rocks* (literally, " fire broken "), a name which refers to their mode of origin.

Poorly consolidated tuffs from the Naples area were used by the Romans for making " hydraulic " cement, and were called *pozzclina* ; mixed with lime they harden under water. Similar material from the Eifel volcanic district of Germany, has also been used : tuffs known as *trass*, when mixed with an equal amount of limestone, form a cement. These pozzolans, as they are now called, are still used at the present day.

The famous diamond mines of Kimberley are located in old volcanic necks, which are filled with the diamond-bearing breccia known as " blue ground." The breccia has the composition of serpentine (*q.v.*) ; it is easily weathered, and is crushed for the extraction of the diamonds which are sparsely distributed through it.

(4) **Paroxysmal Eruptions.** Some volcanoes, notably a group in the West Indies, are characterized by sudden and rapid activity which consists mainly in the discharge of large quantities of deadly gases, with very little outflow of lava.   One such volcano, Mont Pelée on the island of Martinique, has a disastrous history. In May and December 1902 two violent eruptions occurred, each time with the emission of a hot cloud (*nuée ardente*) of heavy gases, loaded with incandescent dust particles. In the May eruption, the hot cloud rushed down the mountainside, completely destroying the town

---

[1] Materials ejected from a volcanic vent may be classified according to size as follows : Bombs and blocks, greater than 32 mm. ; lapilli, between 32 and 4 mm. ; coarse ash, from 4 to 0·5 mm. ; fine ash, from 0·5 to 0·05 mm. ; dust, less than 0·05 mm. Tuffs may be coarse or fine according to the size of fragments they contain.

of St. Pierre at its foot. Buildings were obliterated and the 30,000 inhabitants perished, except for one survivor. A similar eruption later in the same year, with violent gas discharge through the side of the cone at a weak point, was observed by an expedition afloat. A plug of almost solid lava—the " spine " of Mont Pelée—was pushed up through the volcanic pipe by gas pressure within, to a height of 700 feet above the crater. It crumbled and almost disappeared by weathering after a few months.

Krakatoa, an island of the East Indies, was the scene of four tremendous explosions of the paroxysmal type in August 1883. The island formed part of the rim of a former large crater, much of which had become submerged. After two centuries of quiescence, the eruption began with the emission of steam, culminating with the great explosions which blew away most of the island, estimated at $4\frac{1}{4}$ cubic miles of rock. Shocks were felt virtually the world over, and tidal waves generated near the volcanic centre did great damage to low coasts. The dust from Krakatoa floated round the earth in the upper atmosphere and caused remarkable sunsets for a year after.

Other volcanoes belonging to the same class are Papandayang in Java, and Bandai-San in Japan, both of which have in modern times lost a large part of their bulk by great explosions.

(5) **Fumaroles, Geysers, and Hot Springs.** In areas of dying volcanic activity, the emission of steam and gases (HCl, CO_2, H_2S, and HF) at high temperature from *fumaroles* or gas-vents may continue for a long time. Sulphur is deposited around some of the lower temperature gas-vents, called *solfataras*, as in the Vesuvian area, and commercial supplies of sulphur were obtained from these deposits.

Geysers [1] are eruptive springs of boiling water and steam ; jets of water are blown into the air at intervals by steam pressure generated in fissures in hot rocks below the surface. The Yellowstone Park region in Wyoming, U.S.A., is famous for its geysers and hot springs ; " Old Faithful " is the name given to one geyser which erupts regularly at intervals of about an hour (i.e. after sufficient steam pressure has been generated), and shoots a column of water to a height of 150 feet. Geysers and hot springs are common in Iceland, where the hot water is utilized for domestic heating and cooking, and for laundry supplies. The temperature of hot springs is generally lower than that of geysers, and the former flow constantly, whereas geysers are intermittent. Around the orifice of a spring or geyser there is often deposited a cone or mound of *sinter*, a siliceous substance thrown out of solution from the water of the spring. Sinter is usually white but may be a variety of colours ; pink sinter deposited by hot springs formed the well-known terraces of Rotomahana, New Zealand, which were largely obliterated by a subsequent eruption.

Igneous Intrusions

A body of magma which is under pressure in the earth's crust may be forced to higher levels, penetrating the upper rocks of the crust ; it is then

[1] *Geyser* = roarer (Icelandic).

said to be *intrusive*. It may, during the process of intrusion, incorporate within itself some of the rocks with which it comes into contact, a process known as *assimilation* (see p. 114). In some cases it may also give off mobile fluids which penetrate and change the rocks in its immediate neighbourhood. If the intrusive magma cools under cover at some depth below the surface, the rocks which result are called *plutonic rocks* and are coarsely crystalline ; a large mass of this kind constitutes a *major intrusion*. When magma rises and fills fractures or other lines of weakness in the crust, it forms *minor intrusions*, i.e. smaller igneous bodies. These include *dykes*, which are wall-like masses, steep or vertical, with more or less parallel sides ; and *sills*, which are sheets of igneous rock whose extent is more or less horizontal, and which lie parallel to the bedding planes of sedimentary rocks into which they are intrusive (Fig. 36). Dyke and sill-rocks commonly have a fine-grained texture. *Veins* are smaller and irregular bodies of igneous material, filling cracks which may run in any direction.

In order to complete this outline of igneous rock-forms, it should be added that magma which rises to the earth's surface and flows out as a lava, as described earlier in this chapter, is called *extrusive*, and under these conditions it loses most of its gas content. Igneous rocks so formed are termed *volcanic rocks*, and since they have cooled comparatively quickly in the atmosphere they are frequently glassy (i.e. non-crystalline), or very fine-grained with some larger crystals.

Dykes and Sills. Of the minor intrusions, *dykes* vary in size from a few inches up to hundreds of feet in width. Most dykes, however, are

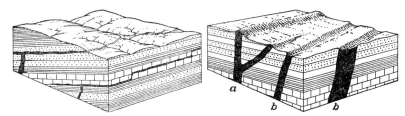

FIG. 36.—Sills (left) and Dykes (right).
(a) Dyke more resistant to weathering, (b) less resistant, than the country-rock.

less than 10 feet across. They tend to outcrop in nearly straight lines, and may extend for a short distance or may run for many miles across country (see Fig. 103). The Cleveland dyke of dolerite in the north of England, for instance, can be traced for 130 miles. The Great Dyke of Southern Rhodesia is several miles wide and 312 miles in length, and is the longest known. If the dyke-rock is harder than the rocks into which it was intruded, as weathering and denudation proceed it will tend to stand up above the level of the surrounding rocks as a wall-like mass (Fig. 36 and Plate VIA).

A group of many parallel or radial dykes is called a *dyke swarm*. A good example of the former is found in Mull, where 375 basaltic dykes running in a general N.W.–S.E. direction form a parallel swarm and cut the south coast of the island within a distance of 12½ miles. Some of the dykes extend across to the Scottish mainland, where they are traceable for a considerable distance farther, and appear to link up with the Cleveland dyke already mentioned. The stretching of the crust which was necessary to open up the dyke fissures points to the operation of tensile stresses across the area, at about the time that the Tertiary basalts of Antrim were being extruded. Another swarm of parallel dykes, which trend east and west, crosses the Midland Valley of Scotland. These dykes are of quartz-dolerite, and are closely related to the Whin Sill and other intrusions of the north of England (p. 217). A radial swarm occurs in the island of Rum, off the west coast of Scotland, where 700 basic dykes have been recorded and are grouped about a centre in the south of the island. Dyke swarms in Iceland have recently been described by Dr. G. P. L. Walker.[1]

Ring dykes are intrusive masses filling curved fractures, sometimes appearing as a complete circle or loop in plan. Other fractures which are shaped like the surface of a cone with its apex downwards, and are filled with igneous material, are called *cone-sheets*. These two types are well seen in the Ardnamurchan peninsula in the west of Scotland,[2] and a theory to account for the origin of the stresses causing the two sets of circular fractures has been worked out.

Sills, like dykes, may vary greatly in thickness and extent. One of the best known sills is the Whin Sill in the north of England, a sheet of basic rock (dolerite) which has an extent of more than 1500 square miles. Its average thickness is a little less than 100 feet, and it is exposed along the sides of many valleys and escarpments, where denudation has cut down through it, and in coastal cliffs (Plate VB). It yields a good road-metal, locally called " whinstone." Another well-known sill of dolerite forms the Salisbury Craigs at Edinburgh, and shows prominent columnar jointing ; the columns run from roof to floor of the sill and were formed by the contraction of the igneous rock on cooling. The sediments above and below a sill are baked by the heat of the intrusive rock. A sill may sometimes be stepped up from one level to another, the two flat parallel sections being connected by a short length of dyke (Fig. 36). If the rocks into which the sill is injected are later tilted or folded, the igneous mass will also partake of those movements.

Sills, and also dykes, are sometimes *composite*, i.e. having contrasted margins and centres due to successive injections of different material; successive injections of similar material produce a *multiple* sill or dyke. Fine-grained *chilled margins* are formed by rapid cooling where an intrusion has come into contact with the colder " country-rock " into which it was injected.

Laccoliths and Phacoliths. A *laccolith* is a " mushroom-shaped " body (Fig. 37) of relatively small size, up to several miles in diameter, having a flat floor and up-arched roof. The roof-rocks were lifted or arched by the pressure of the incoming magma, and their form is therefore due

[1] " The Breiddalur Volcano," *Quart. Journ. Geol. Soc.*, 119, 1963, p. 50.
[2] J. E. Richey, " Geology of Ardnamurchan," Mem. Geol. Surv. Gt. Brit., 1930.

to the process of intrusion. Laccoliths were first described by G. K. Gilbert from the Henry Mountains, Utah, where they are intruded into mainly horizontal strata and exposed in all stages of erosion. They are found in many regions, including Iceland and Skye (gabbro laccoliths) ; a laccolith

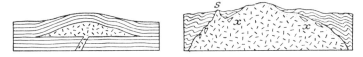

FIG. 37.—CROSS-SECTIONS OF AN IDEAL LACCOLITH (left) AND A BATHOLITH (right). Igneous rock stippled. s = stock, x = detached masses of country-rock enclosed within the igneous body during intrusion. Scales of the two diagrams are not the same.

of porphyrite occurs in the Tinto Hills, Lanark, and the rock has been much quarried for road stone.

The *phacolith* is a somewhat similar intrusive form, but with both floor and roof curved ; this is due to the magma having been intruded into rocks which were already folded. An example of a phacolith is the dolerite intrusion of Corndon, Shropshire.[1] This igneous body occupies the crest of a dome, about $1\frac{1}{2}$ miles in length, in folded mudstones. Both laccoliths and phacoliths are classed here as minor intrusions (p. 97).

Batholiths, Stocks, and Sheets. Of these major intrusions the name *batholith* (literally " depth-rock ") is given to very large igneous masses, bounded by steep walls of sedimentary or other rocks across which the igneous body cuts without having any apparent floor (Fig. 37). The largest known igneous masses of the world are among the batholiths and, where exposed at the surface, may cover thousands of square miles. Projections from the upper parts of such masses are called *stocks* and *bosses* ; stocks have cross-sectional areas up to 40 square miles (as defined by R. A. Daly), while bosses are smaller and roughly circular in cross-section. Both have steep walls and cut across the structures in the country-rocks (*i.e.* the rocks penetrated by the igneous body). Batholiths are found in regions of folded rocks, especially in the cores of mountain fold-belts (p. 192), and are dominantly acid (granitic) in composition. The Cordillera of North America, for example, contain many batholiths, elongated parallel to the length of the folds.

The Leinster granite, which lies to the south-west of Dublin and occupies 625 square miles of surface, is the largest granite mass in the British Isles and may be batholithic. It is elongated in a north-north-east direction (Fig. 94), not quite parallel to the folds which affect the slaty rocks of the area. Recent studies have shown that its western contact is steep, and in places faulted, while the eastern contact dips more gently under the country-rocks.[2] Large bodies of granite of similar age, the forms of which are not completely known, are found in Galloway, and others in the Scottish

[1] F. G. H. Blyth in *Quart. Journ. Geol. Soc.*, 1943, p. 178.
[2] J. C. Brindley, *Proc. Roy. Irish Acad.*, 56, 1954.

Highlands (Fig. 94). The term *pluton* is used to denote any large igneous mass (other than a batholith), irrespective of its size and shape. Among the granites of Donegal several different styles of intrusion are represented; a new map of these granites and their envelope rocks has recently been completed (1967).

The granites of Devon and Cornwall are a group of plutons of related composition, and are probably connected underground at a lower level, perhaps as a large scale system of intersecting veins (or stockwork). The granites are now exposed where their sedimentary roof-rocks have been removed by denudation. Other buried plutonic masses probably exist, whose cover has not yet been denuded sufficiently to reveal the igneous rock beneath. One such mass underlies the northern part of the Pennines between Alston and Stanhope (Co. Durham), where mineral veins are found injected into the sedimentary rocks of the district; geophysical surveys had suggested a buried granite, which was reached by a boring at Rookhope, in 1961, at a depth of 1281 feet.[1]

Many large and small fragments of the country-rocks in which a batholith is emplaced are frequently found enclosed within it, especially near its margins, and are known as *xenoliths* (= " stranger-stone "). Certain ores are commonly associated with the roof- and wall-rocks of granite masses, e.g. the tin veins of Cornwall (p. 116).

Large *sheets* of igneous rock, which are much thicker in proportion to their extent than sills, and often basic in composition, may occupy many square miles of country although not everywhere exposed at the surface. Some of the gabbro masses of Aberdeenshire are probably irregular sheets of this kind, e.g. the Huntly mass. Another example is the Duluth gabbro of Minnesota, which is a great sheet of basic rock with an extent of 2500 square miles and a thickness estimated at 20,000 feet.

We can now construct the following grouping for igneous rocks, based on their mode of occurrence as described above, and leading to the classification given in the next chapter :

EXTRUSIVE (Volcanic) . . **Lavas** . . . . . Glassy or very finely crystalline.

INTRUSIVE
{
Minor . . . **Dykes and sills, laccoliths** . . . Mainly fine-grained rocks.

Major . . . **Batholiths, stocks, and sheets** . . Coarsely crystalline rocks.
(Plutonic)
}

---

[1] K. C. Dunham *et al.*, *Quart. Journ. Geol. Soc.*, 121, 1965, p. 383.

CHAPTER 5

IGNEOUS ROCKS

The different ways in which igneous rocks occur were described in the previous chapter. The rocks themselves, their textures and mineral composition, have now to be discussed. References to their economic value and uses are also included in the descriptions of the different varieties.

Textures. The texture, or relative size and arrangement of the com ponent minerals, of an igneous rock corresponds broadly to the rock's mode of occurrence. Plutonic rocks, which have cooled slowly under a cover perhaps several miles thick, are entirely crystalline or *holocrystalline :* their component crystals are large (2 to 5 mm. or more) and can easily be distinguished with the naked eye. Rocks of medium or fine grain generally have crystals less than 1 mm. across. When the texture is so fine that individual crystals are indistinguishable without the aid of a microscope it is called *microcrystalline,* and when even the microscope fails to resolve the rock into its component minerals, yet its crystalline nature is apparent between crossed nicols, it is said to be *cryptocrystalline.* These textures are all even-grained, i.e. composed mainly of crystals of much the same size ; but, in contrast to this, some rocks show the *porphyritic* texture, in which a number of larger crystals are set in a uniformly finer base or groundmass. The large, conspicuous crystals are called porphyritic crystals or *phenocrysts,* e.g. the large pink felspars in Shap Granite (see also Plate VIIA).

Extrusive rocks, which have cooled more rapidly at the earth's surface, are often entirely glassy or *vitreous* (without crystals), or partly crystalline and partly glassy. Within a single lava flow the outer layers may be glassy, because rapidly chilled, and the inner part crystalline. Expanding gases in the magma during its extrusion as lava give rise to cavities or *vesicles,* resulting in a vesicular texture ; the vesicles are frequently elongated and somewhat almond-shaped, and may subsequently become filled with secondary minerals, when they are called *amygdales* (amygdaloidal texture). Basalts are frequently amygdaloidal. Banding or *flow-structure* is produced by differential movement between layers in viscous lava during the process of flow, as in rhyolite.

Composition of Igneous Rocks. The mineral composition and colour of rocks are related to their chemical composition. When the chemical analyses of an acid rock like granite and of a basic rock (e.g. basalt) are compared, important differences are seen, such as the greater proportion of silica and alkalies (Na_2O and K_2O) in the acid rock, and the higher content of lime, magnesia, and iron oxide in the basic. This is shown by the following figures, which are averages of a large number of analyses :

	Average Granite %	Average Basalt[1] %
SiO_2	70·2	49·1
Al_2O_3	14·4	15·7
Fe_2O_3	1·6	5·4
FeO	1·8	6·4
MgO	0·9	6·2
CaO	2·0	9·0
Na_2O	3·5	3·1
K_2O	4·1	1·5
H_2O	0·8	1·6
rest	0·7	2·0
	100·0	100·0

The higher alkali content in granite corresponds to a greater proportion of felspar in the rock ; conversely, basalt has more minerals containing Fe, Mg, and Ca.

During the cooling of a magma, the different constituents unite to form crystals of silicate (and other) minerals. In a basic magma, for example, minerals like olivine and magnetite may be the first to crystallize, and they take up some of the silica, magnesia, and iron oxide ; the remainder of the magnesia and iron (with some alumina and other oxides) is used up later in augite, hornblende, and perhaps dark mica. On account of their composition, such minerals are called *ferromagnesian* or *mafic*.[2] In contrast to these dark and relatively heavy mafic minerals, the alkalies and lime, together with alumina and silica, form light-coloured or *felsic* minerals, which include the felspars, felspathoids, and quartz. Most of the lime, for example, in a basic magma would enter a felspar like labradorite, a little going into augite. In acid rocks felsic minerals predominate and give the rocks a paler colour, in contrast to the darker basic rocks. Between *acid* and *basic* types there are rocks of *intermediate* composition.

When a magma contains enough silica to combine fully with all the metallic bases and still leave some over, it is said to be *oversaturated* ; the excess silica crystallizes as quartz, and an igneous rock which contains quartz is called an oversaturated rock, e.g. granite. Minerals which can exist in a rock in the presence of free silica are said to be *saturated*. Certain minerals with a low silica content, in particular olivine and the felspathoids, are not normally found in association with quartz and are termed *undersaturated* ; thus olivine (Mg_2SiO_4) with the addition of silica would become enstatite ($Mg_2Si_2O_6$), a saturated mineral. It is convenient, therefore, to speak of igneous rocks as oversaturated (i.e. containing quartz or its non-crystalline equivalent), saturated (containing only saturated minerals), and undersaturated (containing olivine or felspathoids or both).

Classification. A simple scheme of classification can be constructed on the lines indicated on p. 97, for the more common varieties of igneous

[1] Quoted from R. A. Daly, "Igneous Rocks and the Depths of the Earth." New York, 1933.

[2] *Mafic* is coined from *ma* for magnesium and *fe* for iron (ferrum).

rocks. The scheme does not include all igneous types; some of the less common ones are mentioned in the descriptions which follow; but more than this is not within the scope of the book.

In the table below, the rocks are arranged in three columns headed Acid, Intermediate, and Basic, forming the Granite, Diorite, and Gabbro groups respectively.[1] A transitional type, Granodiorite, between Granite and Diorite, is also indicated. Rocks of the Syenite family fall outside this grouping and are treated separately on p. 109, for the reasons stated there. The range from left to right in the table corresponds to a decreasing

TABLE OF IGNEOUS ROCKS

(excluding alkaline rocks)

	Acid	Intermediate	Basic	Ultra-basic
EXTRUSIVE (Volcanic)	RHYOLITE Dacite	ANDESITE	BASALT	
MINOR INTRUSIVE (Dykes and Sills)	Felsite QUARTZ-PORPHYRY	PORPHYRITE	DOLERITE	
MAJOR INTRUSIVE (Plutonic)	Microgranite GRANITE GRANODIORITE	DIORITE	GABBRO	Picrite Peridotite

Oversaturated...............Saturated ....Undersaturated

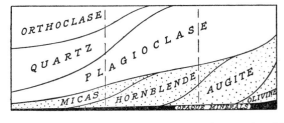

Generalized Mineral Composition

silica content (over-saturated to saturated); an extension to the right of the table would include the Ultrabasic rocks, most of which contain olivine and are undersaturated. In each column there are three divisions, the lowest containing the name of the coarse-grained plutonic member of the group, the middle division the dyke or sill equivalent of the plutonic type, and the top division the extrusive or volcanic rocks. The main minerals which make up the plutonic rocks are shown in a separate diagram below the table. The columns therefore give a grouping based on mineral composition (which in turn expresses the chemical composition), and the

[1] The term *clan* is used by some geologists for groups of igneous rocks; thus, the Gabbro clan would contain the Gabbro, Dolerite, and Basalt families.

horizontal divisions are based on mode of occurrence, which governs the rock texture.

Silica percentage decreases from Granite to Gabbro. In the lower diagram, intercepts on any vertical line give the approximate mineral composition for the corresponding plutonic rock in the table.

DESCRIPTIONS OF IGNEOUS ROCKS

GABBRO, DOLERITE and BASALT. These basic rocks form a large group and are of considerable economic importance on account of the value of certain types as road metal. They have a large content of ferromagnesian minerals, which give the rocks a dark appearance and a range of specific gravity from about 2·9 to 3·2. On account of the relative fluidity of basic lavas, basalt is frequently completely (though finely) crystalline, and locally grades uniformly into dolerite ; similarly dolerite may grade into gabbro as the texture grows coarser. Undersaturated basic types include olivine-gabbro, olivine-dolerite, olivine-basalt, and felspathoidal varieties.

Gabbro.

MINERALS : Essential minerals are plagioclase (labradorite to anorthite) and a monoclinic pyroxene, e.g. augite or diallage. The lime-rich nature of the plagioclase is related to the high CaO and low Na_2O content in a normal gabbro (see analysis, p. 112). Other minerals which may be present (not all in one rock) include enstatite or hypersthene, olivine, hornblende, biotite, and felspathoids. Ilmenite and apatite are common accessories. There is no quartz or orthoclase in a normal gabbro, but a very small amount of interstitial quartz may be present in some varieties. Mafic minerals form about 50 per cent of the rock.

TEXTURE : Coarsely crystalline, rarely porphyritic, sometimes with finer modifications. The hand specimen appears dark in colour, grey to black or greenish black, owing to the high proportion of mafic minerals and the grey tint of the plagioclase. Under the microscope the rock shows interlocking crystal plates (Fig. 38). Olivine if present usually shows well-formed crystals, because of its early separation from the magma. Grains of iron oxide may be enclosed in olivine and other minerals. Frequently decomposition products such as serpentine after olivine or chlorite after pyroxene are present.

VARIETIES : Some are named after the chief mafic mineral present other than augite, thus : enstatite- or hypersthene-gabbro ; olivine-gabbro ; hornblende-gabbro. *Norite* is a gabbro containing enstatite or hypersthene instead of augite. *Troctolite* [1] is an olivine-gabbro without augite. *Quartz-gabbro* (e.g. at Carrock Fell, Cumberland) has a little interstitial quartz, which represents the last siliceous liquor to crystallize from a slightly oversaturated gabbro magma. Felspathoidal varieties include nepheline-gabbro (*essexite*).

Gabbros of many kinds are found in Britain, as in Skye and Ardnamurchan (West Scotland), Northern Ireland, the Lake District, and at the Lizard, Cornwall, where troctolite and other gabbros occur. Norites are found in Aberdeenshire. The important nickel-bearing intrusion of Sudbury, Canada, is largely composed of norite, in which the nickel sulphides are concentrated near the base of the sheet.

Dolerite.

Dolerite occurs in dykes and sills, and is of great importance as a road

---

[1] Greek *troctes*, a trout, from its speckled appearance.

metal because of its toughness, and its capacity for holding a coating of bitumen and giving a good " bind." It is dark grey, sometimes nearly black in colour, except when the proportion of felspar is high ; the texture is usually of medium to fine grain.   Dolerite is included in the trade name " basalt " (as are also andesite, basalt, and other rocks).

MINERALS : As for gabbro.

TEXTURE : When the lath-shaped plagioclase crystals are partly or completely enclosed in augite the texture is called *ophitic* (Fig. 38). This interlocking of the chief mineral components gives a very strong, tough rock. The augite may, however, occur as granules between the plagioclase laths, when the texture is described as *intergranular*. The nearer dolerite approaches gabbro, as the texture increases in coarseness, the less emphatic will be the lath-like form of the felspars. On the other hand, dolerite merges by degrees into basalt as the texture becomes finer.

VARIETIES : Normal dolerite = labradorite + augite + iron oxides ; olivine-dolerite ; hypersthene-dolerite ; quartz-dolerite, with accessory quartz (cf. quartz-gabbro), is a common dyke-rock in the Midland Valley of Scotland and else-where, and forms the Whin Sill; analcite-dolerite (= *teschenite*) is an under-saturated type.   Much-altered dolerites, in which both the felspars and the mafic minerals are decomposed, are sometimes called *diabase*.[1]

Road-metal quarries in dolerite are extremely numerous ; well-known locali-ties among them include Rowley Regis, near Birmingham ; the Clee Hills, Shrop-shire ; many workings in the Whin Sill and other dolerites of the North of England ; and, among others, Hennock, South Devon.

Basalt.

Basalt is a dense-looking, black rock, often weathering to a brown colour, and is the commonest of all lavas.   It is estimated that the basalt flows of the world have five times the volume of all other extrusive rocks together.

MINERALS : Essential minerals are plagioclase and augite.   The normal felspar of basalts is labradorite, but andesine, oligoclase, or albite may occur in different varieties.   Magnetite and ilmenite are common accessories ; olivine occurs in many basalts and commonly shows alteration to serpentine ; calcite, chlorite, zeolites, chalcedony, and other secondary minerals may fill vesicles.   Nepheline, leucite, and analcite are found in undersaturated types.

TEXTURE : None seen in the hand specimen, unless the rock is porphyritic or vesicular.   Seen under the microscope (Fig. 38) the texture is microcrystalline to cryptocrystalline or glassy, often with porphyritic crystals of olivine or augite which are too small to be visible without magnification.   Basalt glass is called *tachylite* and is found as a chilled base to flows of basalt lava, or as the chilled margins of dykes.   Vesicular and amygdaloidal textures are common.

VARIETIES : Basalt and olivine-basalt are the commonest varieties ; others include quartz-basalt (cf. quartz-dolerite), and felspathoidal types like nepheline-basalt and leucite-basalt (e.g. the lavas from Vesuvius).   Soda-rich basalts in which the plagioclase is mainly albite are called *spilites* ; these rocks often show " pillow-structure."   All varieties may be amygdaloidal ; weathered types are sometimes called *melaphyre*.

Some of the great flows of basalt in different parts of the world are referred to on p. 90, and the list given there could be extended.   Olivine-basalt lavas are

---

[1] In American literature *diabase* is synonymous with dolerite.

extruded from volcanoes like Kilauea, Hawaii (p. 90). Plateau-basalts, so called from the topographical forms which they build, are prominent in the west of Scotland and Antrim, in the volcanic region of Auvergne, Central France, and in the Deccan, India, to quote only a few instances.

PICRITE and PERIDOTITE. These rocks consist essentially of mafic minerals and contain little or no felspar. They are coarse-grained, holocrystalline, mostly dark in colour, and have a high specific gravity (3·0 to 3·3). As their silica content is in many cases about 40 per cent or less they are known as *ultrabasic* rocks, and in the classification of p. 100 they form an undersaturated group next to the gabbros. Ultrabasic rocks have relatively small outcrops at the earth's surface. They often form the lower parts of basic intrusions, the heavy crystals of which they are composed having sunk through the body of magma before it consolidated.

Picrite.

Picrite contains little felspar (not more than about 10 or 12 per cent), the bulk of the rock being made of olivine and augite or hornblende, generally with some ilmenite. The olivine crystals are sometimes enclosed in the augite or hornblende. By increase of the felspar content and corresponding decrease in the other constituents, picrite grades into olivine-gabbro and gabbro. The Lugar sill, Ayrshire, contains a thickness of some 25 feet of picrite, which merges downwards into peridotite and upwards into a felspathoidal gabbro.

Peridotite.

Olivine is the chief constituent of this rock, which is named from the French *peridot*, olivine. Other minerals include augite, hornblende, biotite, and iron oxides. Felsic minerals are virtually absent. A variety composed almost entirely of olivine is called *dunite*, from the Dun Mountains, New Zealand ; it is used on a small scale as a decorative stone.

Serpentine-rock may result from the alteration of peridotite by the action of steam and other magmatic fluids, while the rock is still hot (p. 81). Large masses of red and green serpentine occur in the Lizard district, Cornwall, where a local industry exists for the manufacture of ornaments from the rock, which takes a high polish. The fibrous serpentine, *chrysotile*, furnishes one source of commercial asbestos, and occurs in veins.

Other types of ultrabasic rocks consist almost entirely of one kind of mafic mineral, such as *pyroxenite* (all pyroxene), and *hornblende rock* (all hornblende). They are usually associated with basic rocks like gabbro, and are of small volume.

DIORITE, PORPHYRITE and ANDESITE. The intermediate rocks forming the diorite group or clan are saturated with regard to silica, and typically contain little quartz. But by increase of the silica content and the incoming of orthoclase they grade into the acid rocks, thus : *diorite—quartz-diorite—granodiorite—granite.* They are quarried for road-stone and for kerbs and setts, and as stone for rough walling. The average specific gravity of diorite is 2·87.

Diorite.

MINERALS : Essential minerals are plagioclase (normally andesine) and hornblende. Accessories include iron oxides, apatite, and sphene. Biotite and quartz and a little orthoclase are frequently present. The mafic minerals may form from 15 to 40 per cent of the rock. The higher soda and lower lime content as compared with gabbro (p. 112) are reflected by the change in the nature of the plagioclase, from labradorite to andesine; some of the lime, together with magnesia and iron, goes to form hornblende.

TEXTURE : Holocrystalline, of coarse to medium grain, rarely porphyritic; diorites on the whole are rather less coarse than granites, but in the hand specimen the different minerals can generally be distinguished with the aid of a pocket lens. The rock is normally less dark in colour than gabbro, on account of the smaller proportion of mafic minerals and the paler tint of the plagioclase. Under the microscope the minerals show interlocking outlines, with a tendency for the mafic mineral to be idiomorphic.

VARIETIES : Diorite (= andesine felspar + hornblende); augite-diorite, forming a link with gabbro; biotite-diorite; quartz-diorite, perhaps a more common type than normal diorite, and grading into granodiorite as explained below. Fine-grained varieties are called *microdiorite*.

Diorites have a somewhat restricted distribution, and frequently form local modifications to granodiorite and granite intrusions due to assimilation (see p. 114), as in the case of many of the " newer granites " of Scotland (p. 212). Small masses of diorite occur at Comrie and Garabal Hill, Perthshire.

The microdiorite of Penmaenmawr, North Wales, is worthy of special mention since it is extensively worked in large quarries which yield road-metal and stone for setts and kerbs. The intrusive mass is exposed along the coast between sea-level and 1500 feet O.D., and becomes increasingly basic from the top downwards. Quartz and orthoclase are present in the upper part of the intrusion; they decrease in amount at lower levels, and are practically absent in the lowest (visible) part of the mass, while at the same time the plagioclase changes from oligoclase to labradorite and the proportion of mafic minerals increases. Parts of the intrusion would more properly be called porphyrite.

Porphyrite (Diorite-Porphyry).

MINERALS : Similar to diorite.

TEXTURE : Porphyritic crystals of plagioclase and hornblende in a micro-crystalline groundmass consisting mainly of felspar, with some hornblende or biotite. In some varieties the groundmass contains patches of felspar and quartz in micrographic intergrowth (p. 107).

VARIETIES : When mafic minerals other than hornblende occur as porphyritic crystals their name is prefixed to the rock name, giving varieties thus : augite-porphyrite, mica-porphyrite. Minor intrusions of these rocks are found in the Charnwood Forest area, Leicestershire; sills of mica-porphyrite occur on Canisp, Sutherland, and many porphyrite dykes in the Southern Uplands.

Andesite.

The andesites form a large family of rocks occurring mainly as lava flows and occasionally as small intrusives. They are compact, sometimes vesicular, and often brown in colour, and in extent are second only to the basalts. It is estimated that basalts and andesites together have fifty times the volume of all other extrusive rocks combined. The name is taken from the Andes of South America, where many volcanoes have emitted lavas and ash of andesitic composition. Many andesites are useful as road-metal and are worked in numerous quarries.

MINERALS AND TEXTURE : The essential constituents are plagioclase (generally andesine) and a mafic mineral (hornblende, augite, enstatite, or biotite), which occur as porphyritic crystals in a base which may be glassy, cryptocrystalline,

PLATE VII

(A) Biotite-Granite, Cornwall

(B) Biotite-Gneiss with Augen, Sutherland

PLATE VIII

Photo by J. C. Harper.

(A) PEGMATITE VEINS IN FLAGS, NEAR LOCH LAGGAN, INVERNESS-SHIRE.

(B) SMOOTH JOINT SURFACES IN GRANITE, BLACKENSTONE QUARRY, DARTMOOR.

or microlithic [1] (Fig. 38). Microlithic varieties frequently show flow-structure, the microliths having a roughly parallel arrangement (cf. the trachytic texture,

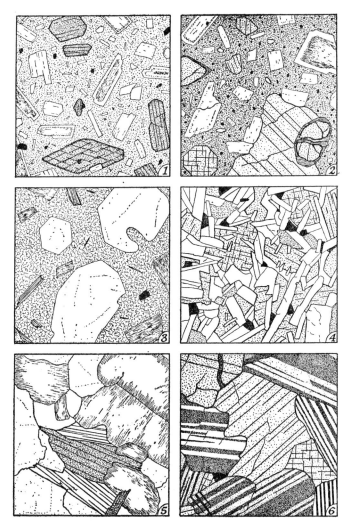

FIG. 38.—IGNEOUS ROCKS IN THIN SECTION.
1. Hornblende-andesite. 2. Olivine-basalt. 3. Quartz-porphyry. 4. Ophitic dolerite.
5. Muscovite-biotite-granite. 6. Gabbro (crossed nicols). (Magnification about × 12.)

p. 111). Hornblende may show resorption borders. Grains of iron oxide are nearly always present as accessories, and quartz may develop in oversaturated types.

---

[1] *Microliths* are very small, elongated crystals, generally of felspar ; a texture in which large numbers of them are present is said to be *microlithic*.

G.E.—H

VARIETIES : Hornblende-andesite ; augite-andesite ; enstatite-andesite ; biotite-andesite ; quartz-andesite (= *dacite*). The term pyroxene-andesite is used if both orthorhombic and monoclinic pyroxenes are present ; these pyroxene-bearing varieties grade into basalts, and are very abundant.

Andesites which have been altered by hot mineralizing waters of volcanic origin, with the production of secondary minerals, are called *propylites.*

In Britain, andesite lavas are found in many areas of volcanic rocks, such as the Pentland Hills, Edinburgh ; the Glencoe and Ben Nevis districts, and the Lorne volcanic plateau, Argyll ; the Cheviot Hills ; and south Shropshire. The Borrowdale Volcanic Group of the Lake District (p. 206) is largely made of andesitic lavas and tuffs, some of which have been subjected to stresses which nduced a slaty cleavage, and thus produced the green Cumberland slates.

GRANITE and GRANODIORITE. These two oversaturated plutonic types form most of the very large acid bodies, the batholiths, which occur in the cores of folded mountain ranges ; they also form many plutons in the upper levels of the earth's crust (p. 97), and are the most abundant of all the plutonic rocks. Granite is the main structural stone from among the igneous rocks, because of its good appearance, its hardness and resistance to weathering, and its strength in compression (the crushing strength of sound granite may reach 20,000 to 40,000 lbs. per sq. inch). Its strength and rough fracture are also valuable properties when it is used as concrete aggregate. The average specific gravity of granite is 2·67, and of granodiorite, 2·72. The trade name " granite " is used for many rocks which are not granite in the geological sense, e.g. diorite or gneiss.

Granite.

MINERALS : Quartz and felspar are the essential minerals. The latter includes both orthoclase and plagioclase (albite or oligoclase), and in some rocks microcline is present, as in certain Scottish granites. Quartz may form 20 to 40 per cent of the rock, and felspar up to 60 per cent (see diagram, p. 100). Mica of some kind is commonly present and may be a dark variety like biotite, or the light mica muscovite, or both. Other minerals which may be present in different granites (not all in any one rock) are hornblende, augite, and tourmaline ; soda-rich minerals like reibeckite and aegirite appear in alkaline types of granite. Accessory minerals include apatite, zircon, sphene, garnet, and magnetite.

The average of over 500 chemical analyses of granite is given on p. 99. The large felspar content of the rock is reflected in the high percentages for soda and potash, though some of the latter helps to form mica ; the low ferromagnesian content is to be noted. The high value for silica results in the formation of free quartz after the metallic bases have been fully combined with silica, and the rock is therefore oversaturated. Small constituents such as titanium (for sphene) and phosphorus (for apatite) are included in the last item of the analysis.

TEXTURE : Hand specimens of the rock are, on the whole, light in colour, with a white or pink tint according to the colour of the felspar, and are coarsely crystalline. Individual mineral grains can be distinguished by eye, flaky micas contrasting with cleaved felspar, and both with the glassy quartz crystals. The texture may be porphyritic (e.g. the Shap granite, with large pink twinned felspar crystals). Sometimes small or large pieces of country-rock have been caught up by the granite during its intrusion and recrystallized by the heat, to appear as dark inclusions or *xenoliths.*

Under the microscope the component crystals are seen to interlock at their contacts with one another, producing the granitic texture (Fig. 38); this texture is not confined to rocks of granitic composition.

Granites, though generally coarse-textured, include less coarse varieties; the fine-grained type called *microgranite* is frequently found as a chilled margin to a larger mass, or as a vein rock. The reibeckite-bearing microgranite from Ailsa Craig is an example; it is noted as the rock from which curling stones are made.

The *graphic* texture is due to an intergrowth of quartz and felspar, in which oriented angular pockets of quartz have crystallized within the felspar (orthoclase or microcline) in parallel positions. The resulting appearance may have a resemblance to Hebrew writing, and for this reason the texture was called " graphic " (Fig. 39); it is also developed on a fine-grained scale (micrographic) in rocks such as *granophyre* (= graphic microgranite).

The proportions of the two minerals in such rocks are nearly constant, about 70 per cent felspar and 30 per cent quartz; the quartz intergrowths run in regular

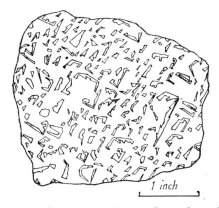

FIG. 39.—GRAPHIC GRANITE, showing angular pockets of quartz in orthoclase. About two-thirds full size.

directions through the felspar crystals. In a thin section, groups of adjacent quartz areas show simultaneous extinction between crossed nicols, indicating that each group forms part of a single crystal structure which extends through the felspar. According to one view, this texture is explained as due to simultaneous crystallization of the two minerals, which form a mixture in the eutectic proportions. The *eutectic* mixture of two solids (which do not form solid solutions) is the one which has the lowest freezing point; this principle has considerable applications in connection with metallic alloys. The proportions for an orthoclase-quartz eutectic are, orthoclase 72·5 and quartz 27·5 per cent—about the same values as are found in graphic granite.

An alternative view is that there has been a replacement of parts of the felspar by quartz; at a late stage in the consolidation of the rock, silica-bearing fluids penetrated the felspar, and potassium and aluminium were exchanged locally for silica. Such replacement could give rise to the " graphic " appearance. Other quartz replacements are also known.

VARIETIES: Varieties of granite are named according to the chief mineral present, other than quartz and felspar, and include: muscovite-granite; biotite-granite; muscovite-biotite-granite (or " two-mica granite "); hornblende-granite; tourmaline-granite (see also p. 150). The list could be extended.

The wide extent of granitic rocks has already been indicated. Great Britain possesses a number of granite masses. In Scotland, as well as in the south, the rock is quarried extensively for building material; in the neighbourhood of Aberdeen a group of quarries yield grey granites, one being the muscovite-biotite-granite from Rubislaw, a much used structural stone. The pale grey muscovite-granite from Kemnay, near Aberdeen, was employed for the piers of the Forth Bridge. The red biotite-granite from the famous Peterhead quarries, north of Aberdeen, is a noted structural stone which has been widely exported.

The porphyritic granite from Shap, Westmorland, has two main varieties, differing in the pink or white colour of the groundmass felspar; this stone was used for facing the piers of the new Inverness bridge in 1961. Rock chippings are made into concrete for a variety of uses, e.g. paving slabs.

In the Dartmoor area, Devon, the Merrivale quarries near Princetown yield a grey, somewhat porphyritic biotite-granite which is a good structural stone; granite is still worked at Blackingstone, near Moretonhampsted, and was formerly quarried at Sweltor, Gunnislake, and Ivybridge. Much good stone on Dartmoor (e.g. that at the Haytor quarries, from which London Bridge was built) is now unworked because transport costs hindered it from competing with other British and foreign stones, which were situated on a seaboard and were cheaper to market. (See Plates VIB and VIIIB.)

The well-known Cornish granites from the Penryn, Carnsew, de Lank, and Cheesewring quarries, among others, are mainly muscovite-biotite-granites, grey in colour and sometimes porphyritic. Cornish granite has been used in the construction of many dock and harbour works both at home and abroad (e.g. Swansea, Belfast, and Colombo, Ceylon), in London bridges and the Rotherhithe Tunnel, in many large buildings, and for the river wall at the South Bank Exhibition site, London (1951).

In Ireland, grey biotite-granites are worked at Newry and Castlewellan, Co. Down, and at other localities. Quarrying localities in the Leinster granite are at Ballyknockan and Ballyedmonduff, Co. Dublin; a granite with large micas is worked at Three Rock Quarries, near Dublin.

Many varieties of Norwegian granite were formerly exported to Britain and used for facing and decorative work.

Granodiorite.

In rocks of this type the proportions of orthoclase and plagioclase are more nearly equal, but with plagioclase in excess of orthoclase. There is rather less quartz, on the whole, than in granite; the dark minerals are mainly hornblende and biotite. Granodiorite generally has a slightly higher mafic content than granite (see diagram, p. 100); the rock has the granitic texture and is similar in appearance to granite. It is transitional between granite and diorite.[1]

A good example of granodiorite (often referred to as granite) is the rock from the Mountsorrel Granite Quarries, near Leicester; these are perhaps the largest producers of road-stone among granite quarries in England. Micromeasurements on thin sections of the Mountsorrel rock give the following mineral composition: Quartz, 22·6; orthoclase, 19·7; plagioclase, 46·8; biotite, 5·8; hornblende and magnetite, 5·1 per cent. The rock has grey and reddish varieties, and a medium to coarse texture; it has a moderately high crushing-strength.

Another granodiorite which is quarried for road-stone comes from the Hollybush Quarry at the southern end of the Malvern Hills, where it occurs with a

---

[1] Special names are used for particular varieties of granodiorite, such as *tonalite* (from the Tonali Pass) and *adamellite* (Mt. Adamello, N. Italy).

number of other igneous types. The mineralogy of this rock is similar to that of the one just quoted.

Many granodiorites (formerly called granites) are found in Scotland, e.g. the Moor of Rannoch intrusion and the Criffel-Dalbeattie mass (see p. 212). The quarries at Dalbeattie, in Kirkcudbrightshire, yield a sound grey rock which has been extensively used in dock construction (e.g. at Liverpool and Swansea), and for the King George V and other bridges at Glasgow.

QUARTZ-PORPHYRY and ACID LAVAS.

Quartz-Porphyry.

This rock is the dyke equivalent of granite, and has a similar mineral composition. It has the porphyry texture (Fig. 38) with porphyritic quartz and orthoclase in a microcrystalline base composed of quartz and felspar; small crystals of mica are often present. Dykes and sills of quartz-porphyry occur in most granite areas; when porphyritic crystals are absent the rock is called *felsite*. A West of England quarrymen's term for quartz-porphyry is *elvan*.

The acid lavas have a restricted occurrence, and their amount is small by comparison with basic lavas.

Rhyolite.

This acid lava characteristically shows *flow-structure,* i.e. a banding in the rock developed by relative movement in the layers of the viscous lava as it flowed during extrusion. It is not a very abundant rock. It may be glassy or crypto-crystalline, and may contain porphyritic crystals of quartz and orthoclase. It frequently contains *spherulitic* structures, which are minute spheres of crystalization formed of quartz and felspar crystals radiating from a centre. In course of time the original glassy rock may become cryptocrystalline, when it is said to be devitrified; any flow-structure originally present is preserved.

Obsidian, a black glassy-looking rock which breaks with a conchoidal fracture, is a variety of rhyolite, almost entirely devoid of crystals. Obsidian Cliff in Yellowstone Park, U.S.A., is a classic locality for this type. *Pitchstone* is another glassy lava, generally with a greenish tint and pitch-like lustre, which approximates to rhyolite in composition but is if anything somewhat less rich in silica. A pitchstone flow occurs on the Isle of Eigg, Scotland. Small curved contraction cracks, formed during cooling and known as *perlitic* structure, are sometimes shown by these glassy rocks.

Dacite is the acid lava which approximates to granodiorite in composition, and is distinguished from rhyolite by having porphyritic plagioclase instead of orthoclase. It is found associated with andesites and is distinguished from them by its content of quartz crystals.

Pumice is a highly vesicular " lava froth," formed by escaping gases and making the rock so light as to float on water. Pumice may have the composition of rhyolite or it may be of a more basic character. Of recent years, pumice has been used in light concrete slabs for interior partitions, with sound insulating properties.

SYENITE, PORPHYRY, and TRACHYTE. This group of igneous rocks, of which syenite (named after Syene, Egypt) is the plutonic representative, is treated separately here because its members do not form part of the diorite—granodiorite—granite series already described. Syenites and their related rocks contain a higher proportion of alkalies than is found in rocks of similar silica percentage such as granodiorite; this is demonstrated for syenite by the curves in Fig. 40. In terms of minerals the same fact is expressed by the large content of alkali-felspars which is common in syenites, and sometimes by the presence of felspathoids. Syenite, with the incoming of quartz, grades on the one hand into quartz-syenite and thence into an alkaline variety of granite ; on the other hand, with decrease of orthoclase and increase in the proportion of plagioclase and mafic minerals, syenite grades into an alkaline type of gabbro.[1]

Rocks of the syenite family, taken as a whole, are not very abundant by comparison with the great bulk of the world's granites. Where, however, they are locally well developed they may be quarried and used in engineering construction ; examples of this are provided by the syenites and alkaline gabbroic rocks which are extensively worked for road-metal and concrete aggregate in the neighbourhood of Montreal, Canada ; and the laurvikites (see below) of Southern Norway, which are popular decorative stones and are exported on a considerable scale.

Undersaturated [2] types, such as nepheline-syenite, are numerous and provide many varieties which are of petrological interest, but their description is beyond the scope of this book and only the chief saturated [2] types will be dealt with.

Porphyry (or felspar-porphyry, i.e. without quartz) is the dyke equivalent, and trachyte the extrusive equivalent, of syenite.

Syenite.

MINERALS : Orthoclase (or some other variety of alkali-felspar) is the chief constituent, forming well over half the rock, with a smaller amount of plagioclase (oligoclase) ; mafic minerals are frequently hornblende and biotite, sometimes augite ; accessories include iron oxides, apatite, sphene, zircon. A small amount of quartz may be present, filling interstices between the other minerals. Felspathoids occur in undersaturated syenites, when their name is used as an adjective to the rock name, e.g. nepheline-syenite.

TEXTURE : Coarse-grained holocrystalline, sometimes porphyritic. Hand specimens appear rather lighter in colour than most diorites, but this depends on the proportion of the dark minerals in the rock. In thin section the texture is granitic, with interlocking crystal plates.

VARIETIES : These are named by prefixing the name of the chief mafic constituent, and include : hornblende-syenite ; augite-syenite ; biotite-syenite ; also quartz-syenite, when quartz is present but is insufficient to make the rock a granite.

The type hornblende-syenite comes from Plauen, Saxony, and is a rock with a light purplish tint. There are few occurrences of syenite or felspathoidal-syenite in Britain, but great developments of these rocks occur in Canada and Norway, as already mentioned, and in the Kola peninsula, Russia, where they are associated with important ore bodies.

The soda-rich syenite (with average Na_2O = 6 per cent) called *laurvikite*, from Laurvik, Norway, is important because of its use as a decorative stone for the facing of buildings. It consists mainly of the felspar anorthoclase (p. 73) with some titaniferous augite, mica, and iron oxides. The felspar shows beautiful blue and green schiller effects which give the rock its value for decorative pur-

---

[1] Such a series of rocks is called an *alkaline* series, as distinct from *calc-alkaline* rocks, which are typically represented by granite, granodiorite, and diorite.

[2] For definition of these terms see p. 99.

poses; it also takes a good polish. Various differently coloured laurvikites are marketed and are known to the trade by names such as " light pearl," " dark pearl," " blue granite," etc.

Porphyry.

Porphyry, sometimes called syenite-porphyry, is the dyke equivalent of syenite, and contains porphyritic crystals of orthoclase in a microcrystalline base made of felspar with hornblende or biotite. *Rhomb-porphyry* is the dyke rock corresponding to laurvikite; boulders of it have been found in East Anglia and owe their transport from Norway to the agency of ice.

Trachyte.

MINERALS AND TEXTURE : Trachyte, the volcanic equivalent of syenite, is typically a pale-coloured, rough-looking lava (Greek : *trachys*, rough). It has porphyritic crystals of orthoclase in a groundmass composed mainly of felspar microliths (orthoclase and plagioclase), with some biotite or hornblende as a mafic constituent. A glassy (non-crystalline) base is sometimes present.

The *trachytic texture* has a characteristic appearance under the microscope, the microliths of the groundmass having a sub-parallel arrangement, and showing lines of flow around porphyritic crystals.

Sanidine-trachyte contains porphyritic crystals of sanidine, a glassy variety of orthoclase (p. 73).

VARIETIES : Trachytes are found at a number of localities in the Central Valley of Scotland, e.g. in the Braid, Garleton, and Eildon Hills. A felspathoidal trachyte called *phonolite*,[1] in which nepheline takes the place of some of the felspar, forms the hill of Traprain Law, Haddington; the Wolf Rock off the coast of Cornwall is composed of a well-known nosean-phonolite. The Eifel district of Germany provides many leucite-bearing trachytic lavas and tuffs, and the Auvergne district of Central France is noted for its trachyte domes, which are extrusions of viscous lava which solidified around the vents as dome-like masses.

Pegmatites and Aplites. *Pegmatites* are very coarse-grained rocks which occur as dykes and veins in the outer parts of an intrusive mass and in the surrounding country-rocks (Plate VIIIA); they are composed of minerals similar to those of the parent igneous body, and represent residual portions of the magma. Thus, granite-pegmatites, containing quartz, microcline, and mica, are common in many granite areas. The mica (e.g. muscovite) used in industry is obtained from pegmatites, where individual crystals may be many inches in diameter, yielding large plates of the mineral; the United States, Canada, and India produce mica from such sources. Syenite-pegmatites in Norway contain large crystals of apatite and rare earth minerals. Some minerals grow to very large sizes under these conditions : crystals 42 feet long of the rare pyroxene spodumene, which contains lithium, have been measured in a granite-pegmatite in Dakota.

These coarsely crystalline growths are the products of residual magmatic fluids which are rich in volatile constituents, and are late injections in the cooling history of an igneous mass. The volatiles, which are largely aqueous, act as fluxes and lower the crystallization temperatures of minerals, which

---

[1] From *phone*, a sound; the name refers to the ringing note emitted by the rock when struck with a hammer.

can continue to grow to large sizes in the mobile medium. Rare constituents (such as lithium, tungsten, cerium, thorium) may become concentrated in these residual fluids, and the resulting pegmatites are sometimes worked as ores from which the metals are extracted.

Aplites are fine-grained, " sugary " textured rocks, which are found as small dykes and veins in and around granites and other intrusives. They are composed chiefly of light (felsic) minerals, such as quartz and felspar, with few or no dark minerals. Their fine texture points to a derivation from more viscous and less aqueous fluids than in the case of pegmatites ; but they are commonly associated with the latter, and streaks of aplite often occur within a pegmatite vein. Aplites also contain fewer of the rare elements that are so often found in pegmatites.

Igneous Rock Series. A series of rocks such as the granite—grano-diorite—diorite suite, in which there are gradations between the different members, can be illustrated by means of a *variation diagram*. This may be constructed in several ways from the chemical analyses of the rocks ; in Fig. 40, the percentages of the different constituents are plotted as ordinates against silica percentages as abscissæ, giving a series of curves. The values used in the figure are taken from the following table of average compositions of plutonic rocks.[1]

	Granite %	Grano-diorite %	Diorite %	Gabbro %	Syenite %
SiO_2	70·2	65·0	56·8	48·2	60·2
Al_2O_3	14·5	15·9	16·7	17·9	16·3
Fe_2O_3	1·6	1·7	3·2	3·2	2·7
FeO	1·8	2·7	4·4	6·0	3·3
MgO	0·9	1·9	4·2	7·5	2·5
CaO	2·0	4·4	6·7	11·0	4·3
Na_2O	3·5	3·7	3·4	2·6	4·0
K_2O	4·1	2·8	2·1	0·9	4·5
H_2O	0·8	1·0	1·4	1·5	1·2
rest	0·7	0·8	1·2	1·4	1·1

It will be seen that the points representing syenite do not fall on the smooth curves given by the other four rock types, indicating that syenite does not belong to the same series as the rest. The curves also show the increases in magnesia, lime, and iron towards the basic end of the series. Variation diagrams can be drawn for other rock series and comparisons made.

Origin of Igneous Rocks. While there are many different sorts of igneous rock, it is thought that there are only a few, perhaps two, kinds of primary magma from which they have been derived. The science of Petro-logy is concerned with the explanation of the origin of magmas and the derivation of different rocks from them. Some of the processes which are believed to have contributed to the formation of igneous rocks are briefly outlined below.

[1] Quoted from " Igneous Rocks and the Depths of the Earth." by R. A. Daly, 1933.

The splitting of a magma into fractions of contrasted composition is called *differentiation*. It may come about in various ways : for instance, a magma might become divided into lighter and heavier parts under the influence of gravity, these being separated and injected as distinct intrusions. A more likely process depends upon the separation of crystals from the fluid. The early formed crystals in a basic magma, for example, are heavier than the fluid in which they grow, and have a tendency to sink. Thus olivine as it formed would sink and accumulate at lower levels. Many instances of intrusive masses having a heavy olivine-layer at the base have

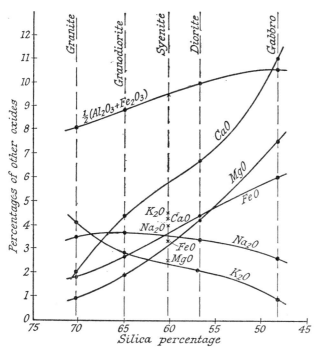

Fig. 40.—Variation Diagram for plutonic igneous rocks.

been recorded, e.g. the Lugar sill (p. 103). As cooling continues, with the separation of pyroxene as well as olivine, the specific gravity of the remaining magma is continuously being reduced, and the pyroxene crystals also tend to settle ; but if viscosity increases, the separation may be less complete than before. The crystallization of the mafic minerals, which use up Mg, Fe, Ca, and some Si and Al, results in the remaining fluid becoming relatively richer in silica, alkalies, water (steam) and other volatiles, and also in rare constituents originally present in the magma as traces. Thus at successive levels in the cooling mass, if crystallization is undisturbed, there might be formed zones containing olivine, olivine and pyroxene, pyroxene and plagioclase, and so on. These layers would consolidate as dunite, peridotite, olivine-gabbro, and gabbro, grading into one another.

The residual fluid, now much smaller in quantity, has a composition completely different from that of the original magma, because of the abstraction of mafic material, with some silica, by crystal growth ; were it to be separated from the crystal phase at this stage and injected (by the operation of crustal stresses), it would consolidate possibly as diorite. Supposing it to remain in place and the process of differentiation by crystallization to continue, with the separation of further crystals such as felspar and hornblende, the final silica-rich residue, relatively small in amount, would consolidate as a quartz-felspar rock (granite or microgranite). Thus a series of rocks could be produced from one basic magma ; and since the intrusion of magma might take place at any stage durin g differentiation, if earth-movements intervened, the production of many sorts of igneous rock becomes possible by a mechanism of this kind. It should be noted, however, that any granite so produced must be in relatively small quantities, which would be quite insufficient to account for the vast areas of granitic rocks which exist in every continent. But the theory helps to explain the many basic and ultrabasic rocks, and some small occurrences of granite.

Other theories of the origin of granite have therefore been put forward. Some geologists have postulated the existence of primary granitic magma. Others have suggested processes such as the melting at depth of sedimentary and other rocks of high silica content. During mountain-building orogenies (p 192), compression has produced intense folding in certain belts of the earth's crust, and the lower parts of the folds must have been pushed down to depths where temperatures were high enough to melt the rocks. Thus magma would be generated, and it would be of acidic composition because of the mainly siliceous nature of the rocks involved. In this way a likely origin for granite magma in bulk is suggested. Its formation is associated with mountain-building, and it is a fact that granite batholiths are found in the cores of the fold-belts of the earth (p. 96).

Another process which could result in the formation of granitic rocks is called granitization, which involves the permeation (or soaking) of rocks of suitable composition within the crust by igneous fluids, particularly by alkaline silicates. The original rock is made over, as it stands, into a rock of granitic composition and appearance. The nature of the " igneous " mass thus formed is therefore dependent not only on the character of the permeating fluids, but also on the composition of the pre-existing rocks which have been granitized : some, such as shales and sandstones, are more readily transformed than others. The hot permeating fluids might also transform solid rocks at depth into a mobile mass, which could then move upwards and become intrusive at higher levels in the crust.

There may thus be more than one way in which granite has been formed, and the problem of its origin is still a matter for discussion.

During the time that a hot igneous mass is in contact with the rocks into which it is injected, reactions take place between the magma and its walls (see also p. 150). Some of the country rock may become incorporated in the magma, a process known as *assimilation* ; and magmatic juices may permeate the zone of country rock next to the contact, thereby producing a variety of new rocks immediately around the igneous body. The assimilation of pre-existing rock by an intrusive magma, if the mixing of the two is complete, will yield a resulting rock different from that which would have been produced by the uncontaminated magma. Incorporation of shale, for example, would render an intrusive granite less acid, i.e. the granite might be changed locally to granodiorite or even to diorite. Field observations have shown that some granite masses have margins of dioritic composition which merge gradually into granite at some distance inwards from the contact; this is attributable to assimilation. Assimilation of country-rock by basic magma may also take place. The partial incorporation of sediments by an igneous body is often observed near a contact, where the process has been frozen solid by the cooling of the mass. In general, therefore, assimilation tends to produce contaminated rocks, different from the normal type which the magma alone would have evolved.

Ores of Igneous Origin. *Mineral deposits* are local accumulations or concentrations of useful minerals; many of these deposits are *ores*, i.e. minerals or rocks from which a *metal* or metals may be profitably extracted.[1] Metalliferous deposits associated with igneous rocks are here discussed briefly, and can be grouped as follows:

(i) those formed by direct segregation from magma.

(ii) those formed as veins or lodes, whose material is largely derived from magma. These may be sub-divided into (*a*) *pneumatolytic deposits*, due to the action of gaseous emanations at a high temperature (500° C. or over), including water in the gaseous state; and (*b*) *hydrothermal deposits*, due to the operation of hot aqueous fluids, at temperatures from about 500° C. downwards. It is difficult to draw a sharp distinction between the higher temperature hydrothermal minerals and those of pneumatolytic origin.

(iii) certain deposits are sometimes formed in the aureole of contact metamorphism which surrounds an intrusive mass such as granite; these *pyrometasomatic deposits*, as they can be called, result from the replacement of the wall-rocks by material from the magma, limestone in particular being often replaced in this way (Fig. 40*a*). They are not further discussed here. As examples, the copper deposits of Clifton, Arizona, and the magnetite deposits of Iron Springs, Utah, may be cited.

(i) *Magmatic segregations.* During the consolidation of a magma, early formed heavy minerals may sink and become concentrated at or near the base of the mass. Such minerals include magnetite (Fe_3O_4) and chromite ($FeCr_2O_4$). The famous magnetite deposits of Kiruna, Sweden, which have yielded millions of tons of high grade ore, were formed by the concentration of the mineral in this way, after crystallization from a magma which consolidated mainly as syenite. Deposits of chromite occur, for example, as

---

[1] As well as ores, mineral deposits include coals, oil, and non-metalliferous minerals such as barytes, gypsum, and sulphur.

segregations at the base of the Bushveld gabbro of the Transvaal, South Africa. The metals chromium, nickel, and platinum are generally associated with basic rocks.

(ii) *Veins and lodes* consist of the infillings of fissures and fractures developed in the outer part of an intrusive body or in the surrounding roof and wall-rocks. Veins which contain metalliferous minerals are termed lodes. Magmas of acid composition (such as granite) are frequently rich in volatile constituents, and may also contain small quantities of many metals. As crystallization proceeds, with the formation of minerals like felspar and quartz which form the bulk of the resulting rock, the metals—which were originally disseminated throughout the magma and were not incorporated in the felspar and other crystals—become concentrated in the residual fluids. These also contain the volatile constituents, and are thus able to remain fluid to lower temperatures than would be possible without the fluxing effect of the volatiles. If, then, fissures are formed in the outer (first consolidated) part of the granitic mass and its surrounding rocks,

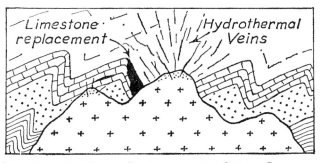

FIG. 40*a*.—VEINS FILLING FRACTURES NEAR A GRANITE INTRUSION.

by the operation of stresses, they become channels into which the residual fluids migrate, there to crystallize as lodes and veins. (See also pegmatites, p. 111.)

Metals which are commonly associated in this way with acid rocks include copper, lead, zinc, arsenic, tin, tungsten, gold, and silver. The volatile constituents, consisting chiefly of water vapour but often also including fluorine, chlorine, boron, and other gases, act as carriers for the metals into the area of mineralization around the intrusion. As they pass outwards into zones where lower temperatures and suitable pressures prevail, they deposit e.g. tin as cassiterite, SnO_2 ; tungsten as wolfram $(Fe,Mn)WO_4$; and copper as chalcopyrite, $CuFeS_2$. Thus tin and tungsten lodes may be formed in and around granite masses, as in Devon and Cornwall ; they may be regarded as of pneumatolytic origin. Minerals such as quartz, pyrite, topaz, and tourmaline are commonly associated with the metalliferous minerals in such lodes. Iron, lead, and zinc may also be carried outwards and deposited as hematite, galena, and blende in joints and fractures in cooler rocks at somewhat greater distances from the igneous source.

Veins of this type grade into the group of *hydrothermal deposits*, which are formed largely through the agency of hot aqueous solutions. These fall into three sub-groups, according to the temperature conditions under which they were formed: (a) those deposited between about 500° and 300° C. are the high-temperature hydrothermal deposits ; (b) those at 300° to 200°C. are the intermediate deposits ; and (c) those from 200° down to about 50° C. the low-temperature deposits.

(a) Minerals generally formed under high-temperature hydrothermal conditions are mainly the sulphides of iron, copper, lead, and zinc (see pp. 84–5). They occur in lodes, as described above, in association with non-metalliferous minerals such as quartz, fluorite, calcite, or dolomite. The non-metalliferous minerals are referred to as the *gangue*, so that a lode consists of gangue and ore.

(b) Among the deposits formed at intermediate temperatures are some lead and zinc veins, certain gold-bearing quartz veins, and some copper and pyrite deposits. Lead and zinc commonly occur as the sulphides, galena and blende, but sometimes as compounds with arsenic and antimony, often in association with pyrite, and quartz, calcite, fluorite, or barytes. In the formation of such veins, mineral-forming materials are carried by the hydrothermal solutions, which may penetrate country-rocks along any available channels for considerable distances from the igneous mass, at a late stage in its cooling history. As the solutions enter cooler regions the minerals are deposited in fissures and cavities. Some replacement of soluble rocks like limestone may be effected (Fig. 40a), as in the Carboniferous Limestone of Derbyshire and Cumberland. Many veins containing galena, blende, and calcite are found in these limestones ; other British occurrences are in Cornwall, Durham, and Cardiganshire.

(c) Deposits formed under low-temperature hydrothermal conditions occur at shallow depths and are often associated with andesites. They include certain gold occurrences, in which the gold (together with some silver) is combined as a telluride. Gold telluride ores are worked at Kalgoorlie, Australia, and were formerly worked at Cripple Creek, Colorado. Mercury, combined as cinnabar (HgS), and antimony, as stibnite (Sb_2S_3), are two other examples of low-temperature hydrothermal minerals. They are sometimes associated in veins with minerals of the zeolite group, indicating a temperature of formation not greater than 200° C.

Secondary enrichment. When ore-deposits undergo weathering and decomposition at their outcrops, secondary alterations take place which are often of economic importance. The weathered upper part of the deposit is known as gossan. Sulphide ores, in particular, are affected in this way. Above the water-table (*q.v.*) there is a downward movement of water percolating from the surface, which carries solutions from the weathered rocks. Below the water-table cementation and reaction take place, leading to the concentration there of metals derived from higher levels. This process is termed secondary enrichment. Thus, soluble sulphates become precipitated as sulphides near the water-table. Copper is an important example: the sulphide covellite (CuS) is formed in the way described, from the primary copper minerals of the ore, giving rise to local enrichment of the deposit.

The above account is a brief outline only of ores associated with igneous rocks. For greater detail reference should be made to books on mineral deposits.

Selected References

HATCH, F. H., A. K. WELLS AND M. K. WELLS. "Petrology of the Igneous Rocks." 12th edition, 1961. Allen & Unwin.

TYRRELL, G. W. "Principles of Petrology." 11th edition, 1956. Methuen.

BATEMAN, A. M. "The Formation of Mineral Deposits." 1955. Wiley & Sons.

CHAPTER 6

SEDIMENTARY ROCKS

The Sedimentary Rocks are, in the main, made of fragments and particles derived from older rocks. The chief ways in which these are disintegrated and weathered at the earth's surface, and the transporting and deposition by wind or water of the fragments thus formed, were discussed in the first chapter, which can be read in conjunction with the present chapter.

Sediments form a relatively thin surface layer of the earth's crust (see p. 165), covering the underlying igneous and metamorphic rocks. This sedimentary layer is discontinuous and of varying thickness ; it averages about half a mile in thickness but locally reaches over 40,000 feet in narrow belts, the sites of former geosynclines (below). It has been estimated that sediments constitute only about 5 per cent of the crustal rocks (to a depth of 10 miles), and the proportions of the three main types have been calculated to be : shales and clays, 4 per cent ; sandstones, 0·75 per cent ; limestones, 0·25 per cent.

Most sediments, especially those which are built up from the breakdown products of older rocks, become subject to the processes of compaction, cementation and hardening, so that in course of time they pass from a loose, unconsolidated condition to a firm, coherent mass of new rock. The consolidation or packing of their loose particles is due primarily to the pressure of superincumbent material. During the process, water between the particles is squeezed out, e.g. a clay passes to the condition of shale by losing much of its water. Cementation processes in time operate on the more sandy sediments and fill the interstices between the particles, which then become bound together by cementing material, e.g. a loose sand becomes a sandstone. The Sedimentary Rocks also include many kinds which are made of the remains of organisms, such as certain limestones, and others which are formed by chemical deposition. The groupings used in the table on p. 125 may be set out briefly thus :

I. *Detrital sediments* (mechanically sorted), e.g. gravels, sandstones, clays and shales.

II. *Chemical, and biochemical (organic)*, e.g. limestones, coals, evaporites.

Environments of Deposition. The composition, texture, and sedimentary structures of any sediment are dependent on the processes which operated during its formation, and on the length of time over which they acted. These factors were governed, in turn, by the environment in which sedimentation proceeded. In turbulent water, for example, sedimentary particles are well sorted and rounded, especially if the processes go on for a long time. This is seen in beach deposits, formed in a stable environment. When, on the other hand, the duration of the formative processes is shortened by the onset of crustal movements such as uplift or depression, or from other causes, the weathering of the sediments is incomplete, the transport is shorter, and the sedimentary particles are deposited rapidly. There is a contrast, therefore, between *stable* and *unstable* environments, which is expressed in the characters of the sediments accumulated.

(*i*) *Stable environments.* On the continental shelf, in the marginal part of a sea, deposits of pebbles and sand (of various grades) are formed, together with muds and limestones. The rough water caused by wave action along a coast results in the rounding of rock particles (to give pebbles), and mineral particles (sand) in which quartz is the main constituent. Minerals which are less hard than quartz do not persist for so long ; nor do minerals with cleavages, such as felspar. Still finer particles (silt) also come to consist mainly of quartz. Current-bedding and ripple-marks are common and may be preserved in the resulting sandy and silty rocks. Thin shale beds are formed from muds deposited in the somewhat deeper and less turbulent zone at a distance from a shore, at depths below the limit of wave-action (p. 26). Limestone-forming materials derived from calcareous skeletal remains (e.g. algae, crinoids, shell debris) are commonly associated with such sands and muds. A sequence of fossiliferous sedimentary layers is thus formed, in a marine area, and they may lie uncomfortably on older rocks in which the platform of deposition was eroded (p. 174). Because of its content of fossil shells and shell fragments, such a sedimentary series is often referred to as a *shelly facies*, or *shelf facies*. It is frequently of relatively small thickness (hundreds of feet rather than thousands); but if gentle subsidence has affected the area of deposition during the formation of the deposits, a much greater thickness of these shallow-water sediments may have accumulated. Under these circumstances successive pebbly layers of the fore-shore, for example, have been put down farther and farther inland from the original coast, as in time the water slowly deepened over the area of sedimentation while the fore-shore zone migrated inland (Fig. 11*a*, p. 35).

Other relatively stable environments of deposition include the land areas on the continental margins where *desert*, *piedmont*, and *lacustrine* deposits are accumulated. Desert deposits such as eolian sandstone and loess have been discussed earlier (pp. 5, 9). Piedmont deposits, which are formed during rapid weathering of mountains at the end of an orogenic upheaval and lie at the foot of steep slopes which are undergoing denudation, may include *arkoses* (felspathic sandstones, q.v.). In lakes of still water lacustrine clays are slowly deposited ; and where water is impounded in glacial lakes (p. 42), seasonal melting of ice leads to the formation of *varved clays*, with alternations of coarser (silty) and finer (muddy) layers.

(*ii*) *Unstable environments.* The elongated basins of sedimentation called *geosynclines* (Fig. 41) are at first filled with sediment during slow subsidence extending over a long period of time. In the later part of their development the geosynclines and their adjacent land areas undergo great disturbances. Much coarse detritus and other sediment is then poured into the deepening trough, filling it with elongated lenses of deposit derived from nearby land areas by rapid weathering, often with contributions from volcanic eruptions. The sediment is accumulated rapidly, without having undergone lengthy processes of sorting and rounding. Slumping affects the finer muddy sediment built up on the steepening submarine slopes, and

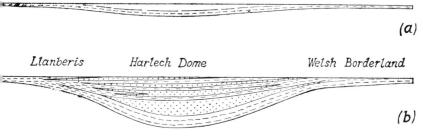

(a)

Llanberis Harlech Dome   Welsh Borderland

(b)

FIG. 41.—SECTIONS THROUGH A GEOSYNCLINE.
(a) the trough in an early stage ; (b) the Welsh geosyncline, filled with thick Cambrian deposits (see p. 204) during deepening ; dots show sediment probably brought by currents along axis of trough (after J. L. Knill).

mud-flows run their course to lower levels. Thicknesses of many thousands of feet of sediment are piled up in the over-deep trough.

Typical *greywackes* are formed under these conditions ; they are badly sorted muddy sediments with much coarse clastic material. With them are associated breccias, and lenses of poorly graded conglomerates in which partly rounded pebbles are set in a matrix of angular mineral grains, the minerals being of more than one variety (in contrast to the predominant quartz of the pebbly beach deposits referred to earlier). The textural features shown by greywackes and associated rocks (p. 130) indicate rapid accumulation with little transport and sorting ; shales which accompany them often show slump structures ; limestones if present are generally thin and represent temporary conditions of greater stability which prevailed for a time, especially when the trough of sediment was nearly filled.

When subsequently all these sediments have undergone compression, their folded and faulted condition at the present day reveals something of the movements which affected them as they became elevated to form fold-mountains on the site of the former geosyncline (p. 192).

I. *DETRITAL SEDIMENTS*, mechanically sorted

This group is subdivided according to the size of the particles into (a) *pebbly* (or psephitic), (b) *sandy* (or psammitic), and (c) *muddy* (or pelitic) sediments, as in the Table. Convenient limits are adopted for the different particle sizes, or *grades*; two scales are given below, the Wentworth scale which is in common use among geologists, and the Atterberg (or M.I.T.) scale, frequently employed in soil mechanics. (Other scales have been proposed.)

Wentworth			*Atterberg*		
Grade	*Size*		*Grade*	*Size*	
Pebbles	over 2 mm.		Gravel	over 2 mm.	
Sand — very coarse	2	−1	Sand — coarse	2	−·6
coarse	1	−½	medium	·6	−·2
medium	½	−¼	fine	·2	−·06
fine	¼	−⅛	Silt — coarse	·06	−·02
very fine	⅛	−1/16	medium	·02	−·006
Silt	·06−·002		fine	·006−·002	
Clay	below ·002		Clay	below ·002	

A particular sediment generally contains particles of several different grades and not all of one size, e.g. a " clay " may contain a large proportion of the silt grade and even some fine sand, as in the London Clay (see Fig. 42, *B*). The determination of the grades or sizes of particles present in a sample of sediment, known as the *mechanical analysis*, is briefly discussed below. Unconsolidated sands, silts, and clays are of considerable importance in civil engineering and are known to the engineer as *soils*. Mechanical analysis may give valuable information about the physical properties of a deposit. The proportion of clay present in a sediment, for instance, affects the engineering properties of the material. A good moulding sand should contain a small proportion of particles of the clay grade ; a good sand for glass manufacture would be composed mainly of one grade of clean grains (Fig. 42, *C*). It is to be noted that in general sand and silt particles are physically and chemically inert, but clays (0·002 mm. and less) are often highly reactive.

Mechanical analysis. The methods commonly employed include:

(1) SIEVING. Sieving is necessarily used for samples of coarser sediment, and is useful for grains down to 200 mesh, or about ·07 mm. Sieves are made in a graded series with a minimum size of 300 meshes to an inch. Two series are in common use in this country, (*i*) the British Standard Screen (B.S.S.), and (*ii*) the Institution of Mining and Metallurgy series (I.M.M.) in which the thickness of wire equals the size of mesh. The sample is passed through a set of sieves and the weights of the fractions thus separated are obtained. They can be plotted to give a size-distribution curve for the sample, as in Fig. 42 ; or the percentage passing each sieve can be plotted against size of mesh. A sieve measures the minimum " diameter " of a particle, since elongated grains of small cross-section can pass through it ; (elutriation, by contrast, measures the *maximum* dimension of a grain). Data from a sieve analysis can be combined with that from elutriation or pipette methods, which are employed for the finer sedimentary particles, in a size-distribution curve.

(2) ELUTRIATION. This method utilizes the natural principle of sorting by a current of water.[1] The velocity of a particle falling freely in a fluid is

Air elutriation is also used in some industrial processes, such as cement manufacture.

a function of (a) its size, (b) its specific gravity. The mathematical expression connecting these quantities is known as Stokes' Law :

$$V = \frac{2(G - \rho)g}{9\eta} \cdot r^2 \text{ (for particles below 0·05 mm. only)}$$

where $2r$ = diameter of grain.
  ρ = density of liquid.
  G = specific gravity of particle.
  η = viscosity.

Some approximate falling velocities for quartz in water at 15° C. are:

Diam.	0·035	0·05	0·10	0·15	0·20	0·25	0·30 mm.
Vel.	1	2	7	13	19	25·5	32 mm./sec.

A sample of the sediment is placed in the elutriator, which is an elongated tapering glass vessel usually of circular cross-section, through which an upward current of water is passed. The flow is controlled by varying (a) the head of water and (b) the size of a jet which is the outlet from the apparatus. The maximum internal diameter of the vessel determines the minimum velocity of flow, which in turn controls the size of grain which is carried up by the current. The smaller grades in a sample are separated first, the flow through the elutriator being gradually increased to carry off successively larger grains. The grades are collected separately and weighed, and the results can be represented graphically as shown in Fig. 42, in which grade size is plotted on a logarithmic scale against cumulative percentage weights. Thus curve A (for Thanet Sand) shows that no grades greater

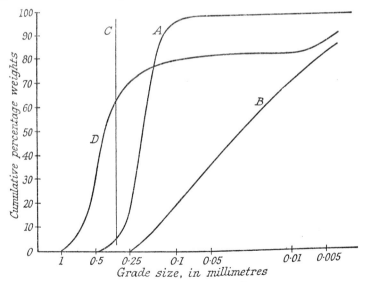

FIG. 42.—MECHANICAL ANALYSIS GRAPHS.

A) Thanet Sand, Charlton.   (B) London Clay.   (C) Ideal glass sand.   (D) Ideal moulding sand.   (B, C, and D, after P. G. H. Boswell.)

than 0·5 mm. are present, and there is 16·2 per cent of medium sand, giving the ordinate 16·2 at 0·25 mm. This value together with 79·6 per cent of fine sand make a cumulative percentage of 95·8, which is plotted at 0·1 mm. The rest of the sample consists of silt and clay grades (3·1 and 1·1 per cent respectively).

(3) SEDIMENTATION METHODS. These are used for the analysis of the finer particles, as in clayey and silty sediments. A suspension is made of the sediment in a measuring cylinder, from which samples can be taken at intervals by means of a pipette. The particles in suspension settle at different rates in water, according to their size. In the standard method, a 10 millilitre pipette is inserted into the suspension to a depth of 10 cms., at pre-determined times, and the successive pipette samples are dried and weighed. From this data a grading curve for the sediment can be constructed. The full procedure is described in British Standard No. 1377, " Soil classification and Compaction." (See also Dapples, Chap. 2, for methods of plotting ; reference on p. 144.)

In the descriptions which follow, the rocks will be treated under the general headings of (1) Pebbly Deposits, (2) Sands, (3) Sandstones, (4) Clays and Shales ; and in Group II, (5) Limestones, (6) Siliceous Deposits, (7) Evaporites, (8) Coals and Ironstones, (9) Residual Deposits. The general relations of raw materials to the consolidated rocks are shown in the Table (p. 125).

(1) Pebbly Deposits.

Pebbles are generally pieces of *rock*, e.g. flint, granite, and by definition are greater than 2 mm. in diameter; most pebbles are much larger than this. Sand grains, on the other hand, usually consist of *mineral* particles, of which quartz, because of its hardness and resistance to weathering, forms the greater part of most sands.

Marine pebbly deposits are formed at the foot of cliffs from the break-up of falls of rock and from material drifting along the coast. Sorting by wave action may result in a graded beach, as at Chesil Beach, Dorset. The pebbles consist of the harder parts of the rocks which are undergoing denudation, wastage of the softer material being more rapid ; thus, a gravel derived from flint-bearing chalk is composed mainly of rounded flints. Pebbles derived from the denudation of boulder clay deposits, as on the Yorkshire coast, are generally of many kinds (e.g. granite, gneiss, vein quartz), and may have travelled far from their source.

River gravels are laid down chiefly in the upper reaches of streams, after being carried over varying distances, and often contain an admixture of sand ; at a later date a river may lower its bed and leave the gravels as terraces on the sides of its valley, marking its former course. In the Thames valley area such gravels are mainly composed of flint and are extensively used for concrete aggregate ; " Thames Ballast," for example, is a gravel containing 98 per cent flint and is obtained from the alluvium of the River Colne below Uxbridge. Gravels laid down by rivers in areas where many different rocks have contributed fragments have a more varied composition ; e.g. deposits of the River Tay, Scotland, contain pebbles of granite, gneiss,

Dominant character	Raw materials	Rocks (consolidated)

I. DETRITAL (terrigenous, mechanically sorted)

Dominant character	Raw materials	Rocks (consolidated)
PEBBLY (psephitic)	Pebbles, gravel (over 2 mm.) Scree (talus) Boulder clay	CONGLOMERATE BRECCIA Tillite
SANDY (psammitic)	mm. Sand { very coarse (2 to 1) coarse (1 to $\frac{1}{2}$) medium ($\frac{1}{2}$ to $\frac{1}{4}$) fine ($\frac{1}{4}$ to $\frac{1}{8}$) v. fine ($\frac{1}{8}$ to $\frac{1}{16}$) Silt (·06 to ·002 mm.)	GREYWACKE, ARKOSE SANDSTONES : Varieties according to cements { siliceous (orthoquartzite) calcareous ferruginous clayey (argillaceous) Micaceous, felspathic, glauconitic and other varieties according to constituents Ganister, brickearth, loess
MUDDY (pelitic)	Clay, clay minerals (less than ·002 mm.)	SHALE, MUDSTONE, CLAY Fireclay, Fuller's Earth

II. CHEMICAL, and BIOCHEMICAL (organic)

	Raw materials	Rocks (consolidated)
CALCAREOUS	Shells, calcareous algae, corals, crinoids, foraminifera Coccolith fragments $CaCo_3$ precipitated from solution $CaMg(CO_3)_2$ of precipitation or replacement origin	LIMESTONES : shelly, algal, crinoidal, reef (bioherm), and other varieties CHALK Oolitic limestone, pisolite, travertine, stalactite, tufa DOLOMITE Dolomitic limestone
SILICEOUS	Silica gel, radiolaria, diatoms	Flint, chert, jasper Radiolarite, diatomite
SALINE	Salt lake precipitates marine precipitates	EVAPORITES : gypsum, anhydrite rock-salt, potash salts
CARBONACEOUS	Peat Drifted vegetation Liquid hydrocarbons	COAL SERIES : lignite, (brown coal), humic (" bituminous ") coals, anthracites Cannel coal Oil-shale, bituminous shale
FERRUGINOUS	Ferrous carbonate Ferrous silicate Colloidal ferric hydroxide	Siderite ores Chamosite ores Bog-iron ores

etc. Some gravels are accumulated by the action of sudden storms which wash down much detritus.

Lens-shaped beds of sand are often intercalated in deposits of river gravels, the variation in size of material being related to the currents which carried it.

Pebbly deposits or gravels when cemented are known as *conglomerate*; the spaces between the pebbles are often largely filled with sand. Two groups of conglomerates may be distinguished : (1) the beach deposits (p. 120) in which rounded pebbles are well sorted, and commonly derived from one kind of rock (such as flint, quartzite). These often occur at the base of a formation which follows above an uncomformity, e.g. the ortho-quartzite at the base of the Ordovician in South Shropshire (p. 207). (2) those conglomerates in which the pebbles are less well rounded and are derived from several different sources. Pebbly layers of this kind are often found within thick beds of sandstone, as in the Old Red Sandstone of Herefordshire, Scotland, and other districts. Such deposits represent rapidly accumulated coarse detritus washed into place by storms.

The Dolomitic Conglomerate of the Mendips is a deposit of Triassic age, containing partly rounded fragments of dolomitic limestone of Carbon-iferous age ; it is well seen at Wookey Hole and on the neighbouring hill-sides. " Hertfordshire Pudding-stone " is a flint-conglomerate formed by the cementing of pebble beds in the Lower Tertiary sands, and is locally found as loose blocks lying on the surface of the Chalk. *Banket* is the gold-bearing conglomerate, composed of pebbles of vein quartz in a siliceous matrix, from the Witwatersrand System, South Africa ; alluvial gold washed into stream gravels was cemented into a hard rock.

The name *breccia* is given to cemented deposits of coarse angular frag-ments, such as consolidated scree. Such angular fragments, after limited transport, have accumulated at the foot of slopes and have not been rounded by water action, in contrast to the rounded pebbles which are distinctive of conglomerates. Breccias composed of limestone fragments in a red sandy matrix are found in Cumberland, e.g. near Appleby, and are called *brock-rams* ; they represent the screes which collected in Permian times from the denudation of hills of Carboniferous Limestone (see p. 218). The forma-tion of scree or talus is specially characteristic of semi-arid or desert conditions.

Breccias may also be formed by the crushing of rocks, as along a fault zone, the fragments there being cemented by mineral matter deposited from percolating solutions after movement along the fault has ceased. These are distinguished as *fault-breccias*. The explosive action of volcanoes also results in the shattering of rocks at a volcanic vent, and the accumulation of their angular fragments to form *volcanic breccias*.

(2) Sands.

Mineral Content. Most sand-grains, as stated above, are composed of quartz ; they may be rounded, sub-angular, or angular, according to the degree of transport and attrition to which they have been subjected. Wind-blown grains, in addition to being well rounded often show a frosted surface.

Other minerals which occur in sands are felspar, mica (particularly white mica), apatite, garnet, zircon, tourmaline and magnetite ; they are commonly present in small amount in many sands, but occasionally may be a prominent constituent. They have been derived from igneous rocks which by their denudation have contributed grains to the sediment. Ore mineral grains of high specific gravity are present in stream sands in certain localities, e.g. alluvial tin or gold.

Heavy Mineral Separation. A quartz sand generally contains a very small proportion of heavy grains, the separation and identification of which may be desirable, either as a source of information concerning the derivation of the sand or as a means of comparison with other samples. In order to separate the " heavies," as they are called, from the abundant lighter material, resort may be had to panning or to the use of heavy liquids. *Panning* is useful for testing a deposit in the field, and is the method used by prospectors. A sample (e.g. of a stream sand) is placed in the pan, a shallow metal dish with preferably not too smooth a surface, and the whole is agitated under water. The heavier grains gradually work their way to the bottom of the sample, and the lighter material (quartz, felspar, etc.) can then be allowed to escape over the edge of the pan, the grains possessing considerable buoyancy in water. When the operation is carried out in a stream, the running water is made to assist the panning. A rough separation into light and heavy fractions is obtained in this way.

For small samples and more accurate separations, liquids of high density are used, in which only the heavier grains sink. Three commonly used liquids are bromoform, methylene iodide, and Clerici's solution (see Chapter 2, p. 47). The sample of sand is placed in a small funnel fitted with a short length of rubber tubing and with a clip to close the tubing, and is stirred in the heavy liquid to ensure the grains are thoroughly moistened. Grains which are denser than the fluid sink and can be withdrawn by opening the clip for a moment, the lighter material still floating ; they are then washed, dried, and mounted (if required) for microscopical examination. A temporary mount on a glass slip may be made with cedar wood oil (refr. index = 1·52) instead of with Canada balsam. The heavy liquid and any washings are recovered for further use. The commoner minerals found in sediments, and their specific gravities, are given in the following list :

Glauconite	2·3	Tourmaline	3·0–3·2	Rutile	4·2
Felspar	2·56–2·7	Sphene	3·5	Zircon	4·7
Quartz	2·65	Topaz	3·6	Ilmenite	4·8
Muscovite	2·8–3·0	Kyanite	3·6	Monazite	5·2
Apatite	3·2	Staurolite	3·7	Magnetite	5·2
Hornblende	3·2 (av.)	Garnet	3·7–4·3	Cassiterite	6·9

Further separation of heavy grains into magnetic and non-magnetic varieties is sometimes useful and is carried out by means of an electro-magnet ; thus, in the above list, magnetite is strongly attracted, ilmenite and iron-rich garnets are moderately magnetic, tourmaline and monazite weakly magnetic, while cassiterite, topaz, sphene, rutile, and zircon are non-magnetic.

(3) Sandstones.

A sandy sediment, after natural compaction and cementation has gone on, is converted into a relatively hard rock called *sandstone*. It has a texture of the kind shown in Fig. 43 ; there is no interlocking of the component grains, as in an igneous rock, and the mineral composition is often simple. Bedding planes and joints develop in the consolidated rock, and form surfaces of division ; these often break the mass into roughly rectangular blocks and are useful in quarrying. Sands laid down in shallow water are subject to rapid changes of eddies and currents, which may form current-bedded layers between the main bedding planes, and this current-bedding is frequently seen in sandstones (see Fig. 5).

Cementation occurs in two main ways : (1) By the enlargement of existing particles ; rounded quartz grains become enlarged by the growth of " jackets " of additional quartz, derived from silica-bearing solutions, the new growth being in optical continuity with the original crystal structure of the grains (a fact which can be tested by observing the extinction between crossed nicols). This is seen in the quartz of the Penrith Sandstone (Fig. 43 (1)), or of the Stiperstones Quartzite of south Shropshire.[1] (2) By the deposition of interstitial cementing matter from percolating waters. The three chief kinds of cement, in the order of their importance, are :

    (i) silica, in the form of quartz, opal, chalcedony, etc.

    (ii) iron oxides, e.g. hematite, limonite.

    (iii) carbonates, e.g. calcite, siderite, magnesite, witherite ($BaCO_3$).

There are also rarer sandstones cemented by sulphates (e.g. gypsum, barytes), sulphides (pyrites), and phosphates. Sometimes there is a clay bond between the grains. Sandstones are classified according to their cementing material or according to constituents other than quartz (see table, p. 125).

Siliceous sandstone, with a cement of quartz or cryptocrystalline silica between the grains of quartz (Fig. 43 (1)), is generally a very hard rock because of its high content of silica, and is therefore resistant to weathering. The Craigleith Sandstone, much used in the past in Edinburgh buildings, is an example, some varieties of this rock having 98 per cent silica. Darley Dale Sandstone, from the Millstone Grit of Derbyshire, has over 96 per cent silica, and contains a little felspar and mica.

The term *orthoquartzite* is now used for nearly pure, evenly graded quartz-sands,[2] which have been cemented to form a sandstone. An example is the Cambrian quartzite of Hartshill, near Nuneaton (p. 205).

Ferruginous sandstone is red or brown in colour, the cement of iron oxide forming a thin coating to each grain. Rocks of Old Red Sandstone age, such as the red sandstone of the Wilderness Quarry, Mitcheldean, have been much worked for building stone in the past. The red sandstones of the Trias are another example ; Bunter Sandstone (*q.v.*) from Woolton,

---

[1] An orthoquartzite (see below) ; for another use of the term *quartzite* see p. 148.

[2] The term " graded " is used in two senses : in engineering literature a " well graded " deposit is one containing a mixture of different sized particles ; whereas in geology the same phrase means well-sorted, i.e. a deposit having a preponderance of particles of one size (or grade).

Liverpool, has been used in the building of Liverpool Cathedral. Red Permian sandstones from Ballochmyle, Ayrshire, and from Locharbriggs, near Dumfries, are two other valuable structural stones of this type.

Calcareous sandstone has a cement of calcite, a relatively weak material, easily weathered by acids in rain-water. The " Calcareous Grit " of Yorkshire, of Corallian age (see p. 225), and the Calciferous Sandstones (Lower

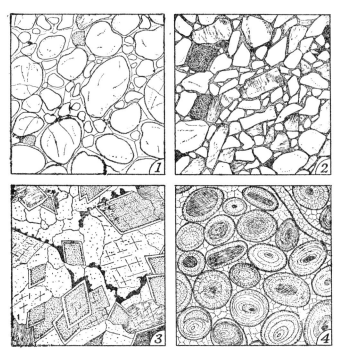

FIG. 43.—SEDIMENTARY ROCKS IN THIN SECTION.
1. Penrith sandstone, showing enlargement of grains by new growth of quartz. 2. Felspathic sandstone (arkose). 3. Dolomitic limestone. 4. Oolitic limestone. (Magnification × 15.)

Carboniferous) of Scotland are examples, as also the Sandgate Beds in Surrey (Lower Greensand). In the Downton Castle sandstone of Shropshire, among others, calcite crystals have grown around the quartz grains, which are thus enclosed in them. Reflection of light from cleavage surfaces in the calcite reveals the crystals, when the rock is handled ; the appearance is described as " lustre mottling."

Argillaceous sandstone has a content of clay, which acts as a cement ; it is relatively weak and unsuitable as building material. Rocks of this type are found in the Carboniferous of Scotland, and some are crushed down to make moulding sands for the steel industry.

Sandstones cemented with barytes ($BaSO_4$) are found at Alderley Edge, Cheshire, and at Bidston, Notts ; this is a very hard cement, and it has resulted in the preservation of isolated stacks of rock, such as the Hemlock Stone, near Nottingham, on account of its resistance to weathering. Sandstones cemented by gypsum are found in arid regions like the Sahara.

Sandstones which are named after constituents include *micaceous sandstone*, in which mica flakes (generally muscovite) are present, dispersed throughout the rock. Other sandstones have parallel layers of mica flakes, spaced at intervals of a few inches ; along these layers the rock splits easily, and it is called a *flagstone*. The structure arises when a mixture of mica and quartz grains is gently sedimented in water ; the micas settle through the water more slowly than quartz because of their platy shape, and are thus separated from the quartz grains and form a layer above them. This may be repeated many times. Flagstones are used in slabs with the bedding vertical for facing steel-framed buildings ; e.g. the Moher Flags from the coast of Co. Clare, west Ireland.

Felspathic sandstone has a small but noticeable content of felspar. *Glauconitic sandstone* contains the green clay-mineral glauconite (a hydrated silicate of iron and potassium, of marine origin), for example the Greensands of the Lower Cretaceous. The glauconite may occur as rounded grains and as infillings to the cavities of small fossils. Some of the Upper Eocene marine sands are rich in glauconite, e.g. part of the Bracklesham Beds (p. 232).

Greywacke (German " grauwacke ") is a dark grey coloured, badly sorted rock in which many coarse angular grains of quartz and felspar are present, together with mica and small rock-fragments (e.g. slate) and fine matrix material. Greywackes were formed in an unstable environment (p. 121) during the infilling of a geosyncline, when much coarse detritus was being washed into the trough of deposition. As a result of the eventual compression of the contents of the trough, typical greywackes are now found in areas of sharply folded strata, for example among the Lower Palaeozoic sediments of central Wales and the Southern Uplands of Scotland. Many greywackes show *graded-bedding*, in which the sediment passes from coarser to finer particles from the bottom of a bed upwards ; this structure is produced by the settling of a mixture of sand and mud in water, after movement over the sea floor as a turbidity current.[1] Elongated projections called *flow-casts* or *sole-markings* are frequently found on the undersides of greywacke beds ; these show the direction of currents which operated at the time of their formation.

The term *arkose* is used to denote typically pale-coloured sandstones, coarse in texture, composed mainly of quartz and felspar in angular or partly rounded grains, usually with some mica ; the minerals were derived from acid igneous rocks such as granites, or from orthogneisses, which were being rapidly denuded at the end of an orogenic upheaval (p. 121). The felspar may amount to a third of the whole rock in some instances ; the constituents are cemented by ferruginous or calcareous materials. Much arkose is found in the Torridon Sandstone of Ross-shire (Fig. 43 (2)).

---

[1] Turbidity currents give rise to a mass of disturbed sediment which on later consolidation gives rocks known as *turbidites*.

Ganister is a fine-grained siliceous sandstone or siltstone and is found underlying coal seams in the Coal Measures ; it is an important source of raw material for the manufacture of silica bricks and other refractories. *Loam* is a deposit containing roughly equal proportions of sand, silt, and clay.

The term *freestone* is used for sandstones *or* limestones which have few joints and can be worked easily in any direction, yielding good building material ; e.g. the Clipsham Freestone of Rutland, a Jurassic limestone.

(4) Shales and Clays.

Shales are compacted clays, and possess a finely laminated structure by virtue of which they are fissile and break easily into parallel-sided fragments. This lamination is parallel to bedding-planes and is analogous to the leaves in each book of a pile of books. Starting from a deposit of very fluid mud with a high water content, water has been slowly squeezed out from the sediment as a result of the pressure of superincumbent deposits, until the mud has passed into the condition of clay, with a water content of perhaps 10–15 per cent or more. With further compaction and loss of more water, the deposit has ultimately taken on the typical shaley parting parallel to bedding ; there is thus a gradation from mud to clay to shale. In some cases the shaley parting is not developed and the rock is called *mudstone*. A calcareous clay is known as *marl*.

Muddy or argillaceous rocks are of many colours ; when they contain finely divided carbon or iron sulphide they appear grey to black. The presence of iron oxide gives a red, brown, or greenish colour, according to the state of oxidation of the iron ; thus, greenish-blue London Clay turns brown on exposure to the atmosphere owing to the change from ferrous to ferric oxide.

Argillaceous rocks are composed of minute particles of the order of 0·002 mm. diameter or less, which were deposited very slowly in still water on the continental shelf or in lakes. Some of the particles are of colloidal size, and in some cases colloids may form a high proportion of the clay. Soon after the deposition of a mass of muddy sediment, sliding or slumping may occur on submarine slopes, and the incipient bedding structures are destroyed or disturbed ; considerable thicknesses of disturbed shales are seen intercalated between normal beds at many localities, and are attributable to slumping contemporaneous with deposition. Some silt particles are commonly present, and by lateral variation, with increase in the proportion of the silt, shales pass gradually into fine-grained sandy deposits.

Clays and shales have a complex mineral composition, which is the more difficult to investigate on account of the very small size of the particles involved. Modern X-ray research on clays has established the identity of a suite of *clay minerals* : these are hydrous aluminium silicates, sometimes with magnesium or iron replacing part of the aluminium and with small amounts of alkalies. They form minute flaky or rod-like crystals which have layer-lattice structures, described below, and they build up the greater part of most clays and are important in determining their properties. Clays may also contain a variable proportion of other minerals, such as finely divided micaceous and chloritic material, together with colloidal silica, iron oxide, carbon, etc., and a small proportion of harder mineral grains (e.g. finely divided quartz). Organic matter may also be present. In addition, water is an important constituent and on it the plasticity of the clay depends ; the water forms thin films around the very small mineral particles and fills the minute pore spaces. These films of water which separate the mineral flakes act as a lubricant between them and endow the clay with plastic properties. The water-absorption capacity of clay in turn depends on the flaky nature of the clay minerals.

The term " fat clay " is used in some engineering literature for a clay which has a high content of colloidal particles, and is greasy to the touch and very plastic ; a " lean clay", in contrast, has a small colloidal content and is less plastic.

During the expulsion of water from clay in the process of compaction, mineral re-constitution takes place and the resulting shale consists essentially of sericite (cf. illite), chlorite, and quartz ; small crystals grow out of the raw materials available and form part of the shale, which, however, is not completely crystalline. Chemically, shale is characterized by a high content of alumina and is also generally rich in potash.

CLAY MINERALS. These, in common with other flaky minerals such as the micas, chlorites, and talc, are built up of two-dimensional atomic layers which are stacked one upon another. The layers are of three kinds : (i) a silicon-oxygen layer, formed by the linking together of tetrahedral SiO_4-groups, as described on p. 62 (" sheet " structures) ; the composition of this layer or sheet is a multiple of Si_2O_5, or with attached hydrogen, $Si_2O_3(OH)_2$.

(ii) an aluminium-layer, $Al_2(OH)_6$ (gibbsite), constructed so that each metal atom lies at the centre of a group of six hydroxyls which are arranged at the corners of an octahedron, as in Fig. 43A. Octahedra are linked by sharing hydroxyls.

(iii) a magnesium-layer, similar to the aluminium-layer but with three magnesium atoms instead of two aluminium atoms, giving a composition $Mg_3(OH)_6$ (brucite). Different arrangements of the above layers build up the units of which the clay minerals are composed, the flat surfaces of the flaky crystals being parallel to the atomic layers. When these are stacked closely together there is some elimination of water.

The commoner clay minerals include :

(a) *Kaolinite*, $Al_4Si_4O_{10}(OH)_8$, made up of alternate silicon- and aluminium-layers; each pair, $Si_2O_3(OH)_2 + Al_2(OH)_6$, with loss of water becomes $Al_2Si_2O_5(OH)$. Kaolinite occurs in hexagonal flakes of minute size, and forms the greater part of kaolin (china clay) deposits ; it is also found in soils and sedimentary clays, of which it forms a variable and often small proportion. It is the main constituent of fire-clays (*q.v.*).

Dickite has the same composition as kaolinite, but the layers in the structure have a different relative arrangement to one another. *Halloysite*, $Al_2Si_2O_5(OH)_4.2H_2O$, may be included in a group with dickite and kaolinite ; it occurs as minute tubes, the rolled-up " sheets " of silicon-oxygen and Al-hydroxyl composition. Certain clays having a high content of halloysite possess special properties, which are discussed on p. 298.

(b) *Montmorillonite*, which has important base-exchange properties, is built up of 3-layer units comprising two silicon-layers separated by an aluminium-layer, and has the ideal formula $Al_4Si_8O_{20}(OH)_4$. Some aluminium

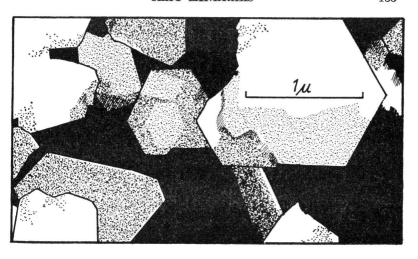

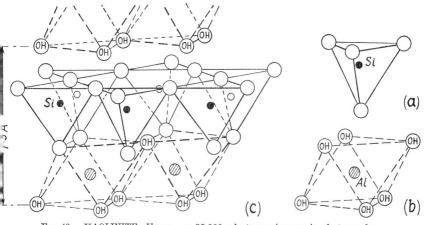

Fig. 43A—KAOLINITE. *Upper.* × 35,000, electron-microscopic photograph.

Lower. Atomic structure of kaolinite (open circles represent oxygen atoms). (*a*) tetrahedral group ; (*b*) octahedral group ; (*c*) unit of structure, consisting of a silicon-oxygen layer of linked tetrahedral groups, combined with an aluminium-hydroxyl layer. (*c*-axis of mineral is vertical).

is usually replaced by magnesium or iron, and small amounts of sodium or calcium are then attached. These alkali atoms (ions) when present lie on the flat surfaces or around the edges of the flakes and are exchangeable, giving rise to the high base-exchange capacity of the mineral. In addition, layers of molecular water may occur between the 3-layer units. A typical Ca-montmorillonite would be represented by the formula: $Ca_{0.5}(MgAl_3)Si_8O_{20}(OH)_4.xH_2O$; the calcium is replaced by sodium in Na-montmorillonite. The proportion of water is variable, and water absorption between the 3-layer units gives rise to the considerable swelling properties possessed by clays containing much montmorillonite.

The mineral occurs sparsely in soils together with kaolinite, but is the chief component of clays such as fuller's earth and bentonite, which are described below, with a note on their uses. The related minerals *saponite* and *nontronite* are formed when the aluminium in montmorillonite is all replaced by magnesium or ferric iron respectively.

(*o*) The mineral *illite* (named after Illinois by R. E. Grim, 1937) has come to be recognized as a distinct species of recent years. It is similar in many respects to white mica, but has less potassium and more water in its composition, and gives a distinct X-ray pattern. It has a much lower base-exchange capacity than montmorillonite. Illite is built up of units comprising two silicon-layers separated by an aluminium-layer, and forms minute flaky crystals in a similar way to montmorillonite. Some of the silicon is replaced by aluminium, and atoms of potassium are attached, giving a general formula of the type : $K_xAl_4(Si_{8-x}Al_x)O_{20}(OH)_4$, the value of x varying between 1·0 and 1·5. (By comparison with the white mica muscovite, illite thus contains about half as much K.) The OH-content may exceed 4, out of total $(O+OH)=24$.

According to Grim, sedimentary clays are mostly mixtures of illite and kaolinite, with some montmorillonite, and shales have illite as the dominant clay mineral. Illite is probably the most widely distributed clay mineral in marine argillaceous sediments.

The property of base-exchange (see above and p. 82) was used e.g. to render impervious a leaky clay lining to the artificial freshwater lake constructed at Treasure Island, San Francisco. The material used for the lining was a sandy clay, having a small content of calcium which was probably attached as ions to aggregates of colloidal particles, by virtue of which the clay was " crumby " and to some extent permeable. By filling the lake with salt water the clay was enabled to take up sodium in exchange for the calcium ; this resulted in a considerable decrease in its permeability and a 90 per cent reduction in the seepage losses. The colloidal aggregates were dispersed by the exchange of bases, thus changing the physical properties of the clay and filling the voids with a sticky gel which rendered it largely impervious to water.[1] This treatment is the reverse of the common agricultural process of adding calcium (in the form of lime) to a heavy, sticky soil in order to improve its working qualities.

Fuller's earth, a clay largely composed of montmorillonite, has low plasticity and disintegrates in water. It readily absorbs grease and is used for the bleaching and filtration of oils, for cleaning cloth and taking grease out of wool, and for medical purposes. Deposits of fuller's earth are worked in the Sandgate Beds (part of the Lower Greensand) at Nutfield, Surrey, and in Jurassic rocks at Combe Hay near Bath and at Woburn. Supplies of commercial bentonite (below) are obtained by processing these deposits.

Bentonite is a clay derived from the alteration of volcanic dust and ash deposits, and is mainly composed of montmorillonite. Owing to the capacity of this mineral to absorb water within the crystal lattice (p. 133), as well as acquiring a film of water around each particle, bentonite clays swell enormously on the addition of water, yielding a viscous mass. This property renders the material useful for various purposes, such as the thickening of drilling mud in sinking oil wells ; it is also used in America as an ingredient

---

[1] *Proc. Amer. Soc. Civ. Engrs.*, Vol. 66, February 1940, p. 247.

of moulding sands for foundries, and as an absorbent in many processes. Commercial deposits are worked in the Black Hills of Wyoming and South Dakota. In civil engineering bentonite is employed as a sealing layer in trenches and cofferdams to prevent the percolation of water, and as a slurry pumped into sands or gravels to fill the voids and render the mass impervious. It was used, for example, in the construction of the Hyde Park Corner underpass, London, to help support gravels in the walls of the excavations.

Fire-clays are rich in kaolinite, and commonly contain small amounts of quartz and hydromica. They occur beneath coal seams in the Coal Measures, and characteristically have a very low content of alkalies. They can be exposed to high temperatures, 1500 or 1600 degrees C., without melting or disintegrating and are used in the manufacture of refractories.

Bituminous shale or *oil-shale* is black or dark brown in colour and contains natural hydrocarbons from which crude petroleum can be obtained by distillation. It gives a brown streak and has a " leathery " appearance, with a tendency to curl when cut ; parting planes often look smooth and polished. The oil-shales of the Lothians of Scotland provide raw material for the production of crude oil and ammonia.[1]

Alum-shale is a shale impregnated with alum (alkaline aluminium sulphate) : the alum is produced by the oxidation and hydration of pyrites, yielding sulphuric acid which acts on the sericite of the shale.

Certain argillaceous deposits are formed on land ; these include *loess*, a wind-blown deposit of fine particles of the clay and silt grades, which is widely distributed in Central Europe and Asia (see p. 9) ; and *brick-earths*, brown and red silty clays which are thought to have been formed in glacial waters in front of the ice-sheets during the Pleistocene period (*q.v.*), and were formerly used in the making of bricks.

For a description of the *Red Clay* and other muds of deep-sea origin, and also of *varves* or *varved clay* (glacial), see Chapter 1.

Apart from uses mentioned above, clays are employed in industry in many ways such as for bricks, tiles, terra-cotta, tile drains, earthenware and porcelain, firebricks, crucibles and other refractories, puddle for engineering structures (e.g. the cores of earth dams), and in cement manufacture. The suitability of a deposit for any particular purpose probably depends on the presence of different clay minerals, and as knowledge of these increases the whole story of clays will gradually be written.

II. *CHEMICAL AND BIOCHEMICAL (ORGANIC) SEDIMENTS*

(5) Limestones.

Limestones consist essentially of calcium carbonate, with which there is generally some magnesium carbonate, and siliceous matter such as quartz grains. The average of over 300 chemical analyses of limestones showed 92 per cent of $CaCO_3$ and $MgCO_3$ together, and 5 per cent of SiO_2 ; the proportion of magnesium carbonate is small except in dolomite and dolomitic limestones. Limestones are bedded rocks often containing many

[1] See " Oil-Shales of the Lothians," Mem. Geol. Surv. Scotland, 1927 ; and Wartime Pamphlet No. 27, *Geol. Surv. G.B.*, 1942.

fossils ; they are readily scratched with a knife, and effervesce on the addition of cold dilute hydrochloric acid (except dolomite). The distance between bedding-planes in limestones is commonly one or two feet, but varies from an inch or less in thin-bedded rocks (such as the Stonesfield " Slate" p. 224) to over 20 feet in some limestones (e.g. the Clipsham Stone, p. 131).

Calcium carbonate is present in the form of crystals (calcite or aragonite), as amorphous calcium carbonate, and also as the hard parts o organisms (fossils) such as shells and calcareous skeletons, or their broken fragments. Thus, a consolidated shell-sand is a limestone by virtue of the calcium carbonate of which the shells are made. On the other hand, chemically deposited calcium carbonate builds limestones (e.g. oolites) under conditions where water of high alkalinity has a restricted circulation, as in a shallow sea or lake. Non-calcareous constituents commonly present in limestones include clay, silica in colloidal form or as quartz grains or as parts of siliceous organisms, and other hard detrital grains. Though usually grey or white in colour, the rock may be tinted, e.g. by iron compounds or finely divided carbon, or by bitumen. The types listed in the table are now described.

Shelly Limestone is a rock in which fossil shells, such as brachiopods and lamellibranchs (see p. 226), form a large part of its bulk. It may be a consolidated shell-sand (cf. the " crags " of East Anglia).

Algal, Coral, and Crinoidal Limestones take their names from prominent fossil constituents. *Algæ* are aquatic plants allied to sea-weeds ; some kinds secrete lime and their remains may build up large parts of some limestones. Some fresh-water algæ precipitate calcium carbonate and silica. Crinoids (or " sea-lilies," Fig. 92f) have a calcareous casing supported on a stem made of innumerable small discs ; these disintegrate when the animal dies and help to build up deposits on the sea floor. Corals (Fig. 92) are marine animals of very simple structure, with radial symmetry, often living in colonies which build reefs in warm, shallow seas, as in the South Pacific at the present day. Parts of the Carboniferous Limestone contain many corals, and the remains of ancient coral reefs are found in the Wenlock Limestone. The *reef-limestones* are mounds of unbedded rock (reef-knolls or bioherms), rich in fossils, which are found adjacent to bedded limestone with fewer fossils, as in the Carboniferous Limestone of Clitheroe, Lancs. Reef-knolls may be several hundred feet long ; they are often very porous, and may be reservoirs for oil which has accumulated in them under a cover of shale.

Chalk is a soft white limestone largely made of finely divided calcium carbonate, much of which has been shown to consist of minute plates, 1 or 2 microns in diameter. These plates are derived from the external skeletons of calcareous algæ, and are known as coccoliths. The Chalk also contains many foraminifera, which differ in kind and abundance in different parts of the formation ; and other fossils, such as the shells of brachiopods and sea-urchins (Fig. 96). The *foraminifera* are minute, very primitive jelly-like organisms (protozoa) with a hard globular covering of carbonate of lime ; they float at the surface of the sea during life, and then sink and accumulate on the sea floor. *Radiolaria* are similar organisms which have siliceous frameworks, often of a complicated and beautiful pattern ; these too are found in Chalk but are not so numerous as the foraminifera. Parts of the rock contain about 98 per cent $CaCO_3$ and it is thus almost a pure limestone. It was probably formed at moderate depths (round about 100 fathoms) in clear water on the continental shelf. The English Chalk is a bedded and jointed rock, the upper parts of which contain layers of flints (p. 139) along some bedding planes and as concretions in joints. Chalk is used for lime-burning and, mixed with clay, is calcined and ground for Portland Cement.

Limestones which contain a noticeable amount of substances other than carbonate are named after those substances, thus : *siliceous limestone, argillaceous limestone, ferruginous limestone, bituminous limestone* ; these terms are self-explanatory. *Cement-stone* (or hydraulic limestone) is an argillaceous limestone in which the proportions of clay and calcium carbonate are such that the rock can be burned for cement without the addition of other material, e.g. the cement-stones of the Lower Lias (p. 223).

Among the limestones which have originated by chemical deposition two important types are oolite and dolomite.

Oolitic Limestone, or *oolite,* has a texture resembling the hard roe of a fish (Greek, *oon* = egg). It is made up of rounded grains formed by the deposition of successive coats of calcium carbonate around particles such as a grain of sand or piece of shell. These particles are rolled to and fro between tide marks in limy water near a limestone coast, and become coated with calcium carbonate ; they are called " ooliths," and their con-centric structure can be seen in thin section (Fig. 43 (4)). Sometimes the grains are larger, about the size of a pea, when the rock made of them is called *pisolite.* Ooliths are forming today in the shallow seas off the coasts of Florida and the Bahamas.

In course of time the ooliths, often mixed with fossil shells, become cemented, and then form a layer of oolite. When few shells are present the rock has an even texture and is easily worked, and makes a first-class building stone. Bath Stone, quarried at many localities in the Bath district, is an oolitic limestone of Jurassic age (p. 224) ; Portland Stone is perhaps the best known of British oolites and has been used in many London buildings, where over a long period it weathers evenly. It is a pale cream-coloured stone, and is quarried from several beds of the Portland Series at Portland, Dorset, the best material coming from the Whit Bed and the Base Bed ; the Roach is a coarser, shelly layer used for rough walling.

Dolomitic Limestone and *Dolomite* are rocks which contain the double carbonate $MgCO_3.CaCO_3$, dolomite ; [1] the mineral occurs as rhomb-shaped crystals (Fig. 43 (3)). Dolomite is made entirely of the mineral dolomite, but dolomitic limestone has both dolomite and calcite, the full ratio of magnesium to calcium needed for the double carbonate not being present.

---

[1] The name is used for the mineral as well as for the rock.

Dolomite does not effervesce readily on the application of cold dilute hydrochloric acid. *Magnesian limestone* is the term used for a limestone with a small content of magnesium carbonate, which is usually not present as the double carbonate but is held in solid solution in calcite crystals.

The mineral dolomite often replaces original calcite in a rock, the magnesium being derived from sea-water and introduced into the limestone by solutions passing through it. The replacement process is called dolomitization. The change from calcite to dolomite involves a volume contraction of 12·3 per cent and hence often results in a porous rock. Magnesium carbonate may also be precipitated direct from solution.

Beds of dolomite are found in the Carboniferous Limestone, e.g. in the Mendips, and at Mitcheldean, Forest of Dean ; in some cases the process of dolomitization has been selective, the non-crystalline matrix of a limestone being dolomitized before the harder calcite fossils which it contains are affected. The Magnesian Limestone of Permian age (p. 218) is mainly a dolomitic limestone. A boring in the coral atoll of Funafuti, in the South Pacific, showed progressive dolomitization of the calcite of the limestone reef with depth,[1] indicating that the change takes place in shallow water. This has been confirmed by more recent borings.

Metasomatism [2] is the general name given to replacement processes such as that outlined above ; original minerals are changed atom by atom into new mineral substances by the agency of percolating solutions, but the outlines of original structures in the rock are frequently preserved. The dolomitization of a limestone thus involves the replacement of part of the calcium by magnesium. Another metasomatic change which takes place in limestones is the replacement of calcium carbonate by silica ; in this way silicified limestones and *cherts* are formed, as in parts of the Carboniferous Limestone. Silica from organisms such as sponges and radiolaria is dissolved by water containing potassium carbonate, and re-deposited as chert, which is a form of cryptocrystalline silica. The Hythe beds of the Lower Greensand in Kent have beds of chert of considerable thickness. Replacement of calcite by siderite ($FeCO_3$) is another important metasomatic change ; it is seen in some Jurassic limestones such as the Cornbrash of Yorkshire and the Middle Lias marlstone of the Midlands. It was formerly thought that the Cleveland Ironstone of Yorkshire originated in this way, but it is now believed that the siderite of this deposit, which is oolitic, was a primary precipitate on the sea-floor.

Travertine, stalactite, and *calc-sinter* are made of chemically deposited calcium carbonate from saturated solutions. Calc-sinter (or *tufa*) is a deposit formed around a calcareous spring. Stalagmites and stalactites are columnar deposits built by dripping water in caverns (see Chapter 1) and on the joint planes of rocks. Travertine is a variety of calc-sinter, cream or buff-coloured, with a cellular texture due to deposition from springs as a coating to vegetable matter. The latter rots away, leaving cavities in the rock.

---

[1] Described by C. G. Cullis in " The Atoll of Funafuti," *Roy. Soc. Report.* 1904.

[2] Metasomatism = " change of substance " (Greek derivation), cf. metamorphism = change of form).

An important economic deposit of travertine occurs in Italy, on the banks of the River Anio near Tivoli. It is 400–500 feet thick, is soft when quarried, but hardens rapidly on exposure. Travertine has been much used in slabs for non-slip flooring, as in many London buildings (e.g. Bush House), and for interior and exterior panelling, with or without a filler in the cavities.

Decay of Limestones in City Buildings. The presence of carbon dioxide and sulphur dioxide in the atmosphere of towns and cities results in the formation of weak solutions of these gases in the rain-water, giving carbonic acid and sulphurous acid. The effect of the former is to dissolve away slowly the surface layers of a limestone, in a similar way to the chemical weathering of limestones mentioned on p. 2. The sulphurous acid in rain, however, attacks the calcium carbonate and forms the compound $CaSO_4$, which on hydration becomes crystalline gypsum. A sulphate skin is thus formed on the surface of the limestone, except where the products of the chemical action are washed away (as may be the case for parts of a building exposed to much rain), and this skin gradually splits off and falls away, a process known as *exfoliation* A full account of this and other processes of decay is given in " The Weathering of Natural Building Stones," by R. J. Schaffer (Building Research Special Report No. 18, published by H.M. Stationery Office, London).

(6) Siliceous Deposits.

Under this head are included both the organically and chemically formed deposits mentioned in the table (p. 125). The deep-sea siliceous oozes are briefly described in Chapter 1, p. 36. *Diatomite* is the consolidated equivalent of *diatom-earth*, a deposit formed of the siliceous algæ called diatoms, which accumulate principally in fresh-water lakes. It is found at numerous Scottish localities and at Kentmere in the Lake District, where there is a deposit of Pleistocene age. The United States and Canada have large deposits from which considerable exports are made.[1] Diatom-earth is also known as *kieselguhr* or as *Tripoli-powder*, and was originally used as an absorbent in the manufacture of dynamite. It is now employed in various chemical processes as an absorbent inert substance, in filtering processes, as a filler for paints and rubber products, and for high temperature insulation. Deposits of *sponge spicules*, which are fragments of the skeletons of siliceous sponges, are found today on parts of the ocean floor ; older deposits of this kind provided the raw material for the cherts which occur in certain limestones.

Flint is the name given to the irregularly shaped siliceous nodules found in the Chalk. It is a brittle substance and breaks with a conchoidal fracture ; in thin section it is seen to be cryptocrystalline. The weathered surface of a flint takes on a white or pale brown appearance. Flints occur most abundantly in the Upper Chalk, where they may lie along bedding planes or fill joints in the form of tabular vertical layers. The silica of flint may have been derived from organisms such as sponge spicules and radiolaria in the Chalk, which were slowly dissolved and the silica re-deposited probably as silica gel by solutions percolating downwards through the Upper and

[1] V. L. Eardley-Wilmot on Diatomite, *Canada Dept. Mines*, 1931 ; and War-time Pamphlet no. 5, *Geol. Surv. G.B.*

Middle Chalk. The Lower Chalk generally contains no flints. Other modes of origin for flint have been suggested. For *chert* see p. 138.

Jasper is a red variety of cryptocrystalline silica, allied to chert, the colour being due to disseminated Fe-oxide ; it is found in Pre-Cambrian and Palæozoic rocks.

(7) Evaporites (Salt Lake Deposits).

When a body of salt water has become isolated its salts crystallize out as the water evaporates. The Dead Sea is a well-known example ; it has no outlet and its salinity constantly increases. Another instance is that of the shallow gulf of Karabugas in the Caspian Sea, into which salt water flows at high tide but from which there is no outflow, so that salt deposits are formed, in what is virtually a large evaporating basin which is continually replenished. In past geological times great thicknesses of such deposits have been built up in this way in various districts. The first salt to be deposited is *gypsum* ($CaSO_4 2H_2O$), beginning when 37 per cent of the water is evaporated. *Anhydrite* ($CaSO_4$, orthorhombic) comes next, followed by *rock salt* ($NaCl$). Pseudomorphs of rock-salt cubes are found in the Keuper Marl (see p. 222 for description of the conditions under which these rocks were deposited). Lastly are formed the magnesium and potassium salts like *polyhalite* ($K_2SO_4.MgSO_4.2CaSO_4.2H_2O$), *kieserite* ($MgSO_4.H_2O$), *carnallite* ($KCl.MgCl_2.6H_2O$), and *sylvite* ($KCl$). All these are found in the great salt deposits of Stassfurt, Germany, which reach a thickness of 4000 feet, and have been preserved from solution through percolating water by an overlying layer of clay.

Gypsum and rock salt are found in the Triassic rocks of Britain, e.g. in Cheshire, Worcestershire, and near Middlesbrough, but until recently nothing beyond the rock-salt stage was known in Britain. New deep borings, however, at Aislaby and Robin Hood Bay near Whitby, have penetrated important potash salt deposits lying above rock salt and covered by marl, at depths of about 4000 feet. The development of these valuable deposits is rendered difficult owing to the depth at which they occur.

Gypsum is also mined at Netherfield, Sussex, where a deposit in the Purbeck Beds is found between 100 and 200 feet below the surface. Gypsum is used extensively in the building trades, for Plaster of Paris, as a filler for various materials (e.g. rubber), and for a variety of other purposes. Rock salt, apart from domestic uses, is employed in many chemical manufacturing processes ; potash salts are used as fertilizers, as a source of potassium, and in the manufacture of explosives.

Sodium Salts.—*Soda nitre* (or " Chile salt-petre," $NaNO_3$) occurs in Chile in sandy beds called " caliche," of which it forms from 14 to 25 per cent. It is exported largely as a source of nitrates, iodine (from sodium iodate) being an important by-product. Other sodium and magnesium salts were deposited from the waters of alkali lakes, e.g. in arid regions in the western U.S.A., and the Great Salt Lake of Utah. Sodium sulphate (" salt cake ") is important in the chemical industry and in paper and glass manufacture. It is produced chiefly in Russia, Canada, and the U.S.A.

The evaporites form an economically important group, of which the foregoing is a brief outline ; for fuller treatment the student is referred to books on economic minerals. (See also Salt Domes, p. 186.)

(8) Coals and Ironstones.

The formation of coal through the burial of ancient vegetation is described in Chapter 11. The average compositions of several varieties of coal are given in the table below, and the carbon-hydrogen proportions in the accompanying graph, which also gives the proportion of oxygen by difference. The coal seams had their origin in extensive peat-bogs, which supported dense vegetation for a time and were then covered by silts and muds when subsidence and inundation took place. *Peat* is thus the first stage in the formation of coal. Upland peat of the present day, derived from compressed mosses and plants such as sphagnum, heather, and cotton-grass, is cut and burned for domestic use ; it has a high ash content and burns with a smoky flame. Peat-fired generating stations for electricity are in use in Ireland, as at Portarlington, south-west of Dublin.

	Average composition of fuels (percentages)				Proportions recalculated with Carbon as 100			
	C	H	N	O	C	H	N	O
Wood	49·65	6·23	0·92	43·20	100	12·5	1·8	87·0
Peat	55·44	6·28	1·72	35·56	100	11·3	3·1	64·1
Lignite	72·95	5·24	1·31	20·50	100	7·2	1·8	28·1
Bituminous Coal .	84·24	5·55	1·52	8·69	100	6·6	1·8	10·3
Anthracite . . .	93·50	2·81	0·97	2·72	100	3·0	1·3	2·9

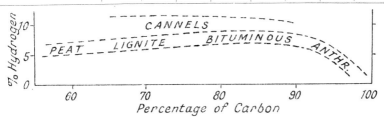

FIG. 43B. RANGE OF COMPOSITION OF COALS (after Raistrick and Marshall). Points plotted for numerous coal analyses fall within the narrow zone between the two lower dotted lines (the " coal belt "). Cannel coals lie outside this belt.

In limited areas of the peat-bogs, slight erosion before deposition of the overlying silts created hollows in which pockets of drifted plant detritus accumulated ; these now form the impersistent seams of *cannel coal* which often accompany the more extensive coals. Cannel is a dense coal of dull grey to black appearance which ignites in a candle flame (hence the name) and burns with a smoky flame. It contains some 70 to 80 per cent carbon, 10 to 12 per cent hydrogen, and much ash, and has a calorific value of 12,000 to 16,000 B.T.U. The ash is attributable to an admixture of sedi-ment which was originally deposited with the drifted vegetable debris.

Lignite (or brown coal) is more compact than peat ; it has lost some moisture and oxygen, and the carbon content is consequently higher (but less than 75 per cent). Its texture is rather like woody peat, and when dried on exposure to the atmosphere it tends to crumble to powder. There are small lignite deposits at Bovey Tracey, Devon ; extensive beds are found in Germany (Cologne), Canada, and the southern United States.

Bituminous coal includes the ordinary household varieties ; it has a carbon content of 80–90 per cent and a calorific value of 14,000 to 16,000 B.T.U. (as against lignite's 7000 to 11,000). Between it and lignite there are coals called *sub-bituminous* (or " black lignites ") with less moisture than lignite and between 70 and 80 per cent carbon. High grade, hard steam coals, sometimes termed *semi-bituminous*, are transitional between bituminous coal and anthracite ; they have the greatest heating value of any, and burn with a smokeless flame.

Bituminous coal has a typical banded structure in which bright and dull bands alternate. The three main kinds of material which are present are known as (i) *fusain*, a soft black powdery substance (" mineral charcoal ") which readily soils the fingers, occurs in thin bands, and is composed of broken spores and cellular tissue ; (ii) *vitrain*, the bands or streaks of bright black coal, a fraction of an inch or more in thickness, representing solidified gel in which the cellular structure of original plants has been detected ; and (iii) *durain*, the bands of dull hard coal, containing spore cases and resins. Blocks of coals break easily along the fusain layers, and are bounded by joints (" cleat " and " end ") which are perpendicular to the layers ; a thin film of mineral matter (e.g. pyrite) often coats the joint surfaces. " Bright " coals have a high content of vitrain, which is the best source of coal tar by-products.

Anthracite contains from 90 to 95 per cent carbon, with low oxygen and hydrogen, and ignites only at a high temperature ; its calorific value is about 15,000 B.T.U. It is black with sub-metallic lustre, conchoidal fracture, and banded structure, and does not mark the fingers when handled. Anthracite appears to have been formed when coal-bearing beds have been subjected to pressure or to increased temperatures ; transitions from anthracite to bituminous coals have been traced, e.g. in the South Wales coalfield, where also shearing structures are present in the anthracites.

Associated with coals are beds of ganister and fireclay (p. 135), which lie below the seams and represent the seat-earth in which the Coal Measure plants grew. Overlying a coal seam is a series of shales, of varying thickness, which grade upwards into sandy shales and then sandstones. These are followed by the next coal seam, with its seat-earth and its overlying shales and sandstones. The repetition of this sequence of rocks over and over again, with minor variations, is referred to as the Coal Measure " rhythm," each unit of which records the submergence of the vegetation of a coal swamp, and the eventual emergence (as the water shallowed) of sandy shoals on which the swamps grew again.

Blackband ironstone and *clay-ironstone* are ferruginous deposits associated with the Coal Measures. In Staffordshire the blackband ironstones contain from 10 to 20 per cent of coal, the iron being present as carbonate, and are found replacing the upper parts of coal seams ; they are economical to smelt on account of their coal content. Clay-ironstones also consist chiefly of chemically deposited siderite ($FeCO_3$) ; they occur as nodular masses in the argillaceous rocks of the Coal Measures, and also in the Wealden Beds, where they are of fresh-water origin.

Bog-iron Ores are impure limonitic deposits which form in shallow lakes and marshes, as in Finland and Sweden today.

The deposition of the iron may be due to the action of bacteria or algæ. The ores were much used in the early days of iron-smelting.

Jurassic Ironstones. Important bedded iron ores of this age contain the minerals siderite and chamosite (hydrated iron silicate) ; some of the ironstones are oolitic and others have small crystals of siderite in a matrix of mudstone. The Cleveland ironstone of the Middle Lias (p. 224) is an oolitic rock containing both the above minerals. A rock of the same age, the marlstone of Lincolnshire and Leicestershire, has a large amount of calcite as well as chamosite and siderite. The Northamptonshire ironstones are partly oolitic rocks with chamosite as the chief constituent, and partly mudstones with siderite and limonite.

Hematite and Limonite Ores. In some cases iron is present as hematite in a shelly limestone, as at Rhiwbina, South Wales, or as limonite, e.g. the Frodingham ironstone. The hematite deposits of Cumberland are replacements of the Carboniferous Limestone by irregular masses of the iron oxide. The Lake Superior region of North America possesses very extensive hematite deposits ; the rocks here are Pre-Cambrian sediments in which iron of sedimentary origin has probably been concentrated as the oxide after alteration from its original silicate or carbonate form.

Magnetite in notable amount occurs in a few sediments, but magnetic iron ores, which are of such importance, for example, in Sweden, are generally of igneous origin and are referred to on p. 115.

(9) Residual Deposits.

In hot, semi-arid regions, where evaporation from the ground is rapid and nearly equal to the rainfall, and where there is little frost action, chemical decomposition of the rocks proceeds to great lengths and a hard, superficial crust is formed by the deposition of mineral matter just below the soil. The water from the occasional rains carries dissolved salts only a short distance below the surface, where they are retained by capillarity, with the result that as evaporation proceeds a mineral deposit is built up. If solutions are saturated with calcium carbonate the deposit will be a calcareous one, like *kankar*, which covers large areas, e.g. in India. If the solutions are ferruginous, such as would result from the decomposition of basic igneous rocks, a red concretionary deposit called *laterite* may be formed, as in many parts of Africa. Laterite is hydrated ferric oxide, generally with some alumina and silica ; its composition varies according to the nature of the underlying rock and the amount of chemical breakdown that has gone on. " Iron pan " is a very hard variety of laterite. This material has been used as rough building stone in tropical countries where it is plentiful.

Bauxite, which consists essentially of hydrated alumina, forms residual deposits resulting from the weathering, under tropical conditions, of igneous and other rocks containing aluminium. It is the raw material from which the metal aluminium is produced, by reduction of the oxide by electrolysis. Important deposits of bauxite occur in Guyana, in the southern United States and elsewhere.

Selected References

Dapples, E. C. " Basic Geology for Science & Engineering." 1959. Wiley and Sons.

Greensmith, J. T. " Petrology of the Sedimentary Rocks." 4th edition, 1965. Murby, London. (Revision of Hatch & Rastall's earlier volume.)

Grim, R. E. " Applied Clay Mineralogy." 1962. McGraw-Hill Co. Ltd., New York.

Gilluly, J., Waters, A. C., and Woodford, A. O. " Principles of Geology," Chap. 21, Mineral Resources. 2nd edition, 1959. Freeman & Co.

Pettijohn, F. J. " Sedimentary Rocks." 1957. Harper & Brothers, New York.

Trask, P. D. " Applied Sedimentation." 1950. Wiley & Sons, New York.

Trueman, Sir A. " The Coalfields of Great Britain." 1954. Arnold, London.

CHAPTER 7

METAMORPHIC ROCKS

Metamorphism [1] is the term used to denote the transformation of rocks into new types by the recrystallization of their constituents. Weathering processes are not included. The changes which occur in metamorphism result from the addition of heat or the operation of pressure, i.e. energy is put into the rocks. New minerals grow out of the old, in a solid environment, and the rock undergoes a transformation or metamorphism. The original rock, which may be igneous, sedimentary, or metamorphic, is subjected to new physical conditions, and the resulting metamorphic product is in equilibrium with the new conditions. Textures entirely different from those of the original rocks are produced. The changes may be aided by the presence of solvents, such as pore-contained fluids, which gradually work through the fabric of a rock and promote new mineral growth. Variations in chemical composition may also play a part in the process, as when the concentration of particular substances is brought about.

Two broad classes of metamorphism, depending on the controls exercised by temperature or pressure, may be distinguished :

1. *Thermal* (including *Contact*) *Metamorphism*, in which rise of temperature is the dominant factor. Thermal effects may be brought about when sediments are down-folded into hotter regions in the crust ; or in contact zones adjacent to igneous intrusions.

2. *Regional Metamorphism*, in which both pressure and temperature have operated, and which commonly affects rocks over a large area. Where stress is locally dominant, as in belts of dislocation, the term *dislocation metamorphism* may be used.

1. *Contact Metamorphism.* By the intrusion of a hot igneous mass, such as granite or gabbro, an increase in temperature in the neighbouring rocks is produced. The general effect of this increase is to promote the *recrystallization* of some or all of the components of the rocks affected, the severest changes occurring nearest the contact with the igneous body. When there are no external stresses acting upon a rock, but only heat, new minerals grow haphazardly in all directions, and the metamorphosed rock acquires a granular fabric, which is known as the *hornfels* texture (Fig. 46).

In addition, transfer of material sometimes takes place at such a contact, and gases or fluids from the igneous mass penetrate the country-rocks ; this process is known as *pneumatolysis*.[2] During contact metamorphism the country-rock is not melted, but is often subjected to the action of emanations (such as water, carbonic acid, and volatile compounds of boron and fluorine) which percolate through it and result in the growth of new minerals ; temperatures probably do not much exceed 500° C.

---

[1] From the Greek *meta*, after (signifying a change), and *morphe*, shape.
[2] Greek, *pneuma* = gases.

2. *Regional Metamorphism.* In this class, the operation of stress results in the recrystallization of the rocks affected, with the formation of new crystals which grow with their length or platy surfaces at right angles to the direction of the maximum compressive stress. It may be suggested that the resulting oriented arrangement of the crystals represents an attempt at offsetting the effects of the external stresses. The minerals have a largely parallel orientation, and in consequence the rocks develop oriented or banded textures ; the oriented texture produced by platy or columnar minerals is known as *schistosity* (Fig. 44), while an alternation of schistose layers with others less schistose produces the banded texture called *foliation* (Plate VIIB). Argillaceous rocks under the influence of moderate stresses without marked rise of temperature develop *slaty cleavage.*

The crystallization form of a mineral partly determines the ease of its

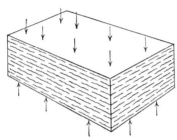

growth under metamorphic conditions, e.g. micas and chlorites, with one cleavage, grow easily in thin plates, oriented with their surfaces at right angles to the maximum stress (Fig. 44) ; amphiboles (such as hornblende) grow in prismatic forms with their length at right angles to the maximum stress. Some minerals which have a high crystallization strength (e.g. garnet, andalusite) grow to a relatively large size in metamorphic rocks, and are then called *porphyroblasts* (in contrast to the porphyritic crystals of an igneous rock, which are produced in an

FIG. 44.—DIAGRAM TO ILLUSTRATE
SCHISTOSITY.

Showing the parallel arrangement of mica flakes (or other flaky minerals) in a schist. Direction of maximum stress shown by arrows.

entirely different way). Felspars and quartz have low and nearly equal crystallization strengths, and thus metamorphic rocks composed of quartz and felspar show typically a granular texture (p. 154).

Contact Metamorphism.

The contact metamorphism of the main sedimentary rock types (shale, sandstone, limestone) is now discussed, assuming temperature to be the controlling factor, stress being entirely subordinate. Consider the contact zone bordering an igneous mass, say a granite, intruded into sedimentary rocks ; the latter are metamorphosed for some distance from the contact, and the area over which this metamorphism occurs is called the *contact aureole* (Fig. 45). Within the aureole metamorphic zones of increasing severity are traceable as the contact is approached ; they are distinguished by the development of certain minerals (see below). The size of an aureole depends on the amount of heat transferred, i.e. on the size of the igneous body. The width of the aureole indicates the steepness or otherwise of the contact (cf. east and west sides of the aureole in the figure).

1. *Contact Metamorphism of a Shale (or Clay).* An argillaceous rock like shale is largely made up of very minute particles ; some are flaky (the clay minerals, p. 132) and are essentially hydrated aluminium silicates ; together

with them are particles of sericite (secondary white mica) and chlorite, and colloidal silica, colloidal iron oxide, carbon and other substances. The two dominant oxides in a clay or shale, as would be seen in a chemical analysis, are thus SiO_2 and Al_2O_3, and when the shale is subjected to heat over a long period the aluminium silicate *andalusite*, or its variety *chiastolite*, is formed (p. 79). *Cordierite* is another mineral frequently formed at the same time; it grows, with andalusite, as porphyroblasts in the meta-morphosed shale.

In the outermost zone of the aureole (Fig. 45, zone 1) small but noticeable changes are produced; the shales are somewhat hardened, specks of opaque

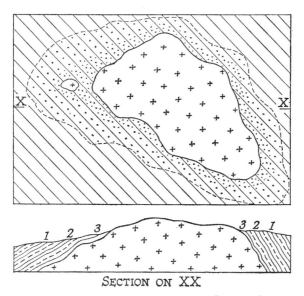

SECTION ON XX

FIG. 45.—METAMORPHIC AUREOLE AROUND AN IGNEOUS INTRUSION.
Aureole dotted. 1, 2, and 3 are zones referred to in the text.

magnetite are formed, and incipient crystals of chiastolite or cordierite appear as small dark spots; the name *spotted rock* is used to describe this low-grade metamorphic product. Nearer the contact (zone 2), chiastolite or cordierite (or both) are better developed, and give very distinct spots, and small flakes of biotite have formed from the chlorite and sericite in the shale. This recrystallization is continued in the next stage (3) still nearer the contact, together with the growth of muscovite flakes (from any sericite remaining) and of quartz; magnetite (from original Fe) and rutile (TiO_2) may also be present, depending on the original composition of the sediment. The shale has now been completely recrystallized, and is called a *hornfels*; it is hard, with a " horny " fracture, and has a typical fine granular texture (Fig. 46). Nearest to the igneous contact a further mineral change may occasionally take place: some muscovite of the hornfels may give rise to crystals of orthoclase, the excess alumina then entering into combination with silica to form needles of *sillimanite* (Al_2SiO_5, acicular).[1] The shale has now become a biotite-cordierite-sillimanite-quartz-hornfels. Hornfelses are often suitable for use as road-metal and ballast ; they are worked, e.g. in the aureole of the Dartmoor granite at Meldon Quarry, Okehampton.

<u>As the igneous rock is approached from outside its aureole the metamorphic sequence passed over is, therefore : hardened shale→spotted rock→cordierite-bearing hornfels.</u> This may be seen, among British occurrences, at places around the granites of Devon and Cornwall and in Scottish aureoles, e.g. around the Ben Nevis granite or the Insch (Aberdeen) gabbro. An interesting case is provided by the Skiddaw granite (Cumberland), which is only exposed over three small areas, each less than a mile across, in the valleys of streams flowing from the north-east side of the mountain ; over a considerable area of adjacent ground, however, there are exposures of chiastolite-bearing rock, indicating the existence of the granite at no great depth below the present surface, which marks a stage in the process of unroofing by denudation.

2. *Contact Metamorphism of a Sandstone.* A siliceous rock like sandstone is converted into a metamorphic *quartzite*. The original quartz grains and siliceous cement are recrystallized into an interlocking mosaic of quartz crystals. Partial fusion of the mass may occur under special circumstances, but rarely. Constituents other than quartz in the sandstone or the cement between the grains may give rise to new minerals, depending on their composition, e.g. biotite (from clay), magnetite (from iron oxide cement).

3. *Contact Metamorphism of a Limestone.* Limestones are essentially made up of calcium carbonate, generally together with some $MgCO_3$ and silica. (i) In the ideal case of a pure calcium carbonate rock, the metamorphic product is a *marble* composed entirely of grains of calcite. The coarseness of texture of the rock depends on the degree of heating to which it has been subjected, larger crystals growing if the metamorphism has been prolonged. Dissociation of the carbonate into CaO and CO_2 is prevented by the operation of pressure. Examples of such rocks, with a high degree of purity, are provided by the statuary marbles. (ii) In the metamorphism of a limestone in which a proportion of silica is present (e.g. as quartz grains or in colloidal form), the following reaction occurs in addition to the crystallization of calcite described above :

$$CaCO_3 + SiO_2 \rightarrow CaSiO_3 \text{ (wollastonite [2]) } + CO_2.$$

The resulting product is a *wollastonite-marble,* as in parts of the Carboniferous Limestone of Carlingford, Ireland, where the rock has been metamorphosed by gabbro intrusions. (iii) During the contact metamorphism of a magnesian or dolomitic limestone the dolomite is dissociated, thus :

$$CaCO_3.MgCO_3 \rightarrow CaCO_3 \text{ (calcite) } + MgO \text{ (periclase) } + CO_2.$$

---

[1] It is assumed in the above discussion that chemically there is neither addition nor subtraction of material during the metamorphism. If chemical transfer does take place across the contact, a variety of entirely new conditions will arise.

[2] The mineral *wollastonite,* which occurs under conditions such as these, forms white or grey tabular, translucent crystals.

The periclase readily becomes hydrated, forming *brucite*, $Mg(OH)_2$, in colourless tabular hexagonal crystals, and the product is a *brucite-marble*. Blocks of this rock have been ejected from Vesuvius ; other occurrences of brucite-marble are in Skye and in the North-West Highlands.

When silica is present, the magnesium silicate *forsterite* (p. 65) is formed together with crystalline calcite, CO_2 being lost in the reaction, thus :

$$2CaCO_3.MgCO_3 + SiO_2 \rightarrow 2CaCO_3 \text{ (calcite)} + Mg_2SiO_4 \text{ (forsterite)} + 2CO_2.$$

The metamorphic product is a *forsterite-marble* (Fig. 46) ; a British locality for this rock is Kilchrist, Skye. If the further change from forsterite to serpentine takes place (by hydration), a *serpentine-marble* is formed (also called *ophicalcite*) ; the white calcite is then streaked with green serpentine, making a very beautiful decorative stone, e.g. the well-known Connemara Marble of Ireland.

When some clay is present as well as silica in the original rock, minerals such as tremolite and diopside (Ca-Mg-silicates) and lime garnets are formed by contact metamorphism, in addition to calcite, and the resulting rock is called a *calc-silicate-hornfels*. Its mineral composition varies according to the proportions of different substances present in the original limestone ; the texture of these rocks tends to be coarse, because of the fluxing action of dissociated $MgCO_3$. (See p. 314 for note on the influence of hard calc-silicate-hornfels in tunnelling.)

The above discussion of some varieties of marble does not exhaust all the possibilities, and other types may arise, some beautifully coloured by traces of impurities in the original sediment. Decorative stones of this kind are exported from Italy and Greece. The rock is cut into thin slabs, with one surface polished, and is often displayed as panels for internal decoration ; advantage may be taken of any pattern due to veining or zones of brecciation, by arranging the slabs symmetrically in groups of two or four.

The term " marble " is also used as a trade name for any soft rock which will polish easily, and therefore includes many limestones which make attractive decorative stones on account of their content of fossils or their colouring. British examples include the Ashburton " Marble " (a Devonian coral limestone), the Hopton Wood stone (a crinoidal limestone of Carboniferous age from Derbyshire), and the Purbeck " Marble " (an Upper Jurassic limestone from Dorset, containing the fossil shell *Paludina*, Fig. 96*j*).

4. *Contact metamorphism of Igneous Rocks.* The effects here are not so striking as they are for the sedimentary rocks, because the minerals of an igneous rock were formed at relatively high temperatures and are less affected by reheating ; but some degree of recrystallization is often evident. A basic rock like dolerite or diabase may be converted into one containing hornblende and biotite (from the original augite and chlorite), the plagioclase being recrystallized. Secondary minerals occupying vesicles, as in amygdaloidal basalt, yield new minerals such as lime-felspar (after zeolite), and amphibole (after chlorite and epidote).

Igneous rocks which were much weathered before contact metamorphism yield calc-silicate minerals (e.g. lime garnet) from the calcite of the original rock, and hornblende from original chlorite.   Andesites and andesitic tuffs on contact metamorphism develop many small flakes of brown mica and crystals of magnetite ; these changes are well seen near the contact of the Shap Granite, Westmorland.

Basic *granulites* (rocks of equi-granular texture, see also p. 154) are produced by the complete recrystallization of a basalt or gabbro, during prolonged metamorphism ; many instances are on record among the Tertiary igneous rocks of Scotland, e.g. the granulitic patches enclosed in the gabbros of Skye and Mull.

Pneumatolysis.

In the foregoing discussion it has been assumed that no transfer of material from the igneous mass has taken place across the contact.   It

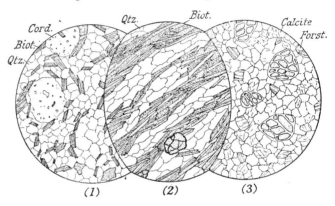

FIG. 46.—METAMORPHIC ROCKS IN THIN SECTION.
1) Biotite-cordierite-quartz-hornfels.   (2) Mica-schist with garnets.
(3) Forsterite-marble.

frequently happens, however, that volatile substances, accumulated in the upper part of a body of magma during its crystallization, pass eventually into the country-rocks, which are impregnated with the vapours at a moderately high temperature stage in the cooling history of the igneous mass.   This gas action is called pneumatolysis.[1]   The vapours include compounds of boron, fluorine, carbon dioxide, sulphur dioxide, etc. ; characteristic minerals which are produced near the contact under these conditions include *tourmaline, topaz, axinite, fluorspar,* and *kaolin.*

Tourmaline (p. 77) is formed by the action of boron-bearing vapours (with some fluorine).   It is a mineral with a high content of alumina, and hence tends to be formed in clay bands in the country-rocks adjacent to the igneous mass.   The biotite in a granite may also be changed to tourmaline by the addition of boron and fluorine, the granite itself often being locally reddened.   The name *luxullianite* (from Luxullian, Cornwall) is given to a variety of tourmalinized granite in which the tourmaline occurs

---

[1] *Pneumatolytic* effects probably take place at temperatures in the neighbourhood of 500° C.   At lower temperatures, especially below the critical temperature of water (375° C.), *hydrothermal* effects are produced by the operation of hot solutions (p. 115).

as radiating clusters of slender crystals (the *schorl* variety) embedded in quartz. Quartz-tourmaline veins, often carrying cassiterite (" tin-stone," SnO_2), are common in some granite areas, as discussed on p. 115.

Axinite is a calcium-boron-silicate which is formed where transfer of boron-bearing vapours into limestone has occurred, at an igneous contact. Axinite crystals are generally flat and acute-edged, brown and transparent, with a glassy lustre.

Kaolinization. The action of steam together with some carbon dioxide on the orthoclase of a granite results in the breakdown of the felspar into kaolin; potassium is removed and silica is liberated:

$$4KAlSi_3O_8 + 2CO_2 + 4H_2O = 2K_2CO_3 + Al_4Si_4O_{10}(OH)_8 + 8SiO_2.$$
Orthoclase $\qquad\qquad\qquad\qquad\qquad$ Kaolinite

Large parts of the granites of Devon and Cornwall, as at St. Austell, have been decomposed in this way into a soft mass of quartz, kaolin and mica, which crumbles at the touch. In the quarries the kaolinized rock is washed down by means of jets of water; the milky-looking fluid is then pumped from a sump and allowed to gravitate down through a series of tanks, the mica and quartz being first removed in the process, and the kaolin finally being allowed to settle out of suspension. This kaolin or " china clay " is used as a paper filler, in pottery manufacture, and for various other purposes, and finds markets in all parts of the world.

China-stone is a granitic rock which represents an arrested stage in the kaolinization of a granite; in addition to quartz and kaolinized felspar, it frequently contains topaz ($Al_2SiO_4F_2$) and fluorspar, both of which minerals point to the action of fluorine during pneumatolysis.

Greisen is a rock composed essentially of quartz, white mica, and topaz, and is formed in small bodies from granite under certain conditions of pneumatolysis; where, for example, the formation of K_2CO_3 is inhibited (see above equation), the felspar of the granite gives rise to white mica (secondary muscovite) and the resulting rock is called greisen.

Regional Metamorphism.

The operation of stresses on rocks on a regional scale has the general effect of inducing growth of new minerals with a parallel orientation, as indicated on p. 146, their length or platy surfaces being developed at right angles to the direction of maximum pressure. Increasing temperature may be associated with the stress conditions. Thus, strong shearing stress and low temperatures arise commonly in the outer part of the crust (epizone); moderate shearing stress and moderate temperatures occur at lower levels (mesozone); and low stress with higher temperature at still deeper levels (katazone), where also hydrostatic pressure reaches high values. Under these different controls (or energy levels), sedimentary rocks of argillaceous composition give rise on metamorphism to *slates*, or *schists*, or certain *gneisses*, respectively. Typical minerals which are formed during such regional metamorphism include chlorite, sericite, epidote, albite (under epizone conditions); and in the mesozone, muscovite, biotite, hornblende, garnet, and kyanite (Al_2SiO_5, in pale blue blade-like crystals, triclinic).

The operation of stresses without much rise of temperature may be locally concentrated in narrow belts of crushing or shearing, where severe mechanical effects are produced in the rocks affected. For this the term dislocation metamorphism is used. Such rocks are badly deformed, and internal rearrangements of a mechanical kind take place among their minerals. Signs of strain which may be observed in individual crystals, in thin sections, include the strain polarization of quartz (a patchy extinction due to the distortion of the crystal structure) ; granulation (breakdown into smaller crystals) ; the bending of mica flakes and of the twin lamellæ of plagioclases ; and the production of strain-slip cleavage (small movements or " slips " along a series of closely spaced shear planes).

An extreme example of the effect of stresses may be seen in the rocks adjacent to a big thrust-plane (e.g. the Moine Thrust, p. 202), where the rocks have been subjected to shearing, together with a considerable vertical load, and are locally transformed into *mylonites* (a name which refers to the " milling " or rolling out of the original mineral grains).

Slate. Under the influence of stresses which may be of regional extent, argillaceous sediments such as shales take on the property of being easily

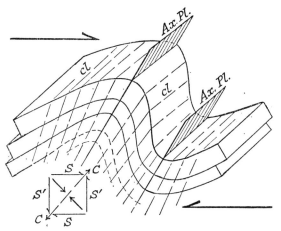

FIG. 47.—SLATY CLEAVAGE IN RELATION TO FOLDS.

Heavy arrows show deforming forces. Cleavage is developed in the direction of easiest relief, which is perpendicular to the principal compressive stress (see small diagram of stresses, where cc = direction of cleavage) ; it is parallel to the axial planes of folds. Note that the angle between cleavage and bedding varies, and is less on limbs of fold than at the axis. cl = trace of cleavage on bedding surfaces ; s, s' = shearing couples.

split along parallel planes which are independent of the original bedding (Fig. 47). This property is known as *slaty cleavage* ; it is often very regular and perfect, yielding thin, smooth-sided plates which are lithologically similar. The cleavage is related to the new texture which is developed in the rock under the influence of the metamorphic stresses ; minute crystals of flaky (layer-lattice) minerals like chlorite and sericite grow with their platy surfaces at right angles to the direction of maximum compressive stress. Some original minerals such as quartz grains may become re-oriented with their length at right angles to the maximum stress. The rock thus develops a preferential split-direction or slaty cleavage (to be distinguished from *mineral* cleavage), which is parallel to the flat surfaces of the oriented crystals. Fossils in the rocks become distorted or broken by the stresses.

Slate is a low-grade metamorphic product, and is essentially a very fine-textured aggregate of chlorite, sericite, and quartz ; it is not always com-pletely crystalline. With the action of continued stresses, and especially if some rise of temperature ensues, the above minerals continue to grow, with the production of larger crystals (muscovite and chlorite flakes), and a lustrous, finely crystalline, micaceous rock called *phyllite* results. With continued metamorphism the size of constituent minerals increases further, leading to the formation of rocks known as *mica-schists*. There is thus a gradation, shale → slate → phyllite → mica-schist, the several meta-morphic types being produced by metamorphism under different energy conditions, from similar material which was originally muddy sediment.

While most slates are derived from fine-grained sediments like shales, the green Cumberland and Westmorland slates are an example of fine-grained volcanic tuffs (andesitic in composition) which have developed slaty cleavage during regional metamorphism.

The commercial value of slate from any particular locality depends on several factors : (i) The perfection of the cleavage ; good roofing slate must be cleavable into thin plates, while poorer slates split less easily, and may be useful only for rough walls and similar purposes. (ii) For high-quality slate the cleavage surfaces must be perfectly smooth. This is the case, for example, with the purplish-coloured slates of Cambrian age from the Bethesda and Llanberis quarries, North Wales. Some slates have a rougher and somewhat corrugated surface (called " puckering " in the quarries), which limits the thinness of the sheets and hence increases their weight. (iii) A good slate should be homogeneous in mineral composition and texture (see above). This affects its water-tightness : its low porosity is due to close packing of the mineral constituents. Colour banding, if due only to iron oxide staining, is not a serious matter ; but if due to differences in composition or texture is open to objection. (iv) Accessory minerals such as calcite, epidote, pyrite, should be very few or, preferably, entirely absent. Calcite is an objectionable constituent if there is much of it, on account of its low resistance to weathering, especially to rain-water acids in city atmospheres. A small content of epidote is not harmful. Pyrite (FeS_2) and marcasite (FeS_2) are objectionable ; they weather rapidly, producing ugly iron staining, and if developed in comparatively large crystals may leave holes of corresponding size in the slate.

The best slates are those in which the stresses which have induced slaty cleavage have operated in a constant direction. Where two sets of stresses have been active at successive periods, two cleavage directions may be superimposed and the smoothness and regularity of a single cleavage destroyed.

British slate localities, in addition to those mentioned above, include Penrhyn and Bangor in North Wales ;[1] Ballachulish, Scotland (black slates, some with pyrites) ; Skiddaw, Cumberland (rough grey slates of Ordovician age) ; Borrowdale, Cumberland (green slates formed from the ash deposits of Ordovician volcanoes) ; and Delabole, Cornwall (grey slates of Upper Devonian age).

Schists. These are crystalline rocks of schistose texture and are moderately coarse-grained, so that their main mineral components can be distinguished by eye. They have been formed from igneous or sedimentary material by the operation of moderately high temperatures and pressures.

Schists are largely composed of flaky minerals such as micas, chlorite, talc, or of prismatic minerals such as amphiboles, which have the predominantly parallel arrangement called *schistosity* (p. 146) ; the flakes or *foliae* into which the rock breaks all have a similar mineral composition and their surfaces are lustrous.[2] When quartz is present, in addition to the flaky minerals, the quartz grains under the influence of stress have often become elongated (Fig. 48) and lie with their length in the surfaces of schistosity. Taking first the schists derived from sedimentary material, a *mica-schist* as already noted (p. 153), is produced by the metamorphism of an original clay or shale. It is composed largely of mica (biotite and muscovite), the flakes having the sub-parallel arrangement described above, with a varying proportion of elongated quartz grains (Fig. 46 (2)). Garnet may occur as porphyroblasts in the schist, and the schistosity is sometimes disturbed by the growth of this mineral during metamorphism. Certain coarsely foliated rocks of the same derivation, and formed during the higher grades of regional metamorphism, are the mica-gneisses (p. 156).

Rocks rich in quartz but with little mica provide the *quartz-schists* and are derived from impure, often felspathic sandstones. The regional metamorphism of purer sandstones yields siliceous *granulites*, i.e. rocks composed of granular quartz and felspar in equi-dimensional, interlocking grains (the granulitic texture). Schistosity is not pronounced in these rocks because platy minerals are scanty, though a little mica is usually present. When the rock is composed almost entirely of granular quartz, the term *quartzite* is used (= quartz-granulite ; cf. another use, p. 148).

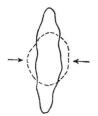

FIG. 48.—CHANGE OF SHAPE OF A CRYSTALLINE GRAIN (e.g. QUARTZ) UNDER STRESS.

Original grain shown dotted. Stress lowers the melting point and is especially prominent where mineral grains touch. Solution proceeds at points of high stress and re-deposition takes place in directions at right angles to the stress direction.

---

[1] See " The Slates of Wales," by F. J. North, 3rd ed., 1946, Nat. Mus. of Wales.

[2] The word " schist " was originally used to denote the property of splitting into foliæ (Gk. *schistos,* divided).

Marbles result from the regional metamorphism of limestones (as well as by contact metamorphism) ; they are composed mainly of interlocking grains of calcite (Fig. 46 (3)). If the original rock was a pure limestone, schistosity is absent in the marble, because the calcite occurs as equidimensional grains. If the original rock had other constituents as well as $CaCO_3$, other minerals arise and the metamorphic product may show a directional texture with streaks of different mineral composition.

The metamorphism of basic igneous rocks such as basalt or dolerite gives rise to chlorite-schists (under epizone conditions) or hornblende-schists (mesozone). *Chlorite-schist* consists dominantly of chlorite flakes, in parallel orientation, often with a little quartz and some porphyroblasts of magnetite or garnet ; it is formed under conditions of high stress [1] and low temperature. *Hornblende-schist* is composed essentially of hornblende and quartz, and is derived from similar basic rocks but under a higher grade of metamorphism, with moderate stress and moderate temperature.[2] Good examples of hornblende-schist are found at the Lizard, Cornwall, and at Start Point, S. Devon. *Eclogite,* a rock composed of pyroxene, garnet, and quartz, is derived from similar original material under conditions of low stress, high hydrostatic pressure [3] and high temperature. This series (*viz.* chlorite-schist, hornblende-schist, eclogite) illustrates the dependence of the metamorphic product on the conditions of metamorphism.

Derivatives of ultrabasic rocks such as peridotite or dunite include some *serpentine-schists* and *talc-schists.* The latter are composed of talc, a very soft mineral, together with some mica. Soft rocks such as chlorite- and talc-schists, which are somewhat greasy to the touch, and sometimes decomposed mica-schists, may be a source of weakness in engineering construction and fail easily by shearing along the foliæ. Several cases are on record where underground works have been hindered when rocks of this kind were encountered, in tunnelling and boring. The schist, when left unsupported in a working face, has begun to move rapidly (or " flow ") under the pressure exerted by the surrounding rocks.[4]

Gneisses. A gneiss has the banded texture called foliation (p. 146), in which light and dark bands alternate ; it is composed essentially of felspar, quartz, and one or more other minerals such as mica, hornblende, and in some cases pyroxene. Garnets are common accessory constituents. The mafic minerals in a gneiss tend to be aggregated into lenses, streaks, or discontinuous bands, within which they have a parallel or schistose arrangement. These bands are in contrast to adjacent bands rich in quartz and felspar, which alternate with the layers rich in mafic constituents (Plate VIIB). A gneiss therefore breaks less readily than a schist, and commonly

[1] By high stress is meant a wide difference between maximum and minimum principal stresses, implying strong shearing stress.

[2] The term *amphibolite* is used as a group name for metamorphic rocks in which hornblende, quartz, and plagioclase are the main minerals ; hornblende-schist is included in this group.

[3] High pressures with small stress differences, i.e. approaching hydrostatic conditions (as here), probably exist at depths of a few miles in the earth's crust.

[4] See *Eng. News Record,* 119, p. 220, 1937 ; and F. Fox, *Proc. Inst. C. E.,* 168, 1906.

splits across the foliation instead of along it; it is often coarser in texture than many schists, though some gneisses are relatively fine-grained.

A gneiss when derived by regional metamorphism from an igneous rock, such as granite, is called an *orthogneiss*; if it results from the metamorphism of a sedimentary rock, the term *paragneiss* is used. An example of the latter is *biotite-gneiss*, the high grade metamorphic derivative of an argillaceous rock such as a shale. It is composed of pale bands made up of quartz and felspar, which alternate with dark, mica-rich bands or streaks. This banding or foliation may result from variations of composition in the original sediments. Biotite-gneiss thus corresponds to mica-schist (lower grade of metamorphism) in the series : phyllite → mica-schist → biotite-gneiss (p. 154).

Some gneisses have the composition of a granite or granodiorite, and result from the metamorphism of such rocks (orthogneiss). They are foliated rocks, bands of quartz-felspar composition being interspersed with streaks of biotite, or biotite and hornblende, in which the mafic minerals are oriented in parallel positions. Generally the felspar is evenly distributed in the quartz-felspar bands ; but occasionally large felspars (or aggregates of felspar crystals) occur in lenticular or eye-shaped areas, to which the name " augen " is given. Such a rock is an *augen-gneiss* Plate VIIB ; the foliation is often deflected around the eye-shaped areas. Augen-gneisses arise by regional metamorphism of granitic rocks, or by injection processes. An example of the former is the metamorphosed granite of Inchbae, Ross-shire; the porphyritic felspars of the granite are now the augen of the gneiss. The granite was intrusive into argillaceous rocks, in which an aureole with andalusite-hornfelses was formed by contact metamorphism. When the mass underwent a second (regional) metamorphism, the hornfelses were converted into kyanite-schists and the granite into augen-gneiss. Several metamorphisms may affect an area, as in the island of Unst, Shetlands; two successive regional metamorphisms followed by a phase of dislocation were demonstrated there by H. H. Read.

Certain beautifully striped gneisses result from the injection of thin sheets of quartz-felspar material of igneous origin along parallel planes in the parent rock ; these are *injection gneisses*. The introduction of igneous material into country-rocks of various kinds produces mixed rocks which are called *migmatites*. In some migmatites the mixing is mechanical, the introduced material veining or striping the original country-rock. In other migmatites the mixing is chemical, and arises from the permeation or soaking of the country-rocks by the invading fluids (see p. 114, for connection with granitization). Migmatites of many kinds are found in the Pre-Cambrian rocks of Scandinavia and Finland ; in parts of the Scottish Highlands ; or in any of the Pre-Cambrian " shields " (p. 203).

The Scottish Highlands are largely built up of metamorphic rocks, gneisses and schists occurring in great variety in the Lewisian and Dalradian groups (see Fig. 94). The Lewisian rocks (p. 202), which form part of a great belt of regional metamorphism in north-west Scotland, include many high-grade gneisses which were derived from earlier igneous rocks, and possess a foliation interpreted as due to recrystallization from a plastic condition. They often contain veins and patches of granitic material and are then described as migmatites. The Dalradian group comprises a series of metamorphosed sediments, with muddy (pelitic), sandy, and limestone bands which have given rise to mica-schists and phyllites, quartzites, and marbles respectively. Dolerite sills intruded into the sediments before their metamorphism were converted into hornblende-schists and related rocks.

In the Alps are found much younger schists and gneisses, the metamorphic equivalents of Jurassic, Cretaceous and Tertiary sediments, which owe their transformation to the great mountain-building movements by which the Alps were raised (p. 192).

Selected References

HARKER, A. "Metamorphism." 3nd edition, 1950. Methuen.

READ, H. H. AND J. WATSON. "Introduction to Geology," chapter 9. 1962. Macmillan, London.

TYRRELL, G. W. "The Principles of Petrology." 11th edition, 1956. Methuen.

BEHRE, C. H. "Slate in Pennsylvania." Pennsylvania Geol. Surv. Bull. Ser. IV, M.16, 1933.

CHAPTER 8

EARTH MOVEMENTS AND EARTH STRUCTURE

The rocky crust of the earth is not stable, but undergoes complex movements. There are slow *vertical movements* of uplift and depression, whose rate is measurable only by lengthy observations, but whose effects are seen in many places. By contrast, *earthquakes* are sudden movements, which can be detected by special instruments and are sometimes felt by the ordinary observer. These two kinds of movement are discussed below. At intervals during geological time *mountain-building movements*, of which earthquakes are often a symptom, have compressed the rocks in weak belts in the crust, giving rise to fold-mountains, as described on p. 192.

Uplift and Depression. Slow vertical movements such as depression or tilting of the sea-floor, or uplift of the land, can only be estimated relative to the datum provided by sea-level. It is not always clear whether, for example, an apparent uplift of a coastal area is a real upward movement or is due to a lowering of sea-level. A large fall in sea-level probably occurred everywhere during the Pleistocene glacial period (or Ice Age, pp. 38 and 233), when much water was locked up in the ice-sheets which covered great areas of the continents in the northern hemisphere. The subsequent melting of the ice eventually restored the water to the oceans, and sea-level rose again. (The isostatic effect of the weight of the ice load is referred to on p. 168.) Evidence of these past changes of level is given by such occurrences as raised beaches, submerged forests, and submerged or " drowned " valley topography. There is also evidence of movement in historical times which is provided by the ruins of former buildings and by the records of precise surveys.

Raised Beaches. These are ancient shore lines, with their deposits of shingle, sand, and shells, standing now above sea-level, and they are

FIG. 49.—RAISED PLATFORM OF MARINE EROSION
formed in pre-Glacial times, covered by gravels of 100-foot beach, Islay. The 25-foot terrace is in the foreground, and to the right the present storm-beach of quartzite boulders.
(After photo by H.M. Geological Survey.)

158

evidence of uplift (Plate IXA). Raised beach terraces are found, for example, around the coasts of Devon and Cornwall, Anglesey, and Scotland. In Norway and Sweden raised beaches sometimes lie more than 600 feet above the present shore. Traceable at places around the Scottish coasts are three beach terraces at 100, 50, and 25 feet respectively above present sea-level (Fig. 49). They were formed when the land was depressed under the load of the Pleistocene ice-sheet, and upon them are deposits including beds of clay in which marine shells are preserved. In the case of the 100-foot beach the Arctic character of the past climate is reflected in the fossils, which include forms similar to those now living in Greenland or Spitzbergen. The 50-foot beach deposits are less Arctic in character, and the 25-foot deposits indicate a temperate climate. The terraces mark successive halts in the uplift of the land during the deglaciation of the British Isles (p. 237). In some places a former line of cliffs with their old sea-caves can be seen, as at Wemyss on the Firth of Clyde. Glasgow and Edinburgh are partly built on old gravel beach deposits.

Evidence of Submergence. Evidence of submergence is more difficult to obtain because it is largely obliterated by the sea. There are places, however, as at Leasowe on the Cheshire coast, where the stumps of trees in the position of growth are seen between tide-marks, indicating a former higher level of the land. The fjords of Norway and some of the Scottish sea-lochs also point to submergence having occurred since they were formed ; the shape of the sides of a fjord above and below water is continuous, and there is no break of slope at sea-level. Further, soundings reveal a profile for the " drowned " part of the valley which points to its excavation under subaerial conditions.

Recent submarine surveys off the eastern coasts of the United States, and elsewhere, have shown the existence of a number of deep channels, or canyons, in the floor of the Atlantic, the Indian Ocean, and other places on the continental slopes. Some of the channels were at first thought to be continuous with valleys on land, and would thus indicate considerable submergence. A case in point was the channel which can be traced for 150 miles out to sea opposite the mouth of the Hudson River, New York. Its apparent connection with the surface valley of the Hudson, however, is no longer thought to be valid, though mud carried out by the river may have played a part in the erosion of the submarine channel. Turbidity currents (p. 128), where unstable masses of mud flow down a submarine slope, are now believed to be largely responsible for the erosion of submarine canyons in general. Many of them have gradients steeper than those of subaerial valleys.

Evidence for changes in level in a volcanic area is provided by historical ruins and is illustrated by the Temple of Jupiter Serapis at Pozzuoli, in the Bay of Naples. Here, during the past 2000 years, slow oscillations in level have been in progress and can be traced by the marks they have left on the structure. Three of the temple's columns, 40 feet high, are still standing : they are smooth for the first 12 feet above their base, and the next 9 feet are pierced by the borings of marine molluscs. After the temple was constructed the land sank and a new floor was built, 5 feet higher than the old one, to place it above the level of the encroaching sea. Volcanic ash from eruptions later filled the building to a depth of 12 feet, thus protecting the lower part of the columns. The land then sank until the sea stood 9 feet above the top of the ash layer, and at that time the columns were bored, the building later being raised once more above the sea. D. V. Ager gives a graph of this (*Proc. Geol. Assoc.*, 66, 1956, 1).

Evidence from Geodetic Surveys. A network of geodetic levelling over Great Britain was completed about 1860 by the Ordnance Survey, and was repeated some 60 years later with modern instruments. When the two sets of precise levels were compared, considerable differences between them were found, the greatest change being a fall of 2 feet at Harwich.[1] The changes were not distributed in a haphazard fashion, but the country as a whole showed a fall in level on the east and south, and a somewhat smaller rise in the west and north. It was considered improbable that these differences could be explained in terms of instrumental or other errors, and they therefore appeared to show that during the period of 60 years there has been a small tilt of the land to the south-east, about a line drawn roughly from Hartlepool to Aberystwyth. The validity of this result was questioned on the ground that the older geodetic levelling did not possess an accuracy of the same order as that of the newer levelling; but more recent measurements of levels at tidal gauges indicate that there is probably a real movement of the land going on at the present time.[2] At Newlyn, this movement is a fall estimated at about 9 in. per century—a figure which agrees with the average rate at which the land surface in the Thames Valley has subsided since Roman times. (Archaeological evidence demonstrates a fall of 12 feet in the Thames Valley since the Roman occupation.) West of a line from Anglesey to Berwick a slow rise appears to be taking place, according to Valentin, with a maximum of 4 mm. per year in the Scottish Highlands.

Earthquakes. In contrast with the slow changes briefly discussed above, sharp movements or *earthquakes* are caused by adjustments to strain in the crustal rocks; the shocks are mainly due to movement along faults (i.e. fracture surfaces, p. 186). Strain accumulates locally in the rocks until breaking point is reached, when slip along the fracture occurs, followed sometimes by a smaller rebound. A very small movement on a fault (perhaps only a fraction of an inch) may produce a considerable shock because of the great masses of rock involved in the movement.

Earthquakes range from slight tremors to severe shocks which break and overthrow buildings, sever supply mains and lines of transport, and leave permanent traces on the surface of the ground. Particularly in loose sandy ground fissures may be opened; fault scarps are sometimes formed, as in the Japanese earthquake of 1891, when an uplift of 20 feet on one

[1] "The Subsidence of London," by Capt. T. E. Longfield, R.E. *Ordnance Survey Prof. Paper*, No. 14 (N.S.), 1932.

[2] H. L. P. Jolly in *Geogr. Journ.*, May 1939, p. 408, and H. Valentin, *Geogr. Journ.*, 99, Sept. 1953, p. 299.

side of the fault was produced at one locality. Damage to water mains has often led to the spread of fires which cause more destruction than the shock itself. In the earthquakes which affected some of the islands of Greece in July and August 1953, domestic fires were scattered by the shocks and caused much damage ; adjacent off-shore areas appeared cloudy from the air, from the disturbance of muds on the sea-floor. Low-pitched earth-sounds frequently accompany earthquakes.

Earthquakes tend to occur mainly in two belts on the earth's surface, one of which extends around the coastal regions of the Pacific, from the East Indies through the Philippines, Japan, the Aleutian Isles, and thence down the western coasts of North and South America ; the other runs from Central Europe across the eastern Mediterranean to the Himalayas and the East Indies, where it joins the first belt. Both these regions are characterized by steep slopes (either on land or submarine), mountain chains, and volcanoes. The Pacific belt is estimated to have about two-thirds of recorded earthquakes, and is a region of present-day crustal movement. Some shocks are associated with the African rift-valley faults.

A few earthquakes, usually of low or moderate intensity, occur in Britain, as at Inverness (1901, 1935), Hereford (1924), and Nottingham (1957). The last had an intensity of 8 locally, near an epicentre 12 miles S.W. of the city, and was attributed to movement on a N.E.–S.W. fault.

Earthquake Records. The intensity of an earthquake is estimated by the effects it produces on people and objects in the district affected. Places where the shock is felt can be marked on a map and lines drawn to include all places where damage of a certain degree is done : these are called *isoseismal lines*. For this purpose a scale of intensity is used, such as the well-known Rossi-Forel scale, which contains 10 grades as follows : 1. Earthquake noticed by experienced observers only. 2. Noticed by a few people at rest. 3. Generally felt by people at rest. 4. Felt by people in motion ; doors and windows rattle. 5. Felt generally ; disturbance of furniture. 6. Hanging objects such as chandeliers made to swing; clocks stopped, sleepers wakened. 7. Causes panic; movable objects overthrown, church bells ring. 8. Damage to buildings ; chimneys fall and walls are cracked. 9. Some buildings destroyed. 10. Widespread damage.

For the Inverness earthquake of 1901 the innermost isoseismal line (8), within which houses were slightly damaged, was an ellipse 12 miles long and 7 miles wide, with its longer axis in the direction N. 33° E. (Fig. 50). This line is correlated with the Great Glen Fault, which passes near the centre of the ellipse and has a direction about N. 35° E. near Inverness. The earthquake was caused by slip along the fault. Comrie, near Perth, on the Highland Boundary Fault (Fig. 94), is the place which experiences the most earthquakes in Great Britain ; small movements are continually taking place along the Boundary Fault, but few of the shocks are severe.

The New Zealand earthquake of 1931 originated near the coast of Hawkes Bay on the North Island, along a fault or fault-zone extending N.E.–S.W., and was felt all over the country. In Napier harbour the sea-bed was raised six or seven feet. Severe damage was done to buildings, and over 250 people were killed, a much larger number being injured. Water-mains were broken, railway tracks buckled, and the landslides and fires which followed the earthquake added greatly to the damage.

One of the best studied shocks is that which ruined San Francisco in 1906. It was due to movement along part of the San Andreas Fault, which passes near the city and can be traced for 600 miles or more to the southward. The motion of the ground was mainly horizontal, and it was found by subsequent surveys that pairs of points formerly adjacent on either side of the fault had been displaced by an average amount of 11 or 12 feet in opposite directions parallel to the fault—a large displacement

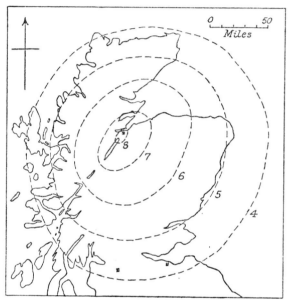

FIG. 50.—ISOSEISMAL LINES FOR THE INVERNESS EARTHQUAKE, 1901
(after Davison).

for a single slip. Fissures were formed in the ground and landslips started, and mud-flats on the coast were arched into ridges ; in the city itself the results were disastrous, with the collapse of buildings, the severing of supply lines, and great loss of life. Later shocks have been felt here, including one in 1952. New surveys of the ground, up to 1957, showed that there had been a further 6 feet of relative movement on the San Andreas Fault since 1935, 4 feet of which had occurred since 1941. A large fault, when once established, may move again subsequently. The Chilean earthquakes of 1960, which occurred during several weeks, were accompanied by volcanic eruptions, and illustrate the connection between some shocks and the movement of magma.

Earthquake-resisting Structures. In countries where earthquakes are of frequent occurrence, important buildings are now designed to withstand all but the most severe shocks. Structures founded on hard rock are generally less damaged than those on soft ground (e.g. alluvium), and it is found that properly designed steel-framed or ferro-concrete structures possess the highest degree of immunity from damage. Thus, a rigid frame carried on a strong foundation would undergo, as a whole, the same movement as the ground ; in soft ground a concrete raft foundation should be used. The height of large buildings should not exceed 100 feet, and heavy loads near the top (e.g. heavy stonework in copings) should be avoided.

The acceleration of the ground when the shock begins is an important factor, of which account must be taken in designing a framed structure, which should be rigid enough to withstand this additional force. In big earthquakes the acceleration may amount to nearly half that of gravity, but it is generally not greater than $0 \cdot 2g$. Bridges present special problems ; after the Bihar earthquake of 1934 it was found that bridges with screw-pile foundations had stood up best to the shock. Brick arches were easily broken, and girder bridges supported on stonework piers also failed. Some references to literature on the design of earthquake-resisting structures are given in the footnote.[1]

Earth Waves and Seismographs. Earth waves are propagated in all directions from the centre of origin or *focus* of a shock. The average depth of focus for normal earthquakes is about 30 km. (18 miles), though many have a deeper or shallower origin. The point on the earth's surface immediately above the focus is called the *epicentre*. The waves which travel out from the focus are of three kinds : 1. Longitudinal vibrations, denoted by the letter P (primary), which are the fastest and the first to arrive at a recording station. 2. Transverse vibrations, called S (secondary), which are somewhat slower than the P waves. 3. Surface or L waves ; these are transverse vibrations of long period which follow the periphery of the earth, and do the greatest damage.[2] As an easily remembered mnemonic, P and S can be thought of as standing for " push " and " shake " waves.

The vibrations can be detected and recorded by suitably placed *seismographs*. The principle on which these instruments work is that of a light beam, pivoted at one end to a frame, and carrying a heavy weight near its free end. When the ground is shaken the frame of the instrument moves with it, but the lightly suspended weight remains relatively fixed in position owing to its inertia. Thus a motion is imparted to the beam, the swing of which is recorded on a rotating drum, on which also intervals of time are marked. Usually two instruments are employed, to record the N.-S. and E.-W. components of the tremors respectively ; a third instrument is needed to detect vertical movements.

From an earthquake record (*seismogram*) obtained in this way, the times of arrival of earth waves are read off, and by assuming values for wave

---

[1] See papers by H. C. E. Cherry, F. W. Furkert, and J. J. Booth, in *Proc. Inst. C.E.*, Vol. 236, 1933, p. 303 ; also Chapter 4 of Milne and Lee's " Earthquakes ", 1950.

[2] Two kinds of L waves are named after Rayleigh and Love, the investigators who first described them. Theories of the propagation of vibrations in an elastic medium are discussed in books listed on p. 168.

velocities (see below) the distance of the epicentre from the recording
station can be calculated. Fuller descriptions of seismographs are given
in larger works on the subject. The sensitivity of a modern seismograph
is illustrated by the fact that the small daily rise and fall of the Wirral
peninsula, Cheshire, which is caused by the change of load produced by
the ebb and flow of a 30-foot tide, has been measured by such an instrument.

Records of Distant Earthquakes. Seismographs situated at distances
up to 105° of arc from the epicentre record the onsets of P, S, and L waves

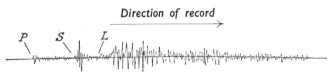

Direction of record

P S L

FIG. 51.—SEISMOGRAM OF DISTANT EARTHQUAKE (after Milne and Lee).
P = longitudinal, S = transverse, L = surface waves.

(Fig. 51). But it is found that for greater distances than this the P and
S waves are not recorded, until at stations 142° or more from the epicentre
P waves are again received. They have, however, taken longer to arrive,
and hence have been slowed down over part of their path through the
earth. There is thus a region, extending from 105° to 142° of arc away

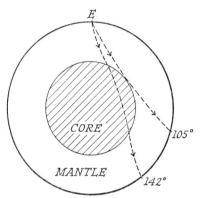

FIG. 52.—PATHS OF EARTHQUAKE WAVES THROUGH THE EARTH.
E = epicentre.

from the epicentre, in which no P and S waves are received. The explanation of these facts was put forward by Oldham in 1906; he suggested
that the earth has a plastic or liquid core, surrounded by a rocky shell
(Fig. 52), called the "mantle," to distinguish it from the crust. Waves
which penetrate deeper than those emerging at 105° enter the core, and
are deflected and slowed down by it. Since the material of the core is
probably in a fluid state (though under great pressure) it cannot transmit
transverse (S) waves, and hence it is the longitudinal (P) vibrations only
which appear at 142° from the epicentre. Later work has shown that

the core extends to within 2900 km. of the earth's surface, i.e. its radius is rather more than half that of the earth (6378 km. at the equator). There is a sharp discontinuity in the nature of the material, disclosed by differences in physical properties, at the boundary between the core and the overlying " mantle."

Near Earthquakes. Records obtained at stations within about 1500 km. of an epicentre have yielded valuable information concerning the composition of the outer shells, or crust, of the earth. On these seismograms two and sometimes three sets of P and S waves can be distinguished ; they are given the symbols P_gS_g, $P*S*$, and P, S, the last-named pair being the first to arrive. The three sets of waves are thought to have travelled in three different crustal layers, along parallel paths (Fig. 53). Their velocities, as determined by Jeffreys from European earthquake data, are as follows :

P_g 5·57 km./sec.	S_g 3·36 km./sec.
$P*$ 6·50 ,, ,,	$S*$ 3.74 ,, ,,
P 7·76 ,, ,,	S 4·36 ,, ,,

These values correspond roughly to those found experimentally for granite, basalt, and peridotite respectively. They are greater than velocities in average sedimentary rocks (2–4 km./sec.) near the earth's surface.

Thus there is evidence from seismology, which is in agreement with geological indications, that the earth has a crust composed of several

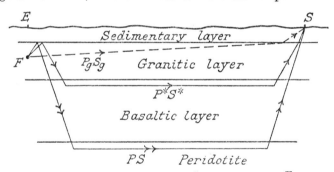

FIG. 53.—PATHS OF WAVES THROUGH THE CRUST FOR A NEAR EARTHQUAKE.
E = epicentre, S = seismograph. Focus (F) in granite layer. Each path represents a small fraction of the energy transmitted from the focus ; refraction occurs at the interlayer boundaries.

distinct layers as shown in the figure (the vertical scale of which is exaggerated) ; the outermost layer is of granitic composition and is covered locally by sedimentary rocks of variable thickness. It rests on a layer whose composition approximates to vitreous basalt, and this in turn rests on ultrabasic rock (peridotite) at a depth of some 30 km. below the surface (variable, between about 25 and 35 km.). The average thicknesses of the granitic and basaltic layers are about 10 and 20 km. respectively. The sedimentary layer is discontinuous ; and the granitic layer is not everywhere present below the oceans.

Structure of the Earth.   The foregoing paragraphs indicate the salient facts concerning the earth's structure which have been revealed by the modern study of earthquakes.

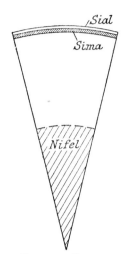

Further information about the fluid core comes from a consideration of the density of the various earth-shells. The density of the granitic layer is about 2·67 and that of basalt and peridotite rather higher; but the average density of the whole earth is 5·5. The core must therefore be composed of material heavier than this to make up for the lighter outer layers; calculations show that a density of 8 for the core would be about right. This figure is slightly higher than the density of iron, and below that of nickel; the core probably consists of a mixture of these two metals, and is therefore called *nifel*, from the symbols for the two metals (Ni and Fe).

Fig. 54. — Sector of Hypothetical Earth.

At the outer boundary of the nifel there is a discontinuity, marked by a change in physical properties, between it and the overlying " mantle." The upper part of the " mantle " probably has the composition of olivine-rock or peridotite. Above this come the layers of the crust (Fig. 54), again with differences in physical properties. The term *sial* has been coined from the initial letters of *si*lica and *al*umina, to express the preponderance of these oxides in the granitic and sedimentary layers; correspondingly, the basaltic layer is called *sima* (from *si*lica and *ma*gnesia), and from its properties is thought to be in a vitreous state (i.e. non-crystalline). The sial is crystalline and rigid, but the sima lacks rigidity and will yield slowly to long-continued stresses. The marked break at the base of the crust, between sima and mantle, is known as the Mohorovicic discontinuity. The several earth-shells may have been formed while the earth was solidifying from an origin-ally fluid condition, though other possibilities have been suggested. The more acid, granitic material being lighter would rise, and the heavier matter would sink, resulting in a rough stratification; the proportion of iron and other heavy metals probably increases with depth until the core is reached.

Continents and Isostasy.   With the above conception of the earth's structure, the continental masses have come to be visualized as large sial blocks supported by the underlying sima. The sial varies in thickness from one region to another, being thickest beneath a mountain chain, and it is absent beneath deep oceans such as the Pacific, which are floored by sima. The continents are thus like granite " rafts " floating in sima (Fig. 55); since the density of sima (nearly 3·0) is not much greater than that of sial (about 2·7), the " rafts " are largely submerged, after the manner of icebergs.

Large topographical features, such as mountains, which project above the general level of a continent, have deep " roots " projecting downwards into the basaltic layer; while under the shallow seas on the continental margins the sial is correspondingly thinner. The state of balance which tends to be maintained between adjacent columns of matter of equal cross-section in the crust, supported by the basaltic substratum, is called *isostasy*.[1] Thus, the weight of a column of matter in a mountainous region where the sial was thick, as at *A* in Fig. 55, would equal that of a column at *B*, where the sial was thinner and displaced less of the denser sima ; the two columns would be balanced at some level in the substratum (called the " level of compensation ").

The concept of isostatic balance has been tested in various ways, such as by gravity surveys which reveal excess or deficiency of density in the rocks of the crust. When all the evidence is reviewed it appears probable that very large topographical features on the earth's surface are bounded

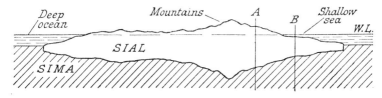

FIG. 55.—DIAGRAMMATIC SECTION THROUGH A CONTINENT (not to scale).

by faults and supported by the upward pressure of the substratum, i.e. they are isostatically compensated on a regional scale. The Alps and the Rockies, for example, are essentially balanced in this way. Local isostatic compensation for smaller masses is unlikely to be complete because their weight is partly supported by the strength of the surrounding crust, i.e. smaller mountains and valleys exist because of the crust's rigidity.

Elevation and Subsidence. The transfer of load from one part of a continental mass to another, by the processes of denudation and sedimentation, results in a local sinking of the area of sedimentation (increase of load), accompanied by the outflow of sima from beneath it. There is a slow rise of the land surface undergoing denudation as it is lightened, with an inflow of denser material below the area. Because of the difference in density, the amount of rise will not equal the thickness of the material eroded. If the densities of sial and sima are taken as 2·7 and 2·95 respectively, then the removal of 1000 feet of sial will be balanced by the inflow of about 920 feet of the denser material, the final level (when isostatic adjustment is complete) being only 80 feet lower than before. It is thought that the height of the Himalayas, for example, has been maintained by this kind of mechanism during the erosion of their many deep gorges, involving the removal of very great quantities of rock, much of which finds its way to the Ganges basin.

In areas of deposition, fresh sediments constitute a considerable load, and geological records show that thousands of feet of deposits have been laid down in shallow water in past ages (see p. 203). It is difficult to account for this unless the area of sedimentation was sinking as the deposits

[1] Meaning " in equipoise."

accumulated. Non-marine regions of subsidence are also known, such as the low-lying Indo-Gangetic plains, which separate the Himalayas to the north from peninsular India to the south ; thousands of feet of alluvial deposits,[1] brought down by rivers from the mountains, have accumulated here as subsidence has gone on. Deep borings in this alluvium, the floor of which has not yet been reached, have penetrated many successive beds of sand and clay with layers of peat and kankar, showing that the deposits are similar throughout. The sinking therefore took place slowly, keeping pace with the gradually increasing load of sedimentation.

During the Glacial period, the load of ice upon a land area would cause a sinking throughout the region affected, isostasy slowly restoring the balance by lifting the area again when the load was removed. Many raised beaches in formerly glaciated countries may be accounted for by this mechanism, and some of the evidence shown by the beaches has been indicated at the beginning of this chapter.

SELECTED REFERENCES

DAVISON, C. " Great Earthquakes." 1936. Murby.
DAVISON, C. " A History of British Earthquakes." 1924. Cambridge.
JEFFREYS, H. " The Earth." 4th edition, 1959. Cambridge.
MILNE, J., AND LEE, A. W. " Earthquakes and Other Earth Movements." 1950. (5th edition.) Kegan Paul, London.
OLDHAM, R. D. " The Structure of the Himalayas and of the Gangetic Plain, as elucidated by Geodetic Observations in India." *Mem. Geol. Surv. India,* XLII, part 2, 1917.
RICHTER, C. E. " Elementary Seismology." 1958. Freeman.
STEERS, J. A. " The Unstable Earth." 5th edition, reprinted 1955. Methuen.
WADIA, D. N. " Geology of India." 2nd edition, 1939. Macmillan.

NOTE. For a discussion of the theory of Isostasy, see Daly's " Strength and Structure of the Earth," 1940. A short statement on the subject is given in Wooldridge and Morgan's " Physical Basis of Geography ".

---

[1] R. D. Oldham in 1917 estimated the thickness to be between 15,000 and 20,000 feet (see reference above), though a recent estimate by E. A. Glennie lowers the figure to 6500 feet. A depth of 1306 feet was bored in these deposits at Garden Reach, Calcutta, in 1938, in connection with a water supply investigation ; the maximum depth bored to date is 1612 feet at Ambala, Punjab (1927).

PLATE IX

(A) RAISED BEACH NEAR SANDY BAY, ISLE OF CALDEY, PEMBROKESHIRE

(B) DUNE-BEDDING IN PERMIAN SANDSTONE, BALLOCHMYLE, AYRSHIRE

PLATE X

Photo by H.M. Geological Survey.

(B) VERTICAL BEDS OF LIMESTONE, MANORBIER, SOUTH PEMBROKESHIRE

(A) HORIZONTAL CURRENT-BEDDED SANDSTONES IN SEA-STACK, YESCANBY, ORKNEYS.

CHAPTER 9

STRUCTURAL GEOLOGY, I:
DEFINITIONS AND GEOMETRICAL PROBLEMS

The purpose of a geological map is to provide a record of geological features on a topographic basis. It shows by tints or shading the *outcrops* of different rocks, i.e. the areas over which they occur at or near the earth's surface, for the particular district represented. If the scale is suitable, the map also shows any lines along which the rocks are arched up (folds), or along which they are broken (faults). A simple example of a geological map is given in Fig. 57, where topography is limited to contour lines, and the outcrops of a series of beds of rock are shown differently shaded. It should be noted that a rock may be *exposed* at only a few points throughout its outcrop, because of the usual cover of soil and vegetation. Quarries and cliffs yield evidence in the vertical direction, as well as the horizontal, which cannot always be completely represented on a map, i.e. in two dimensions ; it may be recorded by means of sections, as described in Chapter 12.

Strata. Sedimentary rocks, whose nature has been discussed in an earlier chapter, cover a considerable part of the earth's surface, and are found in beds or *strata*, lying one above another. A stratum may be of any thickness, from a fraction of an inch to many feet ; each stratum is separated from those above and below it by bedding-planes. We are here concerned with the various arrangements of strata as structural units which build up the upper part of the crust, and how these structures appear on a geological map of their outcrops. The following pages deal with horizontal and simply dipping strata, and the next chapter with folded and faulted beds.

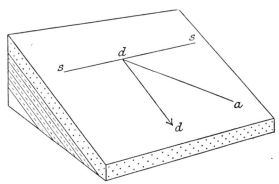

FIG. 56.—DIP AND STRIKE.
ss = direction of strike, *dd* = direction of dip, *da* = an apparent dip.

Dip and Strike. Consider a flat, uniform bed of rock which is tilted out of the horizontal (Fig. 56). On the sloping surface of this stratum there is one direction in which horizontal lines (such as *ss*) can be drawn. This is called the *strike* of the bed; it is a *direction* which can, in practice, be measured and recorded as a compass bearing when part of the surface of the stratum is exposed to view (see p. 247). At right angles to the

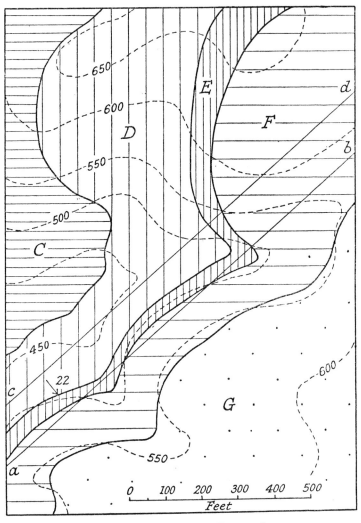

Fig. 57.—Geological Map of Dipping Strata.
ab and *cd* are strike lines.

strike is the direction of maximum slope or *dip* (*dd* in the figure). The *amount* of the dip is the angle of inclination of the bed, i.e. the angle which the line *dd* makes with the horizontal, as seen on the end of the block in the figure; it is measured with a clinometer. The inclination of a line such as *da* is less, and gives an *apparent dip*, the true dip being the maximum slope (in the direction *dd*).   An apparent dip is often shown by beds seen in the vertical face of a quarry (p. 178).

Dip and strike are two fundamental conceptions in structural geology, and represent the geologist's method of defining the attitude of a sloping stratum at any point.   The information is placed on a map in the form of a short arrow with its point at the place of observation and with an adjacent figure, indicating the direction and amount of dip.   In Fig. 57, the beds C to G are dipping south-east at an angle of 22°, as shown by the dip arrow, and *ab* is their strike direction.

Outcrop in Relation to Topography.   A series of dipping beds will have outcrops of different shape and width, according to their thickness and to the form of the ground surface which they intersect.   In general, the flatter the slope of the ground, the wider the outcrop.   Further, if the direction in which the ground falls coincides with the direction of dip, the outcrop of a given bed will be wider than when these directions are opposed (Fig. 58).   When a bed is vertical the width of its outcrop is a minimum.

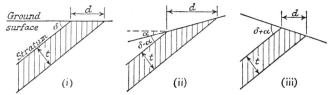

FIG. 58.—WIDTH OF OUTCROP IN RELATION TO SLOPE OF GROUND (α) AND DIP OF STRATA (δ).

(i) Ground horizontal. $d = t.\text{cosec } \delta$.   (ii) Ground slopes in same direction as dip of bed, $d = t.\text{cosec } (\delta - \alpha).\cos \alpha$.   (iii) Ground slopes in opposite direction to dip of bed, $d = t.\text{cosec } (\delta + \alpha).\cos \alpha$.

Where an outcrop runs in the strike direction it tends to keep an approximately even width; thus with the beds *E* and *F* in Fig. 57, for example, where the 500 and 550 topographic contours have a general trend in the strike direction, the outcrops also follow that direction and have a roughly uniform width.

In contrast to this, where an outcrop crosses a valley in the topography it forms a V in plan, as in the case of the bed *E* near the centre of the map. V-shaped outcrops on a comparatively small scale may be frequently seen in mountainous country, where the hill streams have cut steep-sided valleys in dipping beds.

There are three cases of V-shaped outcrop in a valley to be noted :

(*a*) Beds dip in the opposite direction to the fall of the valley floor ; V points *up* the valley (Fig. 59*a*).

(*b*) Beds dip in the same direction as the fall of the valley floor, and at a greater angle ; V points *down* the valley (Fig. 59*b*).

(*c*) Beds dip in the same direction as the fall of the valley floor, but at a smaller angle ; V points *up* the valley and is longer than in case (*a*).

It is easy to remember that when the V points *down*-stream, the beds dip *down* the valley, and this is a useful rule in map-reading.

When beds are horizontal, i.e. their dip is zero, their outcrops run parallel [1] to topographic contours on the map, as in the case of beds P and Q in Fig. 69. A winding outcrop is thus produced in hilly country (Fig. 60, top) : horizontality of strata is denoted on a map by the symbol +.

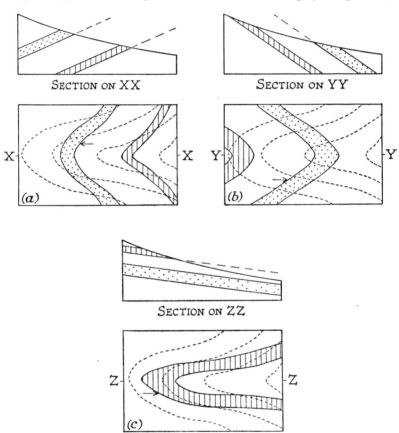

SECTION ON XX   SECTION ON YY

(a)   (b)

SECTION ON ZZ

(c)

FIG. 59.—OUTCROPS OF DIPPING BEDS CROSSING A VALLEY.
(a) Dip upstream. (b) Dip downstream. (c) Dip downstream at low angle.

Vertical strata have a straight outcrop, which crosses all topographical features without deviation (cf. the dykes, in Figs. 36(a) and 103).

Escarpment. A hill or ridge which is formed by hard beds overlying softer rocks generally has a steeper slope on one side than on the other, and is called an *escarpment* (Fig. 60). If the beds are dipping, the length

---

[1] It is assumed here for simplicity that strata maintain the same thickness throughout their extent ; this is an approximation, for a bed may vary considerably in thickness, ultimately " thinning out " and so coming to an end. But for a small area the assumption of constant thickness is often justified.

of the ridge follows the strike direction ; the gentler slope is in the dip direction and is called the *dip-slope.* Wenlock Edge, Shropshire, and the North and South Downs (Fig. 98), are good examples of such escarpments.

Outlier and Inlier. An outcrop of rock which is completely surrounded in plan by older rocks is called an *outlier.* Thus, the beds forming the hills shown in the background of Fig. 60 are detached from their main outcrop, and constitute outliers.

The converse of this is an *inlier, viz.,* an area of older rocks surrounded

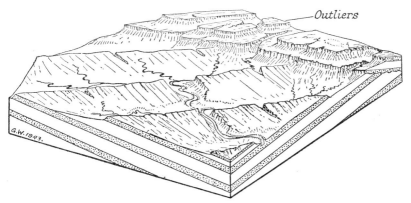

FIG. 60.—ESCARPMENTS AND OUTLIERS.

Hard beds (dotted), gently dipping towards the observer, form a series of escarpments running from left to right. Intervening valleys have been carved out of softer beds. On the extreme right a younger series rests unconformably on the older rocks and is dissected into outliers.

by newer. Inliers are often developed in valleys, where streams have cut down and exposed locally the rocks which are below (older than) those forming the sides of the valley.

Unconformity. One series of strata is sometimes seen to lie upon an older series with a more or less regular surface separating the two. A junction of this kind is called an *unconformity* (see Plate XIIA and Fig. 60) ; there is frequently an angular discordance between the older beds and the newer. Again, Fig. 61 shows an upper series of beds, now gently dipping to the north-west, which has been deposited unconformably upon a lower and older series. The latter were strongly folded by earth-movements, and then denuded during a period of elevation of the sea floor, after which the area was again submerged and the upper beds were laid down. The unconformity thus marks a break in the process of deposition, and represents an interval of time during which no sediments were laid down in the area. This sequence of events is referred to again in Chapter 11.

The appearance on a map of an unconformity is shown in the upper part of Fig. 69, where the outcrops of the newer beds (*P, Q*) transgress those of the underlying beds. The strata above an unconformity may be tilted or folded, together with the beds below them, by earth-movements occurring after their deposition.

Another term used in connection with unconformity may be noted here, *viz.*, *overlap*. As the sea advances over the land during a submergence, and successive layers of sediment are deposited over wider and wider areas, each bed will cover those below it and overlap farther on to the land. This gives rise to an unconformity with overlap (see also p. 228).

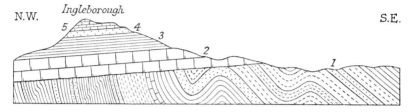

FIG. 61.—SECTION THROUGH INGLEBOROUGH, West Yorkshire, to show unconformity and escarpment (after D. A. Wray, H.M. Geol. Survey).
(1) Silurian and older rocks, below the unconformity. (2) Carboniferous Limestone. (3) Yoredale Series, with sandstones (4). (5) Millstone Grit. Length of Section about 5 miles.

Stratum Contours. The hills and valleys which make up topography are represented on a map by contour lines, often with an interval of 50 or 100 feet, the slope of the ground surface being roughly apparent to the eye by the close or wide spacing of the contours. In a similar way, the buried surface of a dipping bed of rock can be contoured, i.e. lines can be drawn on a map to represent contours *on the stratum* at any desired interval. If the dip is uniform they will be parallel straight lines. They are known as *stratum contours* or *structure contours*, and each has its own value (some multiple of the contour interval). They form an alternative

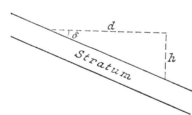

FIG. 62.—SPACING OF STRATUM CONTOURS.

method to the use of dip arrows for showing on a map the structural attitude of a bed of rock. The relation between angle of dip and the spacing of its equivalent stratum contours is seen from Fig. 62. Assuming a uniformly sloping bed (or series of beds), the horizontal distance between stratum contours for a vertical interval h is given by $d = h \cdot \cot \delta$, where $\delta =$ the angle of dip.

Referring again to Fig. 57, the strike-line ab is drawn through the points of intersection of the upper surface of bed E with the 500 topographic contour. Then ab is the 500 stratum contour for the upper surface (or superface) of bed E, or for the under surface (or base) of bed F. In a similar way, the parallel line cd is the 550 stratum contour for the same surface. Thus, stratum contours could be drawn for any of the beds represented, provided their outcrop boundaries intersect topographic contours. If the dip were not known, it could be found from a measurement of the perpendicular distance between ab and cd, using the above formula.

It should be pointed out that, in nature, rocks having a regular dip are generally of limited, though in some cases of large, extent. The example given is a simple geometrical instance.

Construction of Outcrop. The probable outcrops of a series of horizontal or uniformly dipping beds may be obtained by geometrical construction, given (i) the topographic contours of the area, and (ii) *either*, details of outcrop at the minimum necessary number of points ; *or*, one point of outcrop, and data as to the dip and thickness of the beds ; the latter would be obtained, e.g., from a boring through the strata.

1. *Horizontal Strata.* If the beds are horizontal and their thicknesses are known, one point on the outcrop of one of them is sufficient to determine the complete outcrop. For if (e.g.) the top of a bed were known to outcrop at one point at a certain level, its outcrop on the map would run everywhere at the same height, following the topographic contour of that value, and the outcrop could thus be constructed. The altitude of beds lying above or below the given horizon could be obtained by adding their thicknesses successively to the height of the known horizon if they were above it, or by subtracting if they were below it.

2. *Three-point Problem.* If the beds are dipping, three points are required to define the surface of any one of them, assuming that it is a plane. *Example :* In Fig. 63a, let X, Y and Z be three mapped points at which the position of a given bed, say a sandstone, is known. At X and Y the top of the sandstone outcrops at 900 feet and 700 feet above O.D. respectively. At Z the same surface is proved by a boring to occur at 400 feet. It is required to draw in the outcrop of the top of the sandstone.

First find the direction of strike, for which the following construction may be used : Join X and Z, the highest and lowest of the three points, and divide the line XZ into n equal parts, where n is the difference in level between X and Z divided by the stratum contour interval. In this case, $n = 500 \div 100 = 5$. One of the points (y) thus obtained has the same altitude as Y, and the line Yy is therefore a line of constant altitude, i.e. a stratum contour or strike line. Draw Yy and other stratum contours parallel to it through the points of division of XZ, and number them. Draw other parallels as necessary, with the same spacing, for values outside the range from X to Z. The required outcrop is obtained by joining the points of intersection of *equal* topographic and stratum contours, as in Fig. 63b.

To draw the outcrop of the *base* of the sandstone, subtract the thickness of the bed from the value of each stratum contour, and with the new values obtain new intersections with the topographic contours. Through these points draw in the outcrop ; in Fig. 63b a thickness of 100 feet has been taken for the sandstone. Similarly, to obtain the outcrops of other overlying and underlying beds, add the thickness of each successively to the stratum contour values if the beds lie above the stratum for which the construction was first made ; if they are below it, subtract the thickness of each bed. The outcrops can then be drawn in, one after the other, as already described.

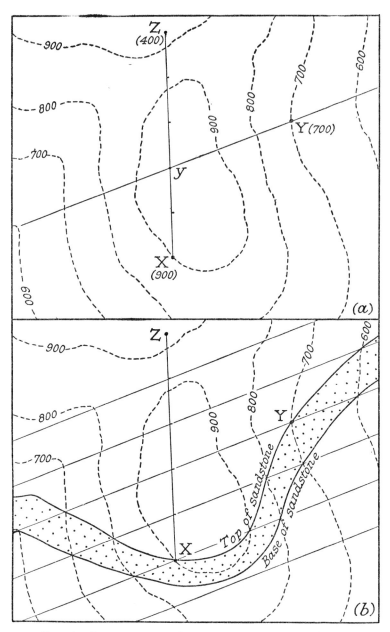

FIG. 63.—CONSTRUCTION OF OUTCROP FROM THREE GIVEN POINTS.

(a) Determination of strike direction (Yy). (b) Completed drawing of outcrop.

Note that (for small angles of dip) the *thickness* of the bed of sandstone is given by the difference in level between the two points where any stratum contour cuts the top and bottom of the bed.

When beds are broken and displaced by a fault, this must be allowed for in the values given to the stratum contours on either side of the line of outcrop of the fault. Suppose, for example, that a fault with a 100-foot vertical displacement traverses the area of the map from north to south, and that the beds on the east side of this line have been dropped relative to those on the west side. Then for any bed, the stratum contours, where they cross the fault, will change in value by 100 feet, being less on the east side and greater on the west.

The effects of faulting are described in the next chapter, and further uses of stratum contours are discussed there.

Another Construction. An alternative construction for finding the strike and dip from three given points on a stratum is shown in Fig. 64. Let P, Q, R be the three points, their altitudes on the stratum being such that P is the highest and R the lowest. Join P and Q, the two higher points. From P draw P*s* perpendicular to PQ, and equal to the height

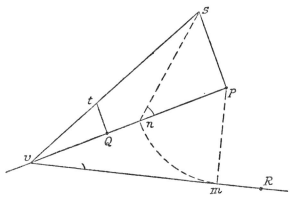

FIG. 64.—CONSTRUCTION FOR DIP AND STRIKE.

of P above R to some convenient scale. At Q erect a perpendicular Q*t* to the same scale, to represent the height of Q above R. Join *st*, and produce it to meet PQ produced in *v*. Then *v* is a point on the stratum at the same level as R, and *v*R is the direction of strike.

To find the dip, draw P*m* perpendicular to *v*R, and set off P*n*, equal to P*m*, along P*v*. Then the angle *sn*P is the angle of dip, and P*m* is the dip direction. (N.B. P*s* must be drawn to the same scale as P*n*.)

This method is useful when it is not required to draw the outcrop of the stratum.

Test Example : A seam of coal is mapped at three points A, B, and C, which form a triangle whose sides are AB = 500, BC = 750, and CA = 900 yards respectively. B is north-east of A, and C is south-east of B. The level of the coal is 700 feet above datum at A, 850 feet at B, and 300 feet at C. Find the dip and strike of the seam by the method of stratum contours, and check your result by the alternative construction.

Assuming a uniform dip, at what depth below surface would the seam be found at D, 545 yards due south of B, if the ground level at D is 650 above datum ? (Solve by finding the stratum contour on which D lies.)

Calculation of True Dip from Two Measurements of Apparent Dip. Let α, β be the angles of apparent dip in two known directions OA, OB respectively (for example, two vertical faces of a quarry). The bearings of OA, OB are known, and hence the horizontal angle AOB (see Fig. 65). It is required to find the direction and amount of the true dip.

Draw ON and OP equal in length and perpendicular to OA, OB, and make the angles OMN, OQP equal to α, β respectively. (Or set off OM, OQ proportional to the cotangents of α, β respectively.) Then MQ is the

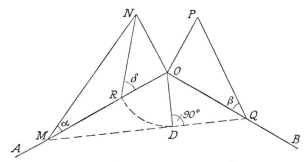

Fig. 65.—Construction for true Dip.

strike direction, and OD, drawn perpendicular to MQ, is the direction of true dip. The angle of dip is the angle ORN, where OR = OD, by construction.

To obtain the direction OD relative to OB (the bearing of which is known), the angle BOD is measured, or calculated from the formula

$$\tan \text{BOD} = \frac{(\tan \alpha . \cot \beta - \cos \text{AOB})}{\sin \text{AOB}},$$

and the dip (δ) is given by $\cot \delta = \cot \beta . \cos \text{BOD}$.

Test Example : A bed of limestone is seen to dip at 15° and 20° respectively on two vertical quarry faces which intersect at 120° in plan. What is the true dip of the bed, and its direction relative to the face with the 20° dip ? (Solve by the construction above and check by calculation.)

CHAPTER 10

STRUCTURAL GEOLOGY, II:
FOLDING AND FRACTURE

Folds.

It is frequently seen that the strata forming the earth's crust have been not only tilted out of the horizontal, but also bent or buckled into *folds*. While simple tilting might result from unequal uplift of sediments on the sea-floor, folding in most cases involves the operation of forces tangential to the earth's surface. The rocks have obtained relief from horizontal compression by rising in the direction of least resistance, i.e. the vertical. Folds are also formed in other ways, for example by the slumping of soft sediments under gravity on an inclined sea-floor.

A complete fold is composed of an arched portion, or *anticline*, and a depressed trough or *syncline* (Fig. 66a). The highest point of an anticline is called the *crest*, and the inclined parts of the strata where anticline and syncline merge are called the *limbs* of the fold. The whole structure extends in length in the strike direction of the beds (here assumed constant).

The plane bisecting the vertical angle between equal slopes on either side of the crest line is known as the *axial plane*. Where this is vertical, as in Fig. 66a, the fold is upright and *symmetrical*; Fig. 66b shows an *asymmetrical* fold. Sometimes the middle limb has been brought into a vertical position by the compression which buckled the strata, and under still more severe conditions an overturned fold, or *overfold*, is produced (Fig. 66c). Here the middle limb is inclined in the same sense as the axial plane, and the beds of which it is composed are said to have a *reversed dip*, i.e. upper beds are now brought to dip steeply beneath lower beds, an inversion of the true sequence.

If the compression is so extreme as to pack a series of folds together so that their limbs are all virtually parallel and steeply dipping, the structure is referred to as *isoclinal folding*, i.e. all limbs have the same slope (Fig. 66d). This structure is found, e.g., in the Southern Uplands of Scotland (Fig. 87).

Where the axial plane is inclined at a low or zero angle, the fold is said to be *recumbent* (Fig. 66e), a type which is met with in intensely folded mountain regions such as the Alps (Fig. 81).

The term *monocline* is given to the kind of flexure which has two parallel gently dipping limbs with a steeper middle limb between them (Fig. 67); it is in effect a local steepening of the dip in gently dipping (or horizontal) beds.

The dimensions of anticlines and synclines vary between wide extremes, from small puckers in sharply folded sediments, to broad archings of strata whose extent is measured in miles. The growth of such structures is, in general, a process which goes on slowly as stresses develop in any particular part of the earth's crust; but superficial folds may develop in a compara-

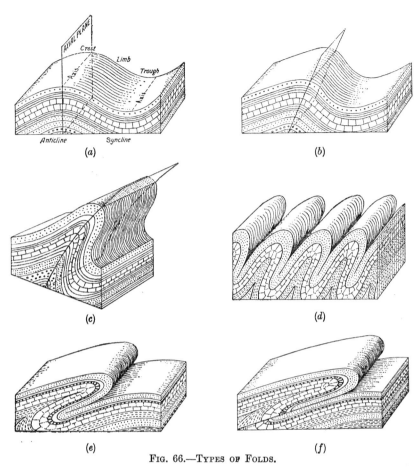

FIG. 66.—TYPES OF FOLDS.

(a) Symmetrical. (b) Asymmetrical. (c) Overturned. (d) Isoclinal. (e) Recumbent.
(f) Recumbent, passing into a thrust.

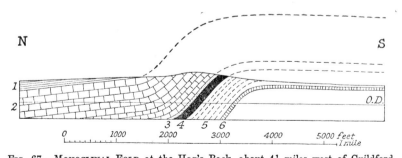

FIG. 67.—MONOCLINAL FOLD at the Hog's Back, about 4½ miles west of Guildford,
Surrey (after H. G. Dines and F. H. Edmunds, H.M. Geol. Survey).

(1) Tertiary Beds. (2) Chalk. (3) Upper Greensand. (4) Gault. (5) Folkestone Beds.
(6) Bargate Beds.

tively short space of time, e.g. earthquake ripples forming quickly in soft sediments.

The length of this period of growth partly determines whether a stratum is broken during the folding process, or whether it can adapt itself to the new pressure conditions by deformation without fracture ; a rapid compression is more likely to lead to fracture than a slow one. The nature of the beds themselves, i.e. hard or soft, resistant or lacking rigidity,[1] is another factor which helps to determine whether the beds break or fold. A third factor is the amount of cover or overburden under which folding takes place.

Frequently an anticline is broken near the crest, where tension stresses are set up by the bending of the strata. Denudation removes more easily the weaker (i.e. broken) parts of the structure, and there is therefore a tendency for valleys to be carved out along the axes of anticlines, and for

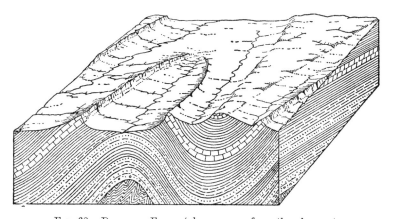

FIG. 68.—DENUDED FOLDS (plunge away from the observer).

hills to be formed over synclines, as shown in Fig. 68. The structure of the Weald of Sussex and Kent, for example, is that of a broad anticlinal arch which has been broken along its crest and denuded in the central area. Its axis runs roughly east and west (Fig. 97). The Chalk which once extended across the Weald is now seen along the North Downs, where the dip is to the north, and along the South Downs, where the dip is southerly (Fig. 98). These represent the limbs of the original fold. The visible structure is now interrupted by the English Channel, and the Chalk of the northern and southern limbs ends in the cliffs of Dover and Beachy Head respectively. Its continuation is seen in the cliffs of Calais and along part of the French coast.

---

[1] The terms *competent* and *incompetent* are used to describe the capacity of a rock for transmitting stress ; competent beds, e.g. limestone, are strong and able to carry their own weight and also that of overlying rocks ; incompetent beds, e.g. shale, are weak and yield by flowage, i.e. change of shape. The form of a fold is controlled by the competent strata which it contains.

Outcrop of Folded Beds. Fig. 69 is a geological map of an area showing the outcrops of beds folded into an anticline and a syncline. The strike of the beds can be found from an inspection of the points of inter-

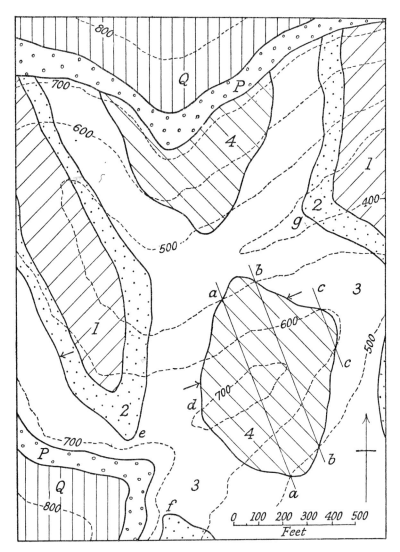

Fig. 69.—Geological Map of Folded Strata and Unconformity.

section of outcrop boundaries with topographic contours; e.g. lines *aa* and *bb*, representing 500-feet stratum contours, may be drawn through the intersections of the 500 topographic contour with the boundary between beds 3 and 4. Similarly, *cc* is a 600-feet stratum contour for the same

boundary. The dip of the strata in this neighbourhood is therefore from
cc (600 feet) towards *bb* (500 feet), and is shown by a dip arrow. In a
similar way it can be deduced that the dip of the strata on the western
side of the same outcrop of bed 4 is in the opposite direction, as indicated by
another dip arrow. The beds are therefore bent into a synclinal form ; the axis
of the syncline lies between the strike lines *aa* and *bb*, and is parallel to them.

This structure could also be inferred, assuming that there were no dip
arrows on the map, by following the course of the boundary 3–4 and noticing
any rise or fall along the outcrop. For example, starting at the most
westerly limit of the boundary, near the point *d*, the outcrop is there at a
level of 700 feet ; but it falls to 600 feet, and further to 500 feet, when
followed to the north. It then falls to a little below the 500-feet level, but
soon returns to it (at *b*), and continues to rise to 600 feet and over. A
synclinal form for the beds is therefore indicated, bearing in mind the strike
direction ; the lowest point on the outcrop (between *a* and *b*) shows the
position of the trough of the syncline, and corresponds to a similar low
point on the southern side of the outcrop. If the hillside carrying this
outcrop be visualized from the map, a three-dimensional picture of the
structure is obtained. In these ways, simple structures can be read from
the shapes of outcrops and topography.

Opposed dips, indicating an anticline, can also be inferred from an
inspection of the boundary 2–3 on the western side of the map. The
anticlinal crest, or " turn-over," is seen from the form of the outcrops on
the hill slopes at *e* and *f*. A line through these points would represent the
axis of the anticline, running parallel with the strike of the beds.[1] The
blunt V-shaped outcrops at *e* and *f* must not be confused with the V due
to beds crossing a valley, as at *g*. In the latter case the V does not point
in the strike direction.

Plunging Folds. It is found in nature that a fold does not continue
indefinitely along its length, but dies away sooner or later. Generally, if
it can be traced along its length in one direction, the crest line is observed
to fall, and the amplitude of the fold may decrease until it becomes merged
into unfolded beds (Fig. 70*a*). When the crest line of an anticline departs
from the horizontal in this way, the structure is said to plunge in the direction in which the crest falls. Similarly, in the case of a plunging syncline,
the trough shallows in one direction along the length of the fold and deepens
in the opposite direction, the latter being the direction of plunge.[2]

The stratum contours representing a plunging fold no longer remain
parallel straight lines, as in the ideal case of a non-plunging structure ;
they converge in the direction of plunge in the case of an anticline, and
diverge in the case of a syncline. The line *lmn* in Fig. 70*a* is a contour on
the surface of the uppermost stratum, and is shown in plan in Fig. 70*b*.
Proceeding from *l* to *m*, the direction of strike veers continually, and with
it the direction of dip, until at *m* the strike is *across* the axis of the fold

---

[1] Compare with a *plunging* fold, Fig. 70, where the strike lies *across* the axis at
the nose of the outcrop.

[2] The term *plunge* is now used generally instead of the older term *pitch*.

and the dip along the axis. This change of strike and dip is characteristic of a plunging fold.

The terms dip, strike and plunge together provide a convenient means of describing the curved surface of a folded stratum. Fig. 71 shows a map of such an anticline and syncline, on the same topography as in part of Fig. 69. The plunge can be detected by comparing the altitudes of two or more points on the outcrop of a bed where it crosses the fold axis ; e.g. between p and q (Fig. 71) there is a difference in level of about 90 feet

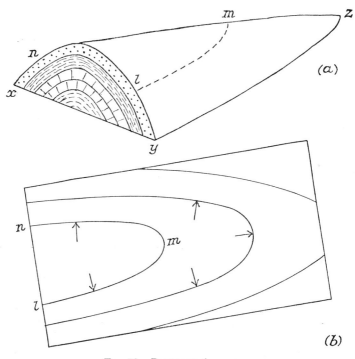

FIG. 70.—PLUNGING ANTICLINE.

(a) Plunging anticline sectioned by horizontal plane xyz ; lmn = contour on curved surface of folded stratum. (b) Stratum contour map of fold, showing lmn and other contours in plan ; note the convergence of the contours in the direction of plunge (to the right).

(estimated from the contours). This can also be expressed as an inclination of the crest-line to the horizontal and called the *angle of plunge*, in this instance nearly 5° in the direction south-south-east.

Domes and Basins. Where strata have been folded so that the dip is everywhere outward from a central area, as in Fig. 72, the structure is called a *dome*. Stratum contours representing this form will appear as complete loops, one within another, though not necessarily regular curves. If the dip is everywhere inwards, the structural form is known as a *basin*.

PLATE XI

Photo by H.M. Geological Survey.

(A) NORMAL FAULT IN COAL MEASURE SANDSTONES, MOSSEND, LANARKSHIRE.

Photo by W. F. Whittard.

(B) FRACTURE CLEAVAGE IN MUDSTONES, NEAR DOLGOCH, CENTRAL WALES
(ANTICLINAL AXIS ON RIGHT)

PLATE XII

(A) Unconformity of Carboniferous Limestone on Silurian Flagstones, Horton-in-Ribblesdale, Yorks.

(B) Anticlinal Fold in Sandstone, Ardross, Fife.

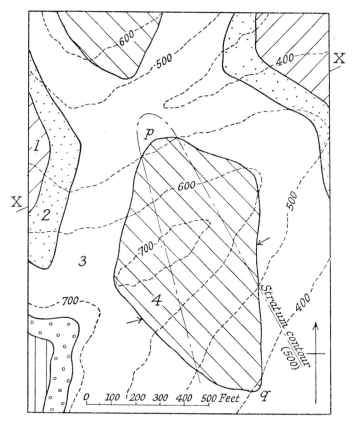

Fig. 71.—Geological Map of Plunging Syncline.
On same topography as part of Fig. 69. XX = line of equal amplitude with
fold in Fig. 69.

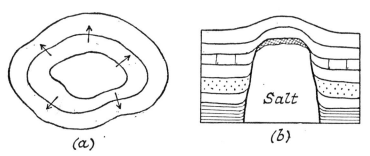

Fig. 72.

(a) Stratum contours for a dome, dip everywhere outwards; (b) salt dome, formed by
intrusive plug of salt, with a cap-rock (shaded).

Generally, these structures are elongated to some extent in one direction ; an elongated dome before denudation, for example, would be something like a long ellipse in shape. A still further elongated dome can be regarded as two plunging anticlines, end to end, with a common axis, and plunging in opposite directions.

Salt domes are formed when strata are upturned by a mass of salt moving upwards under pressure. A layer of salt is a weaker material than other rocks among which it occurs, and undergoes plastic deformation when under pressure, rising as an intrusive plug and penetrating or lifting overlying strata. The dome thus formed is often nearly circular in plan. Many salt dome structures are found in the Gulf Coast area of Texas, in Persia, Germany, and elsewhere.

Faulting.

Faults are rock-fractures along which displacement has taken place; the rocks on either side of the break have moved relatively to one another in opposite directions. The movement may be of any amount and in any direction on the fault plane. The vertical component of the displacement between two originally adjacent points is called the *throw* of the fault.

Two common types of fault are illustrated in section below ; Fig. 73 (left) shows a *normal fault*, where a bed originally continuous at *a* has been broken and the side *A* moved down relative to *B*, or *B* moved up relative to *A*. The side *B* is called the " footwall," and *A* the " hanging wall."

FIG. 73.—NORMAL AND REVERSED FAULTS.

Cross-sections showing the displacement of a horizontal stratum (in black). *Left :* Normal fault ; *A* = downthrow side (hanging wall), *B* = upcast side (footwall). *Right :* Reversed fault ; *C* = upcast side (hanging wall), *D* = downthrow side (footwall).

In a normal fault, therefore, the hanging wall is displaced downwards relative to the footwall. A *reversed fault* is shown in Fig. 73 (right). In this case the hanging wall *C* is displaced upwards relative to the footwall *D*. Notice that the effect of the reversed faulting is to *reduce* the original horizontal extent of the broken bed ; the two displaced ends of a stratum overlap in plan. On the other hand, the effect of a normal fault is to *increase* the original horizontal distance between two points on either side of the fracture.

The custom of describing faults as " normal " or " reversed " originated in English coal-mining practice. Faults which were inclined towards the downthrow side were met most commonly. When a seam which was being worked ran into such a fault, it was necessary to continue the heading a short way (as at *a*, Fig. **73**), and then sink a shaft to recover the seam ; this was the usual or " normal " practice. When a fault was encountered which had moved the opposite way, that was the reverse of the usual conditions, and the fault was called " reversed."

Fault Components. The complete displacement along a fault plane between two originally adjacent points can be described by means of three components measured in directions at right angles to one another. The vertical component, or *throw*, has already been mentioned ; the two horizontal components are the *heave* (*bc* in Fig. 74), measured in a vertical plane at right angles to the fault plane ; and the *shift* (*cd*), measured parallel to the strike of the fault plane. The total displacement, *ad*, is called the *slip*. (There are local variations in this nomenclature.)

Faults in which horizontal movement along the fault plane (the shift or *strike-slip*) predominates, the other components being small or nil, are called *tear* or *wrench* faults. (The term *transcurrent fault* is also used.)

The *hade* of a fault plane is its angle of inclination to the vertical, the angle *bac* in Fig. 74. It is often more convenient to speak of the dip of a fault, i.e. its inclination to the horizontal, than of its hade. Hade + dip = 90°. When a fault is vertical the hade and heave are zero.

Faults are referred to above as " planes " only for ease of description ; they are more often zones of crushed rock which has been broken by the movement, and range in width from a fraction of an inch to many yards. Sometimes the crushed rock along the fault sur-

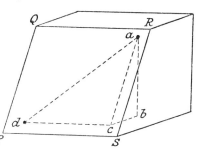

FIG. 74.—COMPONENTS OF FAULT DISPLACEMENT.

PQRS = fault surface. *ad* = total slip. *ab* = throw. *bc* = heave. *cd* = shift. The points *a*, *c*, *d* lie on the fault surface.

face has been ground very small, and become mixed with water penetrating along the line of the fault, producing a clay or *gouge*. Fault surfaces are often plane only for a small extent ; curved and irregular fractures are common.

Fault Groups. Several normal faults throwing down in the same direction are spoken of as " step faults " (Fig. 75) ; two normal faults

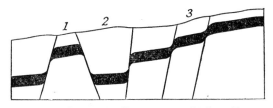

FIG. 75.—(1) RIDGE, (2) TROUGH, AND (3) STEP FAULTS.

The ends of the black bed are shown slightly dragged round as they approach a fault.

hading towards one another produce " trough faulting," and hading apart form a pair of " ridge faults." Where a stratum approaches a fault it is often bent backwards a little, away from the direction of movement along the fault plane, as shown in the figure. A sunken block, bounded on all sides by faults, is called a *graben* ; the Rhine Valley and the Midland Valley of Scotland are examples of this structure on a large scale. A *horst* is a fault-bounded ridge-block, the converse of graben ; an example is the ridge of the Malvern Hills, Herefordshire.

Strike and Dip Faults. Faults are also described from the direction of their outcrops on the ground, with reference to the strata which they displace. *Strike faults* outcrop parallel to the strike of the strata ; *dip faults* run in the direction of the dip of the beds ; and *oblique faults* are those which approximate neither to the dip nor strike direction. These cases are illustrated below.

Effect of Faulting on Outcrop.

I. STRATA HORIZONTAL. On crossing from one side of a fault to the other, the level of the outcrop of any particular bed changes by an amount equal

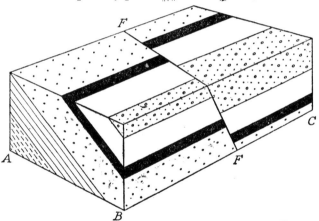

FIG. 76.—EFFECT OF NORMAL DIP FAULT (*FF*) ON DIPPING STRATA.

to the throw. If the faults are vertical they have a straight-line outcrop, or trace. The direction of downthrow is indicated conventionally by a short stroke against the fault trace (Fig. 103, p. 240).

II. STRATA DIPPING. The different examples of normal faulting to be considered here are :

    (i) a dip fault.

    (ii) a strike fault, hading in the same direction as the dip of the strata.

    (iii) a strike fault, hading in the opposite direction to the dip of the strata.

    (i) The general effect of a dip fault is to displace the outcrops of corresponding beds on either side of the fault line. In Fig. 76, the side (*AB*) of the block is parallel to the dip direction, and the side (*BC*) shows a strike section. The normal fault (*FF*) throws down to the right. The outcrops of the beds (seen on the top of the block) are offset on either side of the fault trace ; younger beds, on the downthrow side, are brought opposite older beds on the upcast side.

(ii) Strike faults either *repeat* or *cut out* the outcrop of some parts of the faulted strata. In Fig. 77*a*, a series of beds is broken by a normal strike fault (*FF*) which dips steeply in the same direction as the dip of the beds. The result of this is that one bed (striped) does not appear in outcrop at the surface (the upper surface of the block) ; it is cut out by the faulting. The case where the dip of such a fault is the same as the dip of the strata is referred to as a *slide*, i.e. the fault movement has taken place along a bedding-plane. Where the dip of the fault plane is *less* than the dip of the beds, and in the same direction, there is *repetition* of some part of the outcrop of the beds.

(iii) Fig. 77*b* shows a series of beds broken by a normal strike fault (*FF*)

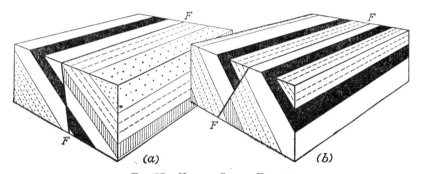

FIG. 77.—NORMAL STRIKE FAULTS.

(*a*) Fault hades in same direction as dip of beds ; outcrop of striped bed is concealed.
(*b*) Fault hades in opposite direction to dip of beds, and outcrops of some beds are repeated.

which dips in the opposite direction to the dip of the beds. The effect is to repeat the outcrop of some beds (the black bed, for instance), as seen on the upper surface of the block.

The above diagrams show outcrops on a plane surface ; irregular topography will modify this simple conception, but the principles remain the same.

Oblique faults to some extent share the features shown by both dip and strike faults ; instances of this kind are seen in Fig. 103.

Reversed Faults. The effects of reversed faulting on outcrop are not always distinguishable from those of normal faulting. For example, a reversed dip fault will still bring older beds on the upcast side against newer beds on the downthrow side (cf. normal faulting, above). On the other hand, a reversed strike fault will have the opposite effect to a normal fault in the same direction ; in the cases illustrated in Fig. 77, a little consideration will show that *repetition* of outcrop would be produced by a reversed fault dipping in the same direction as the dip of the strata, and elimination of outcrop in the other case.

If a fault is not vertical, the shape of its trace or outcrop on a map gives an indication of its hade, which may show whether it is normal or reversed. But, in general, it is difficult to distinguish between normal and reversed faults solely by their relation to outcrops on a map. Field evidence is more definite ; for example, the ends of the fractured beds may be seen in an exposure to be dragged round so as to indicate the direction of relative movement along the fault plane (Fig. 75).

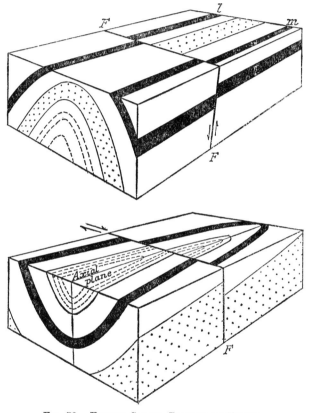

FIG. 78.—FOLDED STRATA BROKEN BY FAULTS.

Above : Faulted anticline; outcrops of limbs are moved apart on upcast side of a normal fault.
Below : Plunging syncline cut by a wrench fault. Note the horizontal shift of the axial plane.

Wrench Faults. A fault in which the displacement is mainly or entirely horizontal may shift the outcrops of dipping beds in a similar way to a normal fault. For example, the staggering of the outcrops shown in Fig. 76 could have come about by a horizontal movement of one part of the block past the other part, along the fault (*FF*). A wrench fault in the direction of strike will not change the order of the strata in outcrop unless there is a vertical throw as well as the horizontal movement.

Criteria for recognizing wrench faulting are also a matter of field observation ; two may be noted here : (i) Parallel grooves have in some cases been cut on a fault surface by projecting irregularities on one block as it moved past the other. These grooves are known as *slickensides*, and they give valuable information about the direction of the fault movement. If they are horizontal, or nearly so, it can be inferred that the faulting which produced them possessed a strong wrench component. (ii) When vertical beds are faulted and displaced laterally in outcrop, a wrench fault is indicated. A third indication of such faulting is given under Folded Strata (below and Fig. 78).

III. STRATA FOLDED. The effect of a normal dip fault cutting an anticline is shown in Fig. 78, where the front half of the block is downthrown relative to the other half, and the top of the block represents a level surface of denudation. The outcrops of a bed such as *l, m*, are brought closer together on the downthrow side of the fault. In the case of a syncline, the outcrops of the two limbs are moved *apart* on the downthrow side. These displacements of outcrop would be similar if the fault were reversed instead of normal.

Where a fold is broken by a wrench fault, with horizontal shift and little or no throw, the outcrops of the limbs of the fold on one side of the fault are moved both in the same direction relative to the other side (Fig. 78, lower diagram). The axial plane of the fold is also displaced ; this fact is often useful in determining the presence of a strike-slip component in a fault movement as seen on a geological map.

Thrust Planes. A common feature of most of the fractures so far described is their steep inclination to the horizontal. They may be thought

FIG. 79.—DEVELOPMENT OF THRUSTS IN FOLDED STRATA. *T* = thrust.

of as roughly radial to the earth's surface, as distinct from tangential. There is another group of fractures which are produced by dominantly horizontal compression ; these are known as *thrusts* or thrust planes (Fig. 83*a*). They have in general a lower angle of inclination, but this varies considerably, and ranges from zero to more than 45°. Many thrust planes are virtually horizontal, especially the great overthrusts which break the much compressed and folded strata in mountain regions.

The development of a thrust from an overturned fold is illustrated in Fig. 79. With continuing compression, the middle limb of the fold becomes attenuated (*A*), then fracture occurs (*B*), and further compression results in a movement along the thrust (or shear) plane so formed (as at (*C*)). The effect of this kind of fracture is thus to shorten the horizontal extent of the beds, in the direction of compression, by increasing their vertical extent.

Examples have been described from many localities, e.g. in cliff sections at Tunnels Beach, Ilfracombe, North Devon, where on a small scale thin bands of limestone in cleaved shales have been folded and thrust repeatedly. This thrusting has left isolated S-shaped (sigmoid) sections of the hard limestone, similar to that between thrusts *TT* in Fig. 79.

A structure involving both major and minor thrusts, known as the *imbricate structure*,[1] was first described from the district of Assynt, in Sutherlandshire. In that region, rocks have been piled up by a series of minor thrusts, as described above, and these have been truncated by flatter major thrusts, or overthrusts, along which large heavy masses of rock have been pushed forward so as to overlap the folded and broken rocks beneath. Fig. 80 shows the type of structure in section (see also p. 206). The outcrops of the nearly horizontal major thrust planes can be traced for miles across the area, and appear on the map as irregular, winding lines. The

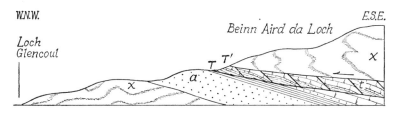

FIG. 80.—SECTION AT LOCH GLENCOUL, SUTHERLAND,

to show imbricate structure (right), with minor thrusts (*t*) between flatter major thrusts (*T,T*[1]). *x* = Pre-Cambrian. *a* = Cambrian.

rocks immediately below these surfaces of dislocation have been crushed and sheared by the over-riding of the heavy masses, and converted into mylonites (p. 152).

Nappes. In intensely folded mountain regions, such as the Alps, overthrusts occur associated with recumbent folds on a large scale. A recumbent fold driven forward on a thrust plane is called a *nappe*, or thrustsheet, and structures of this kind form the basis of one interpretation of the complex geology of the Alps (see Fig. 81).

Fold-mountains. There is evidence that belts of the earth's crust have passed through periods of intense lateral or tangential compression, and these regions have been severely folded and ridged up into mountain ranges. Mountain-building movements of this kind are called *orogenic* movements, and they have operated over the sites of long-continued sedimentation in sinking areas. Such areas of deposition, or geosynclines (p. 120), are generally elongated and from the great thicknesses of sediment which were laid down in them mountain masses have subsequently been elevated by folding and faulting, often with associated intrusive igneous activity. The Alps (Fig. 81) where, as already mentioned, the rocks have been thrown into great overfolds and recumbent folds, and often moved

---

[1] Latin, *imbrex*, a tile; the minor thrust masses overlap like tiles on a roof.

for large distances along nearly horizontal thrust planes, have resulted from the compression of a thick pile of geosynclinal sediments. The horizontal compression resulted in a crustal shortening across the fold-belt of many miles. The Appalachian folds in the eastern United States, formed at a different time, and fold-mountain chains such as the Rockies and the Himalayas show similar features. The Caledonian fold system which trends across the Southern Uplands of Scotland in a north-east to south-west direction represents an ancient mountain-building epoch which strongly affected the British Isles; its place in geological time is described, with other orogenic movements, in the next chapter.

It is beyond the scope of this book to discuss the many geological problems involved in such large-scale structures of the earth's crust, and the theories of their formation; the subject is one of great interest, and leads to a consideration of the earth's internal mechanism. The student must be left to fill in the details for himself, if he wishes, by further reading; a short bibliography is given on p. 197.

In summary, the cycle of events that is inferred from a study of the rocks is—first, the accumulation of thick deposits of sediments over sinking areas (the geosynclines); second, the crumpling of the sediments by lateral compressive forces in the crust, accompanied by balancing movements of sub-crustal material, resulting finally in the elevation of a mountain chain. This then becomes subject to breakdown by the agents of denudation, with the production of new sedimentary deposits. Isostatic forces are continually tending to produce crustal equilibrium. Into this cycle at various

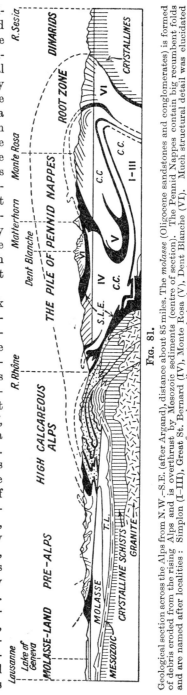

FIG. 81.

Geological section across the Alps from N.W.–S.E. (after Argand), distance about 85 miles. The *molasse* (Oligocene sandstones and conglomerates) is formed of debris eroded from the rising Alps and is overthrust by Mesozoic sediments (centre of section). The Pennid Nappes contain big recumbent folds and are named after localities : Simplon (I–III), Great St. Bernard (IV), Monte Rosa (V), Dent Blanche (VI). Much structural detail was elucidated from deep railway tunnels in the region.

stages, but particularly at the time of mountain formation, may come igneous activity with the injection of magma and the extrusion of lavas.

Fracture Cleavage. Where a series of strata has been subjected to shearing stresses, groups of closely spaced parallel fractures are frequently developed. These are known as *fracture cleavage*, and are dominantly mechanical in their mode of origin ; they are to be distinguished from slaty cleavage (p. 152) on the one hand, and from jointing on the other. The spacing of these shear fractures depends on the hard or soft nature of the material ; incompetent rocks like shale show fracture cleavage planes more closely spaced than is the case with harder (competent) rocks.

When beds are folded, shear stresses incidental to the folding are set up between the layers (Fig. 82), and may lead to slip along the bedding planes, especially if the fold is not broken at its crest ; the slip is greatest on the limbs of the fold. Under these conditions a soft (incompetent) layer lying between two hard beds, as in the figure, may develop a fracture

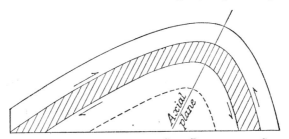

FIG. 82.—FRACTURE CLEAVAGE IN A SOFT BED, SUCH AS SHALE,
FOLDED BETWEEN TWO HARD BEDS.

cleavage pattern, which crosses the bed obliquely. Observation of fracture cleavage in folded rocks is of special value in the interpretation of structure where only a part of the fold is open to inspection. For example, the slope of the fracture cleavage planes on one limb of a denuded anticline will indicate on which side of the limb the axis of the fold is located (cf. Plate XIb). For further discussion of this and other minor structures the reader is referred to text-books of Structural Geology.

Mechanics of Faulting.

Faults are due to the failure of crustal rocks either along shear planes or in tension. It is likely that most faults are shear fractures, and analogies to them are provided by laboratory tests ; but in the earth's crust the state of stress is complex and cannot accurately be imitated in a testing machine.

When a brittle material is broken in compression, failure occurs along shear planes inclined to the direction of loading ; for example, a prism of concrete will, on breaking, yield a rough cone or pyramid. The angle at the apex of such a cone is theoretically 90°, since the maximum shear stresses should occur on planes inclined at 45° to the direction of the maximum principal stress. In practice this angle is generally found to be less than 45°, owing to the operation of frictional forces in the material at the moment of failure. Thus an acute-angled cone is formed ; or, in two dimensions, the shear fractures intersect at an acute angle which faces the direction of maximum compression.

Near the earth's surface, many hard (brittle) rocks which have undergone compression have failed in shear, with the production of single faults or fault patterns. (In other cases the rocks have obtained relief from stress by folding.) Where the dominant compression was horizontal, and the

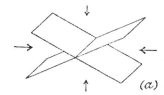

vertical load small, thrust faults would appear to be the characteristic type of fracture, the acute angle between the shears facing the greatest horizontal stress (Fig. 83a).[1] When the greatest stress was vertical (Fig. 83b), the fractures would be steeply inclined to the horizontal, after the manner

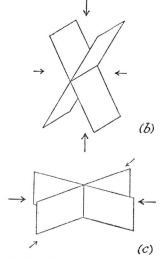

Fig. 83.—SHEAR-PLANES IN RELATION TO COMPRESSIVE STRESSES.

(a) thrusts. (b) normal faults. (c) tear faults. Maximum stress, long arrows. Minimum stress, short arrows. The intermediate stress is omitted, but its direction is that of the line along which the shear-planes intersect.

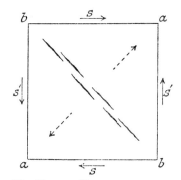

Fig. 84.—TENSION FRACTURES PRODUCED BY SHEARING STRESSES.

aa = direction of tension. bb = direction of compression.

of normal and reversed faults; it is likely that most normal and reversed faults originated in this way. Thirdly, when both the greatest and least stresses were horizontal (Fig. 83c), the resulting fractures are vertical surfaces on which there is horizontal displacement, and correspond to wrench faults.

Soft beds, in contrast to hard, often yield to stress by plastic deformation; this is especially the case when they are at some depth below surface and under confining pressure from overlying beds. Under very high confining pressures, even hard rocks may deform by plastic yielding, as demonstrated experimentally for marble by Adams and Bancroft.[2]

Conditions also arise in which the earth's crust is put locally in a state

[1] Demonstrated experimentally by H. M. Cadell, *Trans. Roy. Soc. Edinburgh*, XXXV, 1888.

[2] *Journ. Geol.*, XXV, 1917, p. 597.

of tension, resulting in the formation of tension fractures, which may appear as normal faults, or may tap sources of hot igneous material which rises and fills them to form dykes. One way in which tension is produced is from the stressing of an area by horizontal shearing forces (couples, *ss* in Fig. 84). The tension breaks are aligned parallel to one diagonal of the rectangular horizontal area, as illustrated, the other diagonal being in compression. (See also Fig. 47, p. 152.)

Tension fractures are also formed by the slipping of rocks under the action of gravity ; this is seen in the case of some landslips, where the ground is torn apart along ragged, gaping lines. A third way in which tension fractures may arise is from a set of torsional forces, for example due to the unequal settlement of a horizontal slab of rock. If opposite corners of such a slab (e.g. *aa* in Fig. 84, neglecting the shearing couples) are raised or lowered relative to the other pair of corners, torsional stresses are then acting on the slab ; a fracture pattern may be developed, as in Daubrée's famous experiment with a sheet of glass. Little is known about the part played by torsion in the deformation of crustal rocks.[1]

Since brittle materials are, on the whole, weakest in tension, it might be expected that tension breaks would be the most common among rock fractures ; the very numerous cases of shear failures, however, may be attributed to the predominance of compressive stresses in the earth's crust.

Joints. Joints are fractures formed as a result of either tension or shear stresses acting on a rock mass. The cause of the stresses may be variously ascribed to contraction, compression, unequal uplift or subsidence (cf. torsion, above), earthquakes, or other earth phenomena. Tension joints arise, for example, by the drying and resultant shrinkage of sedimentary deposits (cf. mud-cracks) ; or during folding ; or in igneous rocks by contraction on cooling. A lava-flow (see p. 90) often develops a hexagonal joint-pattern due to uniform contraction around many centres equally spaced from one another. Shear joints may arise from compression of sedimentary or igneous rocks, the shearing component of the stress being just enough to overcome the shear strength of the material, and then ceasing to operate. The fractures so produced generally form two sets which make an acute angle with one another, as illustrated in Fig. 83, the acute angle facing the direction of the maximum compressive stress. One of the two shear directions may be emphasized, showing many joints, and the other largely suppressed. In dipping or folded sedimentary rocks the direction of one set of joints frequently corresponds to the strike of the beds, and the other set to the dip direction ; they are therefore referred to as *strike-joints* and *dip-joints*.

The spacing of joints varies considerably and is of great importance in quarrying ; some rocks, such as sandstones and limestones, in which the joints may be widely spaced, yield large blocks which are suitable for masonry ; whereas other rocks may be so closely jointed as to break up

---

[1] In this connection see the description of fractures formed in concrete beams under torsional load, by F. G. H. Blyth and W. T. Marshall, *Nature*, Vol. 143, 1939, p. 120.

into small pieces—which, however, may be suitable for road-metal or other purposes. Some joints in sedimentary rocks run only from one bedding plane to the next, but others may cross several bedding planes, when they are known as "master joints." The ease of quarrying, excavating, or tunnelling in hard rocks largely depends on the regular or irregular nature of the joints and their direction and spacing. Joints are also important in connection with water supply (Chapter 13), and their presence helps to promote rock-weathering.

SELECTED REFERENCES

ANDERSON, E. M. "Dynamics of Faulting." 2nd edition, 1951. Oliver & Boyd, Edinburgh.
HILLS, E. SHERBON. "Outlines of Structural Geology." (3rd edition.) 1953.
—— "Elements of Structural Geology." 1963. Methuen.
NEVIN, C. M. "Principles of Structural Geology." 1949. Wiley & Sons, New York. 4th edition.
BILLINGS, M. P. "Structural Geology." 1954. Prentice-Hall.

For a short account of the structure of the Alps see A. HOLMES, " Physical Geology," chap. 18 (reference on p. 43) ; and M. K. WELLS in *Proc. Geol. Assoc.*, 59, 1948, p. 181.

CHAPTER 11

ELEMENTARY STRATIGRAPHY

Sedimentary rocks occupy a large part of the earth's land surface, although as we have seen they form a discontinuous and relatively thin cover to the underlying igneous and metamorphic rocks of the " sial." The sedimentary layers (strata) normally lie one above another in order of decreasing age, the younger beds on older ; but where there has been structural disturbance they are folded and broken. A study of the strata in a particular area enables their sequence or *succession* to be recorded, and this can then be compared with other local successions. From such observations the sequence of sedimentary rocks over a wider area can be established, as has been done for nearly the whole of the British Isles. The study of this branch of Geology is called *stratigraphy*; a list of rock formations is generally shown in the form of a column, with the oldest rocks at the bottom and the youngest at the top. Further, as each stratum was formed during a particular interval of geological time, a succession of strata therefore represents a series of events in the past, a small part of geological history.

The broad divisions of the geological column into Systems and Groups are shown in the Table opposite, which applies particularly to British strata. The names of the geological Systems, and of the larger Groups into which they are collected, are of world-wide application ; the names are also used to express the periods of time during which the rocks of the different Systems were formed. Thus we speak of the Carboniferous System and also of the Carboniferous Period ; or of the Mesozoic Group and the Mesozoic Era. The times of major mountain-building episodes (orogenies), and of phases of igneous activity in Britain, are given in the third column of the Table. The orogenies have been important events in earth-history, and are referred to again later in this chapter.

In any given area the deposition of sediments was not continuous throughout the geological Periods : there are breaks in the sequence of deposits, marked by unconformities (p. 173). These represent intervals of time during which there was not only no deposition, but when denudation took place, the sea floors with their sediments being raised and becoming subject to the action of denuding agents. Thus there were periods of quiet sedimentation, when the seas covered the lands, and intervening episodes of disturbance when uplift and folding took place. This broad pattern of events—the transgression of the seas over the lands, the regression of the seas, followed by orogenic upheaval—has been repeated many times throughout geological history.

Unconformities are often marked by beds of pebble sands and (p. 120), the beach deposits of a sea which inundated the land during its submergence ; examples of this are the pebbly quartzites at the base of the Cambrian, and the rounded flints at the base of the Eocene deposits of south-east England ; both mark the oncoming of marine conditions. Boulder-beds

Name of Geological Group or Era	Name of Geological System or Period (ages in million years)	General nature of deposits, major orogenies, and igneous activity in Britain
Quaternary {	Recent	Alluvium, blown sand, etc.
	Pleistocene	Glacial drifts
CAINOZOIC	Pliocene	⎫
	Miocene	⎬ Sands, clays, and shell beds
Tertiary {	Oligocene	⎪ *Alpine Orogeny*
	Eocene	⎭ *Igneous activity in Scotland and Ireland*
	(70)	
MESOZOIC (or Secondary)	Cretaceous	Sands, clays, and Chalk
	Jurassic	Clays, limestones, some sands
	Triassic	Desert sands and marls
	(225)	
	Permian	Breccias, marls, dolomitic limestone
		Hercynian Orogeny
Newer		*Igneous activity*
	Carboniferous	Limestones, shales, coals, and sandstones
PALÆOZOIC (or Primary)	Devonian	Marine sediments
	(& Old Red Sst.)	(Lacustrine sands and marls)
	(c. 400)	*Igneous activity*
		Caledonian Orogeny
Older	Silurian	⎫ Thick shallow-water sediments, shales,
	Ordovician	⎬ and sandstones. Volcanic activity in
	Cambrian	⎭ the Ordovician
	(c. 600)	
	—*Dalradian*—	—Schists—
	Moinian	Schists and granulites
	(740 +)	
PRE-CAMBRIAN	Torridonian	Sandstones and arkoses
	Uriconian	Lavas and tuffs (Shropshire)
		Pre-Cambrian Orogenies
	Lewisian	Orthogneisses, etc.
	(3500 +)	

and screes formed on an old land surface during erosion, after uplift has taken place, may also be preserved as the lowest members of a newer series of rocks resting unconformably on older rocks ; as for instance the boulders and coarse sands which mark the base of the Torridonian in N.W. Scotland, and lie unconformably on the old land surface carved in the Lewisian rocks (Fig. 85, p. 202). The scree deposits which occur at the base of the Permian rocks similarly represent detritus formed on land by the denudation of folded and uplifted Carboniferous sediments (p. 218).

An old land surface is sometimes evidenced, also, by the presence of a

" dirt-bed " in which some of the old soil has been preserved, as at Purbeck, Dorset ; or by other terrestrial deposits. It indicates an interval of time during which there was locally no deposition of water-borne sediments. In marine deposits a minor unconformity (or non-sequence), representing a local pause in deposition, may be marked by the absence of a few feet of beds over a relatively small area ; it is detected by comparison with other areas where the sequence is complete.

Principles of Stratigraphy. A list of strata for England and Wales was first compiled by William Smith, " the father of English Geology," who also produced the first geological map of the country (p. 239). As a result of his studies he stated two important principles of stratigraphy, namely, that " the same strata are always found in the same order of superposition, and contain the same peculiar fossils." These two principles are still used to determine the relative ages of strata : order of superposition postulates that for an undisturbed series of beds the oldest (i.e. first formed) is at the bottom, and successively younger beds rest upon it ; and strata in different localities can be correlated by means of the fossil remains preserved in them.

Other tests of relative age were formulated later, such as the test of included fragments : fragments of rock found within a deposit must have been derived from a pre-existent formation, which is therefore the older of the two. Current bedding, which is often preserved in sandstones and quartzites, also gives an indication of relative age : the *tops* of the current-bedded layers are truncated by younger layers (Fig. 5b, p. 18). In an old series of metamorphosed sediments, for instance, which may be inverted, this is a valuable means of ascertaining the " way up " (top and bottom) of the beds.

As an example of the application of some of these principles may be cited the Tertiary sands and clays overlying the Chalk near London ; they contain pebbles which are made of flints derived from the Chalk when its upper layers were being eroded. The sands and clays must therefore be younger than the Chalk, as would also be inferred from their position upon it. The latter fact, however, would not be self-evident at a locality where the beds have been brought into the vertical position, as at Alum Bay, Isle of Wight (Fig. 99).

Age of the Earth. The divisions indicated in the Table of Strata enable geologists to speak relatively of parts of geological time ; a very great period of years is represented by the rocks of the geological column, and estimates of its length have been made in the past in various ways, such as by estimating the amount of salt in the oceans and its rate of accumulation, or by estimating the rate of deposition of sediments and dividing this figure into the total known thickness. All these methods gave too low results, and have now been superseded by the time-scale provided by radioactive minerals. The latter contain elements such as uranium and thorium, which are gradually being changed by radioactivity into stable end-products ; this uranium loses helium atoms and passes ultimately to lead, with radium as one stage in the process.

Pitchblende is the chief source of radium and uranium, but other uranium minerals (such as the phosphates torbernite and autunite) also occur, generally in mineral veins penetrating igneous rocks. In one method the lead content is determined for a particular mineral, and from this value the time during which radioactive disintegration has gone on can be calculated. It is given by the " lead-ratio," $Pb/(U + 0.36\ Th)$ if both uranium and thorium are present ; this quantity when multiplied by 7600 gives the approximate age in millions of years, i.e. the time which has elapsed since the mineral and hence the rock containing it were formed. The figures thus revealed are impressive : the maximum so far obtained for Pre-Cambrian rocks is over 3500 million years, and the maximum for Cambrian rocks is 600 millions. The rocky crust of the earth is therefore at least 3500 million years old, and of this vast period Pre-Cambrian time accounts for more than four-fifths of the whole (a point which is not always appreciated from the relatively small space allotted to the Pre-Cambrian in tables of strata). The oldest Mesozoic rocks go back about 225 million years, and the Tertiary era began about 70 million years ago.

Fossils. The main divisions of British strata are discussed in the following pages, with references to occurrences outside Britain when these are of special interest. Distinctive fossils are indicated, but further treatment of Palæontology (the study of fossils) is not within the scope of this book. The civil engineer should, however, have an appreciation of the value of fossils, and if he is in charge of excavations in fossiliferous rocks, should be ready to bring them to the notice of geologists who may be interested and to whom an examination of the rocks and fossils may yield valuable information. Such information is lost once the excavation is lined or filled.

PRE-CAMBRIAN

The oldest rocks of the crust, collectively known as Pre-Cambrian, form an intricate group and represent a very long period of time. In Britain they are of three distinct types, which are named after type localities :

3. *Torridonian.*[1]	Sedimentary rocks, sandstones and arkoses.
2. *Uriconian.*[2]	Volcanic rocks ; acid, intermediate and basic lavas and tuffs. Typically developed in Shropshire.
1. *Lewisian.*[3]	Metamorphic rocks, mainly gneisses of igneous origin with certain schists, and intrusive basic dykes ; found underlying the Torridonian in N.W. Scotland.

The *Moinian* and the *Dalradian* are two groups of metamorphic rocks occupying large areas in the Scottish Highlands (Fig. 94); their age relative to the Lewisian and Torridonian has been uncertain because structural dislocations intervene between them. But recent age-determinations give

---

[1] FromLoch Torridon, West Highlands, the type locality.
[2] After Uriconium, a Roman settlement near Shrewsbury.
[3] Named from the Isle of Lewis, Outer Hebrides.

a minimum of 740 m.y. for the Moine Schists, which are thus Pre-Cambrian ; and a range for the Dalradian which makes that group in part equivalent to the Cambrian.

The Lewisian rocks form the Outer Hebrides and the coastal belt of the N.W. Highlands, where they are overlain by the Torridonian, and both in turn by Cambrian strata. The latter are now tilted as shown in Fig. 85. The belt of outcrop is bounded on the east by a great line of fracture, the Moine Thrust (Fig. 94), which runs from near Durness in the north to south Skye. East of this line the Moine Schists (or granulites), which are metamorphosed siliceous sediments, occupy a large area which extends southwards to the Grampians ; along the line of the Moine Thrust these rocks have been pushed westwards over the Lewisian (together with its overlying Cambrian, see p. 206) for a distance of at least 10 miles. Another big line of fracture, the Great Glen Fault, crosses the Moine area in a N.E.-S.W. direction ; it is a wrench-fault with a large left-handed displacement.[1] South-east of the Moine Schists there follows a belt of mica-schists with

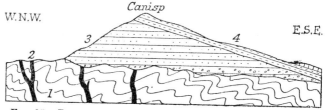

FIG. 85.—DIAGRAMMATIC SECTION THROUGH CANISP, SUTHERLAND.

(1) Lewisian. (2) Basic dykes cutting 1. (3) Torridon Sandstone with basal conglomerate. (4) Cambrian sediments. Two types of unconformity are shown : the old land surface at the base of the Torridonian, and the tilted plane of marine denudation below the Cambrian.

limestones and quartzites, much folded and in places inverted, known as the Dalradian Series ; its southerly boundary is the Highland Boundary Fault, which runs from Stonehaven on the east coast in a west-south-west direction to Loch Lomond, and is further traceable across Northern Ireland, where also Dalradian rocks form the greater part of Donegal. Many granites and related igneous rocks are emplaced in the Moine and Dalradian areas (see Fig. 94). The structural sequence of these groups are matters still under discussion ; for a summary of the different views that are held see " The Grampian Highlands " (*British Regional Geology*, listed on p. 238).

The Torridonian sandstones and arkoses, which have a discontinuous outcrop along the west coast from near Cape Wrath southward to Skye (west of the Moine Thrust), lie unconformably on the Lewisian. They rest on an old land surface eroded in the Lewisian gneisses, with its hills and hollows alike buried by breccias and red sands ; these are succeeded by a group of sandstones (arkoses), up to 8000 feet in thickness, which were deposited largely under desert conditions, and which contain faceted pebbles

[1] An estimated distance of some 65 miles ; this is based on the similarities of the Foyers and Strontian granites, which lie on either side of the fault, and are believed to have been one mass originally, before being separated by the horizontal movement.

and other evidences of eolian origin. Shales occur at intervals among the sandstones.

Apart from Scotland, Pre-Cambrian gneisses and schists of Lewisian type are found in Anglesey. In Shropshire the Uriconian lavas and tuffs form the conspicuous fault-bounded ridges of the Wrekin, Caradoc, and Lawley, and other hills in the neighbourhood of Church Stretton; the extensive plateau of the Longmynd is built of steeply dipping sediments, mainly grits, greywackes, and mudstones, which may correspond in age to the Torridonian of Scotland. In Wales, lavas and tuffs resembling the Uriconian rocks occur in the Lleyn Peninsula, Carnarvon, and at St. David's, Pembroke. Pre-Cambrian rocks outcrop in Charnwood Forest, Leicestershire, and also form the ridge of the Malvern Hills on the borders of Herefordshire. In the Malverns, gneisses and schists of various types have been injected by acid and basic igneous rocks and broken by thrusts and shear zones; they are well seen in numerous road-metal quarries. On the eastern side of Hereford Beacon there is a development of volcanic rocks, called the Warren House Series, which are similar to the Uriconian of Shropshire.

At the Lizard, Cornwall, and at Start Point, Devon, small areas of mica-schist and hornblende-schist of Pre-Cambrian age form the southernmost rocky headlands.

Large areas of Pre-Cambrian rocks occupy the earth's surface in Scandinavia, Siberia, India, Australia, Canada, Brazil, and Antarctica. In Canada they cover about two-thirds of the entire country, and extend into the U.S.A. in the region of the Great Lakes; this area, and similar ones elsewhere, is spoken of as a Pre-Cambrian "shield." Important metalliferous ores are worked in these rocks in Canada, such as the nickel and copper deposits of Sudbury, Ontario, which yield about 90 per cent of the world's output of nickel (see p. 101). Pre-Cambrian sedimentary iron ores are worked on a large scale in the Animikie district (Canada) and in the adjacent Mesabi district (U.S.A.) near Lake Superior, where the ore is quarried in open-cast workings (and see p. 143).

OLDER PALÆOZOIC

The Cambrian, Ordovician, and Silurian systems comprise the big group known as the Older Palæozoic rocks. (The term Palæozoic means "ancient life".) At the end of the Pre-Cambrian a long period of marine deposition began; a large part of the British area was submerged and an elongated trough of deposition, or *geosyncline*, extended across it from south-west to north-east, and across the North Sea into Norway. The north-western margin of the trough was in Scotland, and its south-easterly margin ran from South and Central Wales across England towards the Humber estuary. In this trough were laid down great thicknesses of shallow-water deposits, sands and muds, a slow subsidence of the sea-floor keeping pace with their accumulation. The trough persisted through Ordovician times and into the Silurian, when the sea became shallower. A total thickness of 40,000 feet of sediment was accumulated in the Welsh trough. Near the end of Silurian time, mountain-building movements, which had begun to operate to some extent towards the end of the Ordovician period, developed and became intense ; the sediments of the geosyncline were compressed in a north-west and south-east direction and ridged up into a folded mountain range known as the Caledonian chain, of which the denuded stumps now remain in southern Scotland and northern Ireland (and in Norway). The general direction of these folds in Scotland (i.e. the strike of the folded sediments) is north-east and south-west ; in southern Ireland it is more nearly east–west. Slaty cleavage was impressed on the Palæozoic sediments in the Welsh area and in the Lake District during the Caledonian orogeny.

Cambrian.

The main British outcrops of Cambrian rocks are found in North Wales, with a small area in South Wales near St. David's, in Shropshire, and in the North-West Highlands. The sequence in North Wales, where the sediments reach a thickness of 12,000 feet, is as follows (oldest at bottom) :

4. Tremadoc Slates.
3. Lingula Flags.
2. Menevian Slates (with grit bands).
1. Harlech Grits and conglomerates.

The names are taken from Welsh type-localities, except *Lingula,* which is the name of a fossil. The rocks contain abundant fossils, nearly every order of the animal kingdom being represented except vertebrates ; the more important kinds are described here briefly :

Trilobites are present from the lowest Cambrian upwards, and different species are used for subdividing the strata ; they were three-lobed, segmented creatures with a hard casing (Fig. 88a, d) and lived on the sea-floor. Horny *brachiopods* are represented by such forms as *Lingula* ; a brachiopod has two shells, or valves, one generally smaller than the other, hinged together at one end and forming a chamber in which the animal lived (Fig. 88b, i). Towards the top of the Cambrian, *graptolites* appear in the rocks ; these were simple hydrozoa which lived in colonies (Fig. 88e, g). Each animal occupied a small cup, a number of which were attached to a stem, the whole somewhat resembling a quill pen, hence the name (from *graphein,* to write). Branched forms like *Tetragraptus* are found in the Lower Ordovician rocks. The graptolites are important because they are confined to the Older Palæozoic, and have a restricted range, for which reason they are used for subdividing some formations into *zones,* each zone being a thickness of sediment characterized by particular fossil species which are not found in the zones above or below it.

In the Harlech area the Cambrian strata, with the succeeding Ordovician, are folded into a dome about a north-east axis ; the Harlech Grits which form the core of the structure (Fig. 86) are shallow-water deposits over 5000 feet thick. First quality purple slates are quarried in the Menevian Beds which overlie the Harlech Grits, e.g. at Penrhyn and Llanberis. They are separated from the Upper Cambrian (Tremadoc) slates by several thousand feet of shales with sandstone bands, the so-called Lingula " Flags."

The graptolite *Dictyonema* (Fig. 88c) is characteristic of one band in the Tremadoc beds, and is found in other Cambrian localities.

At the southern end of the Malvern Hills there occurs a small inlier of Cambrian rocks, folded, and intruded by a series of soda-rich dolerite and olivine-basalt sills and andesite dykes. The succession here is:

4. Bronsil (grey) Shales.
3. White Leaved Oak (black) Shales.
2. Hollybush Sandstone.
1. Malvern Quartzite (a pebbly sandstone with siliceous cement).

The Malvern Quartzite is partly conglomeratic, containing pebbles of Pre-Cambrian rocks; it indicates a part of the ancient shore-line of the Cambrian sea. The Hollybush Sandstone is a greenish coloured, micaceous sandstone. In the grey Bronsil Shales, and also in the Shineton Shales (Upper Cambrian) of Shropshire, the fossil *Dictyonema*, mentioned above, occurs at one horizon. In this Malvern area, Cambrian rocks are faulted against the Pre-Cambrian ridge (Fig. 89) and covered unconformably by Silurian.

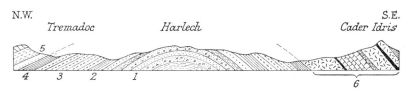

FIG. 86.—DIAGRAMMATIC SECTION ACROSS N. WALES.
(1) Harlech Grits. (2) Menevian Shales. (3) Lingula Flags. (4) Tremadoc Slates. (5) Ordovician sediments. (6) Ordovician lavas and intrusive rocks. Length of section about 18 miles.

Near Nuneaton, Warwickshire, another small Cambrian area is found, and is of economic importance because the lowest beds, known as the Hartshill Quartzite, are worked extensively in road-metal quarries. That Cambrian strata extend farther south under a cover of Mesozoic sediments was proved by a boring at Calvert, Buckinghamshire, where they were penetrated at a depth of 480 feet below surface. Other borings also provide similar evidence.

In the North-West Highlands the Cambrian succession is:

2. Durness Limestone
1. Durness Quartzite, with shales} together about 2100 feet thick.

These beds are shallow-water deposits, and contain fossils almost identical with those found in the Cambrian and Lower Ordovician of eastern North America. It is inferred that the sediments were deposited in a shallow sea which was separated from the main geosyncline (over Wales and southern Scotland) by a land area over central Scotland. They lie unconformably on the Pre-Cambrian of the N.W. Highlands (Fig. 85), and form a nearly north-south belt between it and the Moine Schists on the east (Fig. 94).

Great overthrusts with minor thrusts between them (the imbricate structure, Fig. 80) bring the Pre-Cambrian in places to rest upon the Cambrian beds, which in the imbricate zone are much broken by the repeated fractures.

Ordovician.

The main outcrops of Ordovician rocks are in North Wales, Shropshire, the Lake District, and the Southern Uplands. When the Welsh sequence was being worked out in the middle of last century, a lengthy contention over a part of it arose between two famous geologists, Sedgwick and Murchison, the former proposing to call the rocks Upper Cambrian and the latter Lower Silurian. The matter was finally settled when Lapworth suggested that the rocks should be assigned to a separate group or system, with the name Ordovician (from the district once occupied by the old British tribe of the *Ordovices*). The five subdivisions are named after Welsh and Lake District localities ; an alternative three-fold grouping is shown in brackets :

(Bala)
{ 5. Ashgillian [1] (shales and limestones).
{ 4. Caradocian (volcanic series, with grits and shales).

(Llandeilo)   3. Llandeilian (black flags and shales).

(Arenig)
{ 2. Llanvirnian (shales with tuffs and lavas).
{ 1. Skiddavian [1] (flags and grits with quartzite at base).

Two periods of intense volcanic activity occurred in the Welsh and Shropshire areas in Llanvirn and Caradoc times, when great thicknesses of volcanic ash were deposited and rhyolitic and other lavas were extruded. Some of the volcanoes were submarine and their explosive products became mixed with the muds of the sea-floor. Pillow lavas (thought to have been extruded under water, thus giving rise to sack-like masses which piled up on the sea-floor) are found in the Ordovician of Merionethshire, and at Ballantrae, Ayrshire. Dolerite sills are intruded into Llandeilo slates near Tremadoc, North Wales, and are quarried. Andesitic volcanoes were active in the Lake District in Llandeilo times, and their tuffs and lavas form the Borrowdale Volcanic Series, which covers a large area from Ullswater and Shap in the east to Wastwater and Eskdale in the west. Tuffs which were later cleaved provide the green slates of Honister (p. 154).

It was in the Moffat district of the Southern Uplands, in 1878, that Charles Lapworth, then a schoolmaster and amateur geologist, established the succession of the Ordovician rocks by a careful collection of fossils, mainly graptolites. With the aid of these he was able to demonstrate that an apparently thick group of shales and mudstones was really a comparatively thin series repeated by isoclinal folding (Fig. 87). This masterly piece of work has become a classical illustration of the use of fossils in unravelling a complicated structure. The Moffat rocks become thicker and more sandy when traced westwards to the coast near Girvan, indicating an approach to land, the margin of the geosyncline at that time. New work on the area may lead to a revision of early ideas about the broad structure of the Southern Uplands.

[1] Lake District localities, Ashgill and Skiddaw.

Trilobites (see Fig. 88d and f) and brachiopods are abundant in the Ordovician, together with graptolites (e.g. *Didymograptus*, like a tuning fork, Fig. 88e). The rocks are divided into zones by means of their graptolites.

In the Shelve district of Shropshire, Ordovician rocks from the Skiddavian to Caradocian reach a thickness of 9000 feet, and are folded about north-north-east to south-south-west axes. This folding does not affect the adjacent Silurian rocks which here rest unconformably on the Ordovician, and it is evidence of earth-movements occurring in late Ordovician times (p. 204). The rocks are mainly flags and shales, with the Stiperstones Quartzite (p. 124) at their base and with two thick groups of tuffs. Many dolerite and andesite sills are intruded into these rocks and are quarried for road-stone, among them being the coarse-grained dolerite of Squilver, near Bishop's Castle, a rock easily recognizable by its pale bluish-green

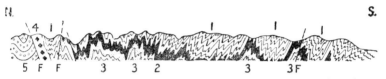

FIG. 87.—SKETCH SECTION ACROSS THE SOUTHERN UPLANDS (near Sanquhar and Kirkcudbright).

(1) Lower Silurian. (2) Ordovician (Arenig to Caradocian). (3) Lower Ordovician Volcanic Rocks. (4) Granite. (5) Old Red Sandstone. F = fault. (After Peach and Horne.)

colour. The dolerite phacolith of Corndon (p. 96) was intruded into Lower Ordovician shales, which are here folded into a structural dome over a mile in length whose major axis trends north-north-east.

Silurian.

The Silurian rocks are well developed in Wales and the Welsh Border country, in the Lake District, and in the Southern Uplands. Their divisions are named after localities in Wales and on the Welsh Border:

3. Ludlow Series (mudstones, with nodular limestones).
2. Wenlock Series (shales and limestones).
1. Llandovery Series (sandstones and shales).

They are succeeded by the Downton Series (sandstones and mudstones, p. 209), which is placed in the Silurian by some authorities but is probably more correctly included in the lower part of the Old Red Sandstone.

In contrast to the preceding period there was little vulcanicity in Silurian times. In Scotland the deposits indicate a shallowing of the geosyncline, and the sea over the Moffat area was divided from that in the Welsh area. Over the English Midlands a shelf sea developed, in which shelly deposits were formed and corals grew at times in warm clear water. The shells and corals are preserved in the limestones of the Wenlock Series. Towards the close of the period the sea became everywhere shallower and finally land-locked, and the great Caledonian mountain-building movements began.

These affected not only the sediments in the British area but also deposits of similar age in Scandinavia.

The Llandovery Series in South and Central Wales, where these rocks occupy large areas, consists of several thousand feet of mudstones with sandstones towards the top of the series. The rocks thin out towards the east, and only the upper part of the Llandovery extends into Shropshire and Herefordshire, where the beds rest unconformably on older rocks. In the Wenlock Series, consisting of the Woolhope Limestone, the Wenlock

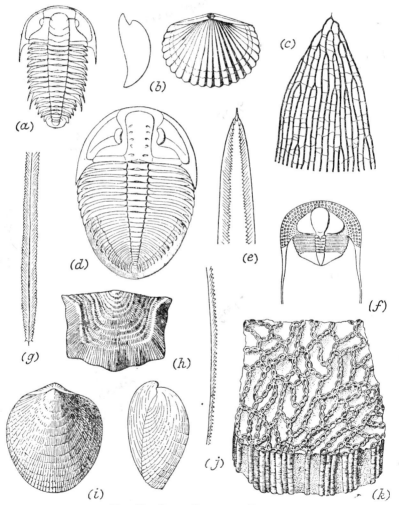

FIG. 88.—OLDER PALÆOZOIC FOSSILS.

Trilobites: (a) *Olenus* (Camb.), (d) *Ogygia* (Ordov.), (f) *Trinucleus* (Silur.). Brachiopods: (b) *Orthis* (Camb.), (h) *Leptaena* (Silur.), (i) *Atrypa* (Silur.). Graptolites: (c) *Dictyonema* (Camb.), (e) *Didymograptus* (Ordov.), (g) *Diplograptus* (Ordov.), (j) *Monograptus* (Silur.). Coral: (k) *Halysites* ("chain coral," Silur.). All × 1 (after drawings published by H.M. Geol. Survey).

Shales, and the Wenlock Limestone (in ascending order), well-developed in Shropshire, the massive limestones form prominent escarpments, of which Wenlock Edge is a well-known example. These rocks are also seen in the Malvern, Woolhope, and Mayhill inliers of Herefordshire (Fig. 89). The limestones, which were formerly much used for lime-burning, contain abundant fossils, including trilobites, brachiopods (such as *Atrypa*, Fig. 88*i*, and *Chonetes*), crinoids (sea-lilies) and corals. Graptolites continue through the Silurian, but are single stem forms like *Monograptus* (Fig. 88*j*). The Ludlow shales and mudstones succeed the Wenlock Series in Shropshire, and a series of shales and grits of Ludlow age and with a graptolitic fauna covers a large area in Denbighshire, North Wales. In the Lake District the Ludlow rocks attain a thickness of 12,000 feet. The Downtonian rocks which follow the Ludlow Series in Shropshire, without apparent break, begin with the yellow Downton Castle Sandstone and Ludlow Bone-Bed at its base, succeeded by greenish Temeside shales, and thick red marls and sandstones. These rocks mark the transition from the marine conditions of the

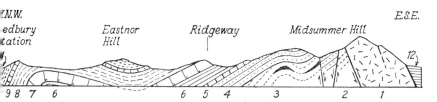

FIG. 89.—DIAGRAMMATIC SECTION FROM LEDBURY TO THE MALVERN HILLS, HEREFORDSHIRE (after Blyth, *Geol. Mag.*, 89, 1952).
Distance about 3½ miles. Vertical scale nearly twice the horizontal. (1) Pre-Cambrian. (2) Hollybush Sandstone (Cambrian). (3) Bronsil Shales (Cambrian) with basalt sills. (4–10) Silurian : (4) Mayhill Sandstone, (5) Woolhope Limestone, (6) Wenlock Shales, (7) Wenlock Limestone, (8) Lower Ludlow Shales, (9) Aymestry Limestone, (10) Upper Ludlow Mudstones. (11) Ledbury Shales (O.R.S.). (12) Keuper Marl.

Silurian to the land period which followed, whose deposits are represented by the rocks of the Old Red Sandstone.

In Scotland, the Silurian rocks of the Southern Uplands are mainly massive greywackes, sandstones, and shales, which are strongly folded along with the Ordovician (*q.v.*) ; not all the divisions are represented.

The Caledonian Movements. These prolonged mountain-building movements began at the end of Silurian time and went on into the middle of the Devonian period. Several phases of the orogenic upheaval can be detected. The sediments of the Older Palæozoic geosyncline were compressed into a great system of folds which extended across Wales, the Lake District and Southern Scotland, and into Norway. The trend of these Caledonian folds in Scotland was N.E.–S.W. and their remnants are seen today in the folded sediments of the Southern Uplands. Probably in early Devonian times, when the movements culminated, the great Moine Thrust and other over-thrusts in Scotland and in Scandinavia were formed. The belt of compression extended from south-west to north-east across Britain and Norway.

The later phases of the movements were accompanied by the extrusion and intrusion of igneous rocks on a large scale ; the lower Old Red Sandstone of Scotland contains many beds of tuff and agglomerate, with lavas, formed at this time, and the great granite masses of the Cairngorms and of Aberdeenshire (see p. 212) came into position, together with many smaller basic intrusions. Farther south, the granites of Cheviot, Skiddaw, Eskdale, and Shap were emplaced, and in Ireland the Newry and Leinster granites.

NEWER PALÆOZOIC

Three systems go to make up the Newer Palæozoic rocks : the Devonian (named after Devon), the Carboniferous (so called because of its coal seams), and the Permian (after the province of Perm, Russia). As a result of the

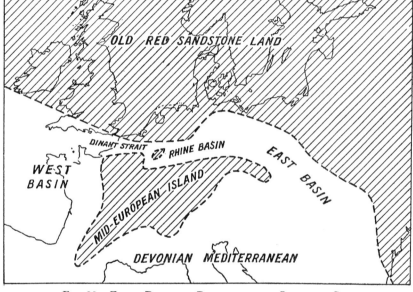

FIG. 90.—EARLY DEVONIAN DISTRIBUTION OF LAND AND SEA.

Caledonian orogeny, a land area of folded rocks had been uplifted (the "Old Red Sandstone Land," Fig. 90) and became subject to denudation during the Devonian period. Britain, except in the south, was part of the land area which extended into northern Europe, with shallow inland seas and gulfs in which sandy deposits were laid down (Old Red Sandstone). At the beginning of Carboniferous times the southern sea, which had covered Devon and Cornwall, began to extend northwards, and marine deposits were spread over the land area. This marine transgression was followed later by the retreat of the sea, leading to the establishment of estuarine and swamp conditions (Upper Carboniferous). At the end of Carboniferous times, mountain-building movements (the *Hercynian*, p. 199) affected much of the European continent ; in the southern part of Britain, these Newer Palæozoic sediments were folded about east–west axes. Subsequently the Permian deposits were accumulated on the newly-formed land area which resulted from the folding.

Devonian.

There are two distinct kinds of deposits of this age : (1) In the sea which covered the Devon area *marine* sediments were laid down ; (2) north of this, *fresh-water* deposits (non-marine) were laid down in large lakes and deltas, and from their predominantly red colour are known as the *Old Red Sandstone.*[1] These constitute two distinct facies (p. 35).

(1) The marine Devonian consists of a lower division with slates and grits (the Dartmouth Slates, Meadfoot Beds, and Staddon Grits) ; a middle division containing shales and limestones (the Ilfracombe Beds, with massive limestones also at Torquay and Plymouth) ; and an upper division with sandstones, shales, and flagstones (the Pickwell Down, Baggy, Marwood, and Pilton Beds). The Delabole Slates of Cornwall, which are extensively quarried for roofing slate, are a formation of Upper Devonian age. The Devonian rocks have broad outcrops in north and south Devon and form a great syncline, in the trough of which lie sediments of Carboniferous age (the Culm of mid-Devon, p. 214). The Devonian strata are much folded, faulted, and cleaved, so that their succession is locally difficult to establish ; another difficulty is that fossils are rare in most of the beds, though plentiful in the limestones. Corals, for example, are abundant in the marine Plymouth Limestone, at the top of the Middle Devonian ; this rock forms the wooded cliffs around Plymouth and is quarried for structural and decorative stone. Fine sections of the intensely folded and thrust Devonian rocks are seen in the cliffs of north Devon, especially where the coast runs north and south (i.e. at right angles to the general strike of the structures), as at Baggy Point and near Ilfracombe.

(2) The " lakes " in which the Old Red Sandstone deposits were laid down occupied large areas in South Wales and Herefordshire, in the Cheviot district, in the Midland Valley of Scotland, in the Orkneys, and in south-west Ireland (Kerry). They may have been the lagoons of coastal plains, with deltaic accumulations. Rivers brought down much sand and mud, especially during storms, when larger particles also would be washed into the areas of sedimentation. The deposits are subdivided into Lower, Middle, and Upper divisions. The Middle Old Red Sandstone is developed mainly in the Orkney area, where flagstones were once quarried from it in large numbers ; these rocks lie unconformably on Pre-Cambrian schists. The Lower and Upper Old Red Sandstones in Herefordshire are separated by an unconformity, and consist of red and green sandstones, conglomerates, and marls with concretionary limestones (" cornstones "). The marls are worked for tile-making and terra-cotta, and the sandstones are quarried for building stone. The predominant red colour of the sandstones is due to a coating of iron oxide on the component sand grains. That they are

---

[1] The Old Red is *older* than the Coal Measures of the Carboniferous ; another group of red rocks occurs *above* the Coal Measures and is called the New Red Sandstone.

fresh-water deposits is shown by their fossil fish remains, which are similar to other fresh-water forms, and by their extent and character.

In southern Ireland, a tract of folded Upper Old Red Sandstone (a thick series of conglomerates, lacustrine sandstones, and marls) extends from the coast of Kerry eastwards through Co. Cork into Waterford. In the west of Co. Cork these rocks grade laterally into the green coloured Glengarriff Grits, which pass upwards into rocks of Carboniferous age.

From the abundance of fossil fishes in the rocks the Old Red Sandstone has been called the " Age of Fishes " ; the earliest fish remains are found in the Ludlow Bone Bed (at base of the Downton Series, p. 209). Lower Old Red Sandstone fishes are primitive armour-plated forms without bony jaws ; other armoured forms, with jaws, occur in the Middle and Upper Old Red (Fig. 92, a and b). The fishes often occur in large numbers in restricted layers or bands in the sandstones, and serve as a basis for subdividing the deposits. Well preserved specimens have been obtained from the Middle Old Red of the Orkneys ; other good examples have been found at Ledbury (Fig. 89).

Igneous activity, which resulted in the intrusion of many of the Scottish granites (called the Newer Granites in distinction from the Older Granites of Pre-Cambrian age), was partly contemporaneous with the later phases of the Caledonian movements, and went on into Middle Old Red Sandstone times. The great granites of the Grampians include the Cairngorm mass, the Hill of Fare intrusion, the Lochnagar and Kincardineshire masses, and many smaller intrusions; the Galloway granites (namely the Dalbeattie-Criffel, Cairnsmore of Fleet, and Loch Doon masses) also came into position about the same time. They invaded the folded Ordovician and Silurian rocks, and a little later belts of shearing were developed in them. High-class structural stone is quarried in Galloway at Dalbeattie (see p. 109) and at Kirkmabreck near Creetown, where a dyke-like body of biotite-granite is intruded parallel to the strike of the country-rocks. In Lower Old Red Sandstone times andesitic lavas were erupted in the Cheviots, the Pentland Hills, the Ochil Hills, and the Ben Nevis area. The granites of Cheviot, Shap, and Ben Nevis, with their associated dykes, and the Moor of Rannoch granodiorite, were also intruded then. In the Cheviot area, andesite lavas are cut by porphyrite and microdiorite dykes with two trends, N.N.W. and nearly N.E. The central granite is later than all but a few of the dykes ; the sequence of igneous activity thus established is (1) lavas erupted, (2) intrusion of dykes, (3) plutonic phase.

The major intrusions of Ben Nevis consist of two granites (Fig. 91), the earlier forming an outer zone around the younger ; a nearly circular down-faulted block of andesite lavas resting on schists lies within the younger granite, which is thought to have welled up around a cylindrical fracture as this block subsided. The mechanism is called " cauldron subsidence " ; it was first described from Glen Coe,[1] where andesitic lavas within a ring fault are surrounded by the Cruachan granite.

---

[1] Clough, Maufe, and Bailey, *Q.J.G.S.*, **lxv, 1909**, p. 611. See also W. S. Pitcher, " The Rosses Ring-Complex, Donegal," *Proc. Geol. Assoc.*, **64**, 1953.

Confirmation of the structure of Ben Nevis, outlined above, was obtained when the fifteen-mile tunnel of the Lochaber Power Scheme was driven through the side of the mountain, to bring water from Loch Treig to the

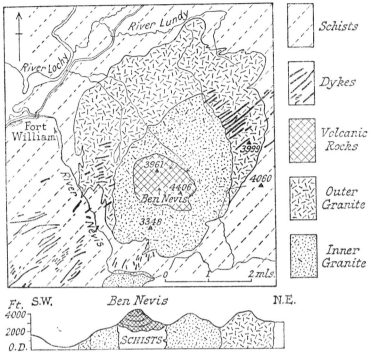

FIG. 91.—GEOLOGICAL MAP AND SECTION OF BEN NEVIS (after H. H. Read, H.M. Geol. Survey).

power house at Fort William. New geological evidence was also brought to light in the tunnel exposures, and the instance provides a good illustration of the way in which geological knowledge may benefit from information made available by engineering construction (see p. 314).

Carboniferous.

There are three divisions of the Carboniferous rocks in Britain :

3. Coal Measures (shales and sandstones with coal seams).
2. Millstone Grit (shallow water, estuarine sands).
1. Carboniferous Limestone (limestone and shales).

After the land period of Old Red Sandstone times, the sea invaded a large part of the British area, covering South Wales, Gloucestershire, Somerset and the south, the greater part of Ireland, Lancashire and Northumberland and the Midland Valley of Scotland. A large area in the Midlands and north of England was not submerged until later, and stood as an island in the early Carboniferous sea. Under these conditions, deposits of limestone were built up in clear and not very deep water, with corals and abundant marine life, deposition beginning in the south and gradually spreading to the north.

The Carboniferous Limestone is divided into zones by means of fossil corals ; their sequence was worked out by A. Vaughan for the rocks of the Avon Gorge, near Bristol, and this is the type succession. Here, and in South Wales and Somerset, the lowest beds are mainly shales, known as the Lower Limestone Shales, up to 550 feet thick ; they lie apparently conformably on the Upper Old Red Sandstone. Following the shales are massive limestones, which in places reach a thickness of over 4000 feet, and above them come shaley beds. Thicknesses vary greatly in different districts. Parts of the limestones are dolomitic, and chert bands are frequent ; other parts of the formation are composed largely of cemented limestone fragments. These fragments represent contemporaneous accumulations of broken-up limestone, resulting from local denudation, and the rock is then virtually a consolidated limestone-sand. Among the many fossils contained in the Carboniferous Limestone, typical corals are shown in Fig. 92; brachiopods are well represented and include *Productus* (Fig. 92d) and *Spirifer*. The rock is extensively quarried in Somerset, and crushed for aggregate.

In Denbighshire the Limestone forms a prominent escarpment near Llangollen, and lies unconformably on Older Palæozoic rocks. The mid-Devon syncline, a broad east–west structure (p. 211), is occupied by a series of shales and grits, with chert bands and black limestones in the lower part, collectively known as the *Culm*. The rocks are often sharply folded, as seen in coastal cliff sections.

The Peak District of Derbyshire is built of Carboniferous Limestone folded into a dome and flanked by the Millstone Grits (Fig. 93b). Intruded into it at various levels are sills of altered dolerite, the Derbyshire " toadstones " ; and lodes carrying lead, zinc, calcite and fluorite are present.

The Carboniferous Limestone of Ireland is a series of limestones and shales, with some dolomites and reef limestones ; in all it reaches a thickness of four or five thousand feet, and covers nearly two-thirds of the country. South of a line passing east and west through Cork Harbour the limestone gives place to a culm facies (referred to as the Carboniferous slate), which passes down into the Devonian (p. 212).

In the Pennine area the massive limestones are succeeded by a thick series of shallow-water sandstones, shales, and thin limestones, known as the Yoredale Series. These rocks are followed by the Millstone Grit Series (grits and sandstones with some shales), which are the shallow-water deposits of a delta, and represent an uplift of the sea floor in this area at the end of Carboniferous Limestone times. The beds outcrop over large areas of West Yorkshire, where they are over 1000 feet thick ; they become thinner both to the north and to the south.

The total thickness of the Carboniferous deposits in the Pennine area is estimated at 16,000 feet ; the Pennine uplift is partly due to faulting as well as to folding (Fig. 93a). Marked differences in lithology are seen in the rocks on either side of the Craven Fault system near Settle, Yorkshire ; this group of faults trends north-north-west and has a combined

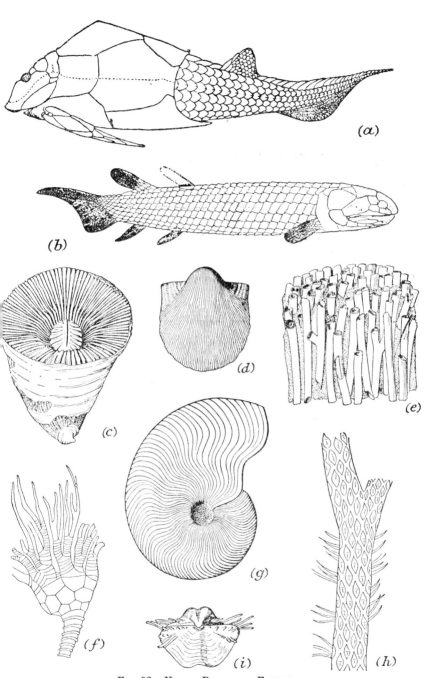

FIG. 92.—NEWER PALÆOZOIC FOSSILS.

Fishes: (a) *Pterichthys*, (b) *Thursius* (Old Red Sandstone; after Watson). Corals: (c) *Dibunophyllum* (Carb.), (e) *Lithostrotion* (Carb.), both × 1. Brachiopods: (d) *Productus* (Carb.), (i) *Productus horridus* (Perm.). (g) A goniatite (Carb.), × 2. Plant: (h) *Lepidodendron* (Coal Measures), × ⅔. (f) A crinoid (Carb.) (c, d, e, and g, after H.M. Geol. Survey. ᶠ and h after A. Morley Davies.)

downthrow of between two and three thousand feet to the west. The differences in the rocks here are probably due to movement on the faults occurring during deposition.

The deltaic conditions of the Millstone Grit gave place gradually to estuarine and swamp conditions, and the formation of the Coal Measures began. The swamps supported vegetation, which from time to time was submerged and covered with muds and sands. Dense forests flourished for a time in a sub-tropical climate, and were then buried by incoming sediment as a result of submergence. This happened many times, as submergence occurred intermittently. The layers of vegetation became compressed under the weight of overlying sediments and were thus preserved, to become ultimately the coal seams of the present day. Plant remains like *Sigillaria*

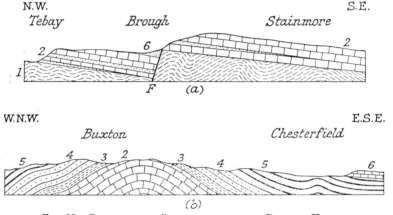

FIG. 93.—DIAGRAMMATIC SECTIONS ACROSS THE PENNINE UPLIFT.

(a) Northern Pennines (after D. A. Wray, H.M. Geol. Survey).   F = Dent Fault. (b) Southern Pennines, from the Lancashire Coalfield to the Yorkshire Coalfield. (1) Silurian and older rocks. (2) Carboniferous Limestone Series, with basement conglomerate dotted. (3) Yoredale Series. (4) Millstone Grit. (5) Coal Measures. (6) Permian.

and *Lepidodendron* (Fig. 92h) and many smaller plants are found in them, and insect life was abundant. The plants, during growth, extracted alkalies from the soil, and the resulting "seat earths" which lie beneath the coals have become seams of fire-clay and ganister, which are of economic value in the manufacture of refractories. Considerable thicknesses of shale and sandstone generally separate individual coal-seams; in South Wales there are about 8000 feet of Coal Measures, of which perhaps 2 per cent is coal. Many seams are very regular and extend over large areas; it is believed that they represent vegetation which grew *in situ*. In some places, however, there is evidence that *drifted* vegetation has accumulated, forming deposits of *cannel coal*, an impure coal with a high ash content (p. 141).

The main coalfields are those of South Wales, Flint and Denbigh, Staffordshire, Lancashire, Yorkshire, Northumberland and Durham, and the Midland Valley of Scotland; in these areas the Coal Measures have been comparatively gently folded into synclinal forms, and are generally broken by many faults. These structural features were impressed on the rocks by the Hercynian folding which came at the end of the Carboniferous period (below). Lower Coal Measures are also preserved in synclines near Carlow and Kilkenny in Southern Ireland. Correlations between important seams in the different coalfields have been worked out by means of fossils such as fresh-water lamellibranchs and goniatites (Fig. 92g).

While Coal Measures outcrop at the surface over large areas, the more important of which are indicated above, they also extend in places below a cover of younger rocks, for example, beneath the Permian rocks of Yorkshire and Durham, thus forming underground reserves of workable coal. The Kent coalfield is entirely concealed ; it is buried beneath a cover of Mesozoic sediments, and its existence was predicted from a study of the older rocks lying beneath the Cretaceous strata, revealed by deep borings in south-eastern England. Its extent is indicated on Fig. 97.

The Scottish Carboniferous rocks differ from the English sequence, the equivalent of the Carboniferous Limestone of the south being the Calciferous Sandstone Series ; coal-forming conditions were present in early Carboniferous time in Scotland (in contrast with the limestone deposits of England and Wales) and later deltaic beds were laid down. The Calciferous Sandstone Series is a group of calcareous sandstones, cement-stones, and marls, with an important oil-shale series towards the top, which outcrop in the Midland Valley of Scotland. Overlying the oil-shales is a group of limestones, and these are followed by the Scottish Millstone Grit and Coal Measures.

Among igneous rocks, lavas of Lower Carboniferous age occur around Glasgow, for example on the Campsie Fells, and the volcanic rocks of Arthur's Seat, Edinburgh, belong also to this period. Many dykes and sills of quartz-dolerite, the former having a general east–west direction, were intruded into the Lower Carboniferous rocks of the Midland Valley ; related intrusions which are found in the north of England include the Hett dyke of Durham, and the Whin Sill. The latter, a quartz-dolerite, is intrusive into the Yoredales of Northumberland and Cumberland, where its outcrop can be traced for some 175 miles ; its intrusion dates from the end of the Carboniferous period. These dolerites locally yield good road-metal.

Hercynian Movements. Towards the end of the Carboniferous period came the onset of the Hercynian mountain-building movements, which affected a large part of north-west Europe and folded the rocks in the south of Britain about east–west axes. Structures having this trend can be traced in Somerset, Devon, and Cornwall ; e.g. the anticlinal folds of the Mendips. Northward of the " front " of the Hercynian folds, structures having a north–south trend were also formed (perhaps a little earlier than the main folding), as in the Malvern uplift. The Coal Measures and underlying rocks were gently folded and the Pennine chain was elevated mainly by faulting. Lakes were formed on the west of the Pennines and in Devon, and a nearly land-locked sea lay to the east of the Pennines, and in these areas the Permian deposits were laid down. Late in the Hercynian orogeny, igneous activity developed and the granites of south-west England came into position, together with similar intrusions on the Continent (e.g. Brittany); these together are called the Hercynian granites.

Permian.

The Permian period was largely one of desert land conditions in the British area; the succession is as follows:

3. Magnesian Limestone (marine dolomitic limestone, with marls and beds of gypsum).

2. Shales (formerly termed the Marl Slate).

1. Lower Sandstones and Breccias (desert sands and scree).

The Lower Permian breccias and sandstones rest unconformably on the Carboniferous rocks and represent scree material and sands derived from the desert weathering of a land mass. On the west of the Pennines, in the Vale of Eden, breccias known as *brockram* contain fragments of Carboniferous Limestone in a red sandy matrix. The red Penrith Sandstone, also from this district, is a well-known building material; it contains wind-rounded quartz grains (see Fig. 43), which point to the existence of desert conditions during their accumulation. Conglomerates, breccias and sandstones of the same age are found in Devon, in the Exe valley and along the coast southwards, where they form striking red cliffs at Dawlish and Teignmouth.

On the east of the Pennines the Lower Permian rocks are only thinly developed, and are succeeded by the " Marl Slate," which is really a hard shale; this formation, although only 15 feet thick, persists over a considerable distance and is a well-marked horizon. It is followed by the Magnesian Limestone, a marine deposit with a greyish-white appearance, whose outcrop runs north from about Nottingham to the coast of Durham near the mouth of the Tyne. The limestone is about 150 feet thick near Nottingham and nearly 800 feet thick east of Durham; it contains a large proportion of dolomite and shows different lithological varieties, one horizon towards the top of the formation containing numerous large calcareous concretions (the " Cannon Ball Limestone " of Sunderland). Parts of the rock are quarried for building stone and for lime; associated with it are beds of gypsum and of rock-salt, as at Middlesbrough. Thin beds of marl lie above the Magnesian Limestone.

Fossils are scarce in the Permian rocks because the high salt content of the sea was unfavourable to marine life; among the few forms, *Productus horridus* (Fig. 92*i*) and *Spirifer* are characteristic brachiopods, and reptile and amphibian remains have been found.

In Scotland there are comparatively small areas of Permian rocks around Dumfries and Annan, whence the red desert sandstone, much used in Edinburgh buildings and elsewhere, is quarried at Locharbriggs and Corsehill. At Mauchline, Ayrshire, a similar building stone of Permian age is worked extensively at the Ballochmyle Quarries (Plate IXB); desert conditions when it was formed are indicated by the coarse dune-bedding and wind-rounded grains in the sandstone. Volcanic necks and sills in Fifeshire belong to the same age, since they cut through Carboniferous rocks.

The Permian is the last of the Palæozoic systems. Its rocks are dominantly red in colour (except the Magnesian Limestone) ; they can be grouped with the red Triassic rocks which lie above them and together are called the New Red Sandstone, or Permo-Trias. While this is a convenient arrangement for the Permian and Trias of Britain, it is usual in other countries to separate the two systems.

MESOZOIC

The Mesozoic rocks comprise three systems, the Triassic, the Jurassic, and the Cretaceous. There is a transition from the Permian strata to the Triassic where the succession is complete, but elsewhere the Trias lies unconformably on older rocks. Another transition, accompanied by a change of colour from red to dominantly grey and buff, occurs between the Triassic and the overlying Jurassic rocks. The Cretaceous beds overlap the Jurassic unconformably, except in the south of England.

Fossils in the Mesozoic include many varieties of lamellibranchs, gastropods, echinoids (sea urchins), and brachiopods, but there are no trilobites or graptolites. Ammonites (Fig. 96a) become specially important in the Jurassic, since they have a wide geographical range, yet certain forms are restricted vertically to a small thickness of strata ; they are chambered shells, coiled in a flat spiral, and originally floated and swam near the surface of the sea ; they belong to the same group (cephalopods) as the modern *Nautilus*. Enormous reptiles, now extinct, flourished in great numbers, together with primitive birds, so that the Mesozoic has come to be called the " Age of Reptiles." Remains of the earliest mammals also appear in these rocks.

Triassic.

There are two main divisions of the Trias in Britain, called the Bunter and Keuper series respectively ; on the continent a group of limestones, the Muschelkalk, lies between them, thus giving a three-fold arrangement to which the name " Trias " refers. The rocks form a large outcrop in the Midlands, with two branches lying on either side of the Pennines (see Fig. 94) and with a southward extension into Devon.

The Triassic deposits were probably accumulated in a large inland basin surrounded by high mountains, with an internal drainage system. The climate was mainly hot and arid, although sometimes tempered by moister and perhaps cooler conditions. The deposits consist of sandstones, pebble beds and marls, having a predominantly red colour, which is considered to be an indication of contemporary desert conditions. The red colour of the sandstones is produced by a thin film of iron oxide coating each of the constituent grains, and is probably connected with a general lack of vegetation at the time of deposition of the rocks. The deposits were partly windborne, partly laid down by torrents, and partly deposited under sheets of standing flood-water. In the latter part of the period shallow salt lakes came into existence, and in them masses of rock-salt were formed, together with gypsum and anhydrite in some places.

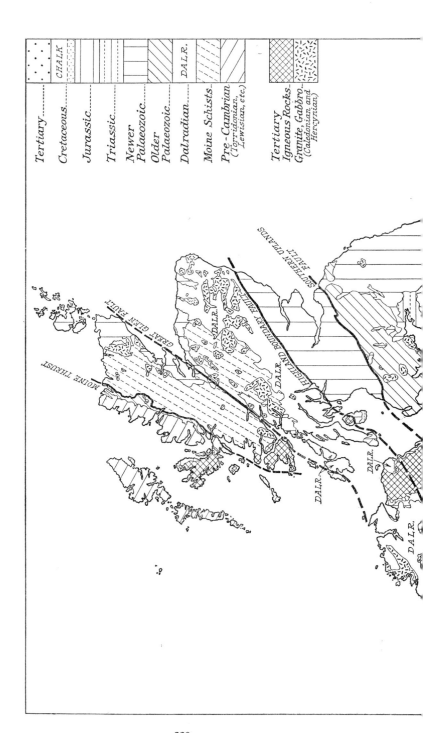

Tertiary

Cretaceous

CHALK

Jurassic

Triassic

Newer Palaeozoic

Older Palaeozoic

D.A.L.R.

Dalradian

Moine Schists

Pre-Cambrian
(*Torridonian.*
Lewisian, etc.)

Tertiary Igneous Rocks

Granite, Gabbro
(*Caledonian and Hercynian*)

MOINE THRUST

GREAT GLEN FAULT

HIGHLAND BOUNDARY FAULT

SOUTHERN UPLANDS FAULT

D.A.L.R.

D.A.L.R.

D.A.L.R.

D.A.L.R.

D.A.L.R.

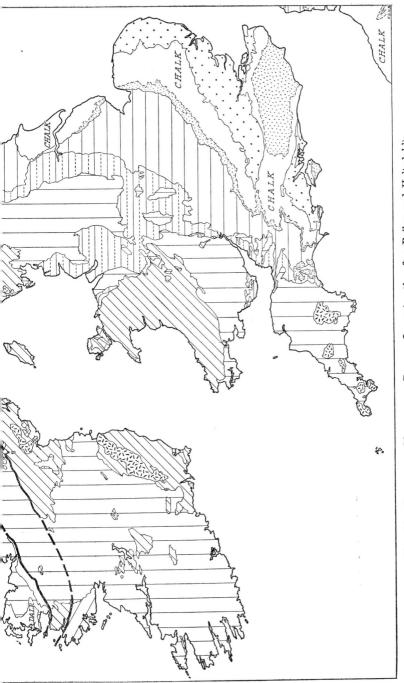

FIG. 94.—GEOLOGICAL MAP OF THE BRITISH ISLES (partly after Bailey and Holtedahl).
Scale approximately 80 miles to an inch.

The succession is as follows :

KEUPER
{
Rhætic (shales and thin limestones).
Keuper Marl.
Lower Keuper Sandstone.
}

BUNTER
{
Upper Mottled Sandstone.
Pebble Beds.
Lower Mottled Sandstone.
}

The Bunter sandstones are well developed in north Shropshire, Cheshire, and S.W. Lancashire, where they reach their maximum thickness of nearly 3000 feet ; they thin out generally to the south-east. They are very important water-bearing rocks in the Midlands (p. 275), and yield good building stone. The Lower Mottled Sandstones are bright red in colour, with yellow bands, and contain a large proportion of wind-rounded grains ; water passes through these rocks very freely. The Pebble Beds (Middle Bunter) are coarse sandstones with thick lenses of pebbles, and are variously coloured ; the pebbles, which were derived from the weathering of a land mass to the south, are often large and sometimes exceed nine inches in diameter. The overlying Upper Mottled Sandstones are softer than the Pebble Beds, and are red and yellow in colour with thin marl bands. The new Mersey Tunnel (p. 315) was driven in the upper part of the Middle Bunter Sandstones, which extend beneath the river from Liverpool to Birkenhead and contain few pebbles at that locality.

The Lower Keuper Sandstones which follow above the Bunter beds are red or buff in colour, mainly fine-grained and often current-bedded, with local breccias at their base and occasional bands of marl. The lower part of the formation is called the "Building Stone Group" and yields good building material, such as the freestone from Grinshill, Shropshire ; the upper part is known as the "Waterstones" (see p. 275). Water from the Keuper Sandstones is used by many industries, for example around Birmingham, and supplies numerous towns in the Midlands ; Birmingham itself drew its supply from this source until the Elan Valley scheme, bringing water from Central Wales, was inaugurated. Towards the top of the series the marl bands increase in number and the Keuper Sandstone passes upwards into the Keuper Marls, which reach a thickness of 2500 feet in Cheshire, but considerably less to the east and south. The marls are mainly red in colour, except towards the top, where a small thickness of "tea-green" marls appear below the beds of the Rhætic. Beds of gypsum and rock-salt, and occasional thin beds of sandstone, occur within the marls ; there is an important salt-field in Cheshire, the salt being pumped up as brine from wells sunk into a synclinal structure.

The Rhætic beds consist of a series of grey or black shales interbedded with thin limestones and sandstones, with a well-known bone-bed at one horizon. They are marine sediments, indicating that at the end of Keuper times the sea once more invaded and flooded the existing land area with its salt lakes ; the beds are a transitional series to the Jurassic rocks which succeed them (Fig. 95). The Rhætic, although not more than 40 to 60 feet thick, has a remarkably persistent outcrop from Devon and Dorset to the Yorkshire coast. Rhætic deposits at Holwell, Somerset, have yielded teeth of the earliest known British mammal.

Jurassic.

The outcrop of the Jurassic [1] strata of England extends from Bridport on the Dorset coast, through the Cotswolds, almost continuously to Whitby on the Yorkshire coast. Over a large part of the outcrop (including the Cotswolds) the beds strike generally north-east and south-west, with gentle dips to the south-east; but in Lincolnshire and Yorkshire the prevalent strike is north and south. The sediments were laid down in a shallow sea which covered a large part of Britain, and which was an enlargement of the Rhætic sea; towards the end of the period the sea withdrew to the south of England, and became at times land-locked, and in these waters the Purbeck beds (the last of the Jurassic deposits) were laid down.

The rocks of the Jurassic system may be broadly described as a series of alternating limestones and clays, with some sands. They form gentler scenery than the older rocks which lie to the west of them. The succession is divided into a lower and an upper group, called respectively the *Lias* and the *Oolites*.

The **Lias** (or Lower Jurassic) is composed of a great thickness of marine clays and shales, in which occur massive bands of limestone and ironstone; there is a three-fold subdivision into Lower, Middle, and Upper Lias, and the total thickness of these rocks exceeds 1000 feet in Gloucestershire, but thins rapidly to the south. Ammonites, lamellibranchs, and oysters are characteristic fossils (Fig. 96). The Lower Lias clays are grey in colour and are used for brickmaking, e.g. at Cheltenham. Near Rugby the lower part of these clays contains impure limestones (cement-stones) which have been extensively worked for the manufacture of cement. Limestones and important ironstones are found in the Middle Lias of Oxfordshire, Leicestershire, Lincolnshire, and Yorkshire (the Cleveland district). These ores are worked in shallow opencasts; the iron occurs as the hydrated silicate,

[1] Named from the Jura mountains, north-west of the Alps.

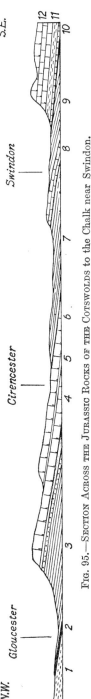

FIG. 95.—SECTION ACROSS THE JURASSIC ROCKS OF THE COTSWOLDS TO THE CHALK NEAR SWINDON. 1, Keuper. 2, Rhætic. 3, Lias. 4, Inferior Oolite. 5, Fuller's Earth. 6, Great Oolite. 7, Oxford Clay. 8, Corallian. 9, Kimmeridge Clay. 10, Lower Greensand. 11, Gault. 12, Chalk. Length of section about 23 miles.

chamosite, and as siderite. The Cleveland iron-ore has an oolitic texture, and may have been formed by the replacement of calcium carbonate by siderite in an original limestone, though some authorities think that the iron carbonate is an original constituent. The Upper Lias is mainly clay with some limestone bands; at Whitby these beds contain bands of *jet,* a hard, black, resinous variety of lignite, formerly fashionable for ornaments.

Small areas of Lias, comprising sandstones with iron ores, are found on the islands of Raasay and Skye.

The **Oolites** (or Upper Jurassic) have numerous subdivisions, many of which yield important economic products:

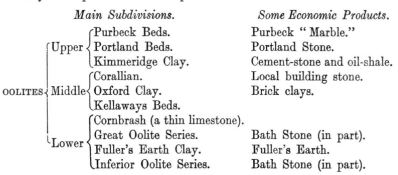

		Main Subdivisions.	*Some Economic Products.*
		Purbeck Beds.	Purbeck " Marble."
	Upper	Portland Beds.	Portland Stone.
		Kimmeridge Clay.	Cement-stone and oil-shale.
		Corallian.	Local building stone.
OOLITES	Middle	Oxford Clay.	Brick clays.
		Kellaways Beds.	
		Cornbrash (a thin limestone).	
	Lower	Great Oolite Series.	Bath Stone (in part).
		Fuller's Earth Clay.	Fuller's Earth.
		Inferior Oolite Series.	Bath Stone (in part).

The Lower Oolites are chiefly oolitic limestones with a few intervening beds of clay; they are about 500 feet thick in Gloucestershire and form the main escarpment of the Cotswolds (Fig. 95). The " freestone " of the Inferior Oolite and the middle beds of the Great Oolite yield first-class building material which is worked in many quarries around Bath, Cheltenham, and other centres. In Northamptonshire the Inferior Oolite is estuarine in character and contains sands and important ironstone (chamositic) deposits. The ore, e.g. at Corby, Northamptonshire, contains over 30 per cent of iron, together with enough silica and phosphorus to give a fluid melt which is specially suitable for the manufacture of iron pipes.

The Great Oolite Series begins with a thinly-bedded sandy limestone at its base, known as the Stonesfield Slate, which provides the picturesque roofing material for many Cotswold houses. Then follow the massive oolites which furnish the building stone (Bath Stone) already mentioned; these are overlain by the Forest Marble, a group of thin limestones and shales. The Cornbrash is another thin limestone used locally for walls and buildings.

The nature of the Lower Oolites gradually changes and beds thin out (others taking their place) as they are traced northwards. Most of the Jurassic formations vary considerably in thickness in different districts.

The Middle Oolites division is well developed from Oxfordshire to Lincolnshire. Its most important member, the Oxford Clay, is a greenish-grey deposit some 400 feet thick in the district from which it takes its name; it forms rich pasture land and is much worked for brickmaking, as at Fletton, Peterborough, and near Bedford. Ammonites, belemnites, and fish and reptile remains are among the fossils found in the Oxford Clay. At its base are beds of shelly sandstone and loam, known as the Kellaways Beds (from Kellaways, Wiltshire). The Corallian formation which overlies the Oxford Clay consists of oolitic limestones, marls, and calcareous sandstones (called " grits "), and extends from near Weymouth to beyond Oxford; near Bedford its character changes and it passes into the Ampthill Clay—a good example of lateral variation in a deposit.

The Upper Oolites division begins with the Kimmeridge Clay (named after Kimmeridge in Dorset), a dark grey bituminous clay containing bands of cement-stone. This is followed by the Portland Beds, a series of fossiliferous oolitic limestones and sands with occasional clays, which have a thickness of about 225 feet in Dorset. High-grade, cream-coloured building-stone is obtained from the Portland quarries at several levels in the series; on account of its uniform texture and good appearance and weathering properties it is a very popular structural material and is much used in London buildings and elsewhere. When these beds were deposited, the Jurassic sea had contracted to a comparatively small size in the south of England, and by Purbeck times had become land-locked. In this lake were laid down the shelly limestones and clays of the Purbeck Series, the uppermost beds of the Jurassic system. One of the limestones, known as the Purbeck Marble, contains many shells of the fresh-water gastropod *Paludina* (Fig. 96*j*), and was formerly much quarried in the Isle of Purbeck for use as a decorative stone. The Purbeck " dirt-bed," with its plant and tree remains, indicates a temporary land surface. Along the Dorset coast the Portland and Purbeck Beds are folded, together with the overlying Cretaceous strata, about east–west axes, and on this account have a steep seaward dip in many places; coves have been eroded, as at Lulworth, in the softer Wealden and Purbeck Beds after the harder Portland limestones had been broken through by the sea.

An exploratory boring for oil, which went to a depth of 6556 feet, was made in 1937 on the crest of the Portsdown anticline, near Portsmouth, and passed through a thickness of 4305 feet of Jurassic rocks below the Cretaceous; no oil was found, but the thickness of the Jurassic encountered was greater than was expected and yielded useful information.[1]

Cretaceous.

The Purbeck Beds at the top of the Jurassic pass upwards without break into the lowest Cretaceous deposits, laid down in a large lake, the site of which extended over the present Weald of Sussex and Kent, and over part of the English Channel. It is known as the Wealden lake; the open sea lay farther to the south-east. Into this lake sediments were brought by rivers from the west and north, and these deposits now form the Wealden Series of sands and clays, the earliest beds of the Cretaceous system. Marine sediments were being deposited contemporaneously in France and Germany. Around the shores of the Wealden lake there lived large numbers of great

[1] G. M. Lees and P. T. Cox, *Q.J.G.S.*, Vol. xciii, 1937.

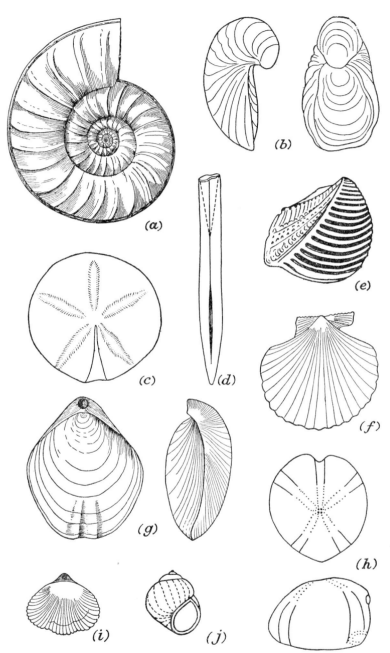

Fig. 96.—Mesozoic Fossils.

Ammonite: (a) *Asteroceras* (Jur.). Brachiopods: (g) *Terebratula* (Chalk), (i) *Rhyn-chonella* (Jur.). Lamellibranchs: (b) *Gryphaea* (Jur.), (e) *Trigonia* (Jur.), (f) *Pecten* (Jur.). Sea-urchins: (c) *Clypeus* (Jur.), (h) *Micraster* (Chalk). (d) A belemnite (Cret.). (j) Gastropod: *Paludina* (L. Cret.). All × ½ except (a), which is × ⅜ (after A. Morley **Davies**).

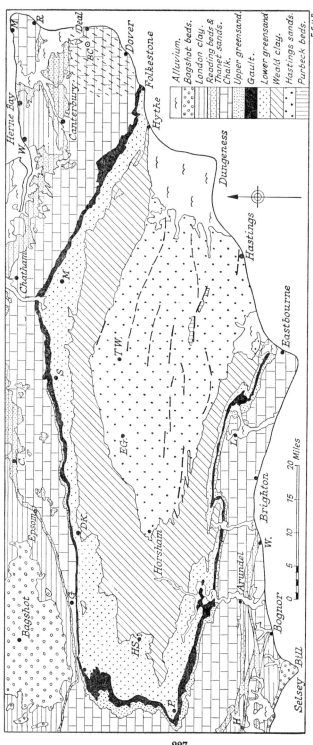

Alluvium.
Bagshot beds.
London clay.
Reading beds &
Thanet sands.
Chalk.
Upper greensand.
Gault.
Lower greensand.
Weald clay.
Hastings sands.
Purbeck beds.

FIG. 97.—GEOLOGICAL MAP OF THE WEALDEN AREA, SOUTH-EAST ENGLAND.

Heavy broken lines are faults. Diagonal shading on the Chalk in E. Kent indicates approximate extent of the concealed Kent Coalfield;
BC = Betteshanger Colliery. Croydon, C; Dorking, DK; East Grinstead, EG; Farnham, F; Guildford, G; Havant, H; Haslemere, HS;
Lewes, L; Maidstone, M; Petersfield, P; Ramsgate, R; Tunbridge Wells, TW; Whitstable, W; Worthing, W.

227

reptiles, such as the dinosaurs and iguanodons, as is evidenced by their remains found in the deposits ; they were soon to become extinct. Subsidence
recommenced while the Upper Wealden beds were being laid down ; gradually the Wealden lake became again an estuary and the sea advanced
farther and farther west and north. Successive layers of sediment were
thus deposited over a widening area in the Cretaceous sea, and the later
beds extend beyond those that lie below them and overlap in places on
to Jurassic rocks (Fig. 95). This is an example of unconformity with overlap, produced by the marine transgression. At its greatest extent, in
Upper Cretaceous times, the sea extended over part of Scotland and across
England into Devon. The following are the divisions of the Cretaceous
system :

$$
\left.
\begin{array}{l}
\text{Upper} \left\{
\begin{array}{l}
\text{Chalk (fine-grained marine limestone).} \\
\text{Upper Greensand (marine sands).} \\
\text{Gault (marine clay).}
\end{array}
\right. \\
\text{Lower} \left\{
\begin{array}{l}
\text{Lower Greensand (marine sands and clays).} \\
\text{Wealden} \left\{
\begin{array}{l}
\text{Weald Clay (estuarine).} \\
\text{Hastings Sands (freshwater).}
\end{array}
\right.
\end{array}
\right.
\end{array}
\right.
$$

The chief British area for Lower Cretaceous rocks is the Weald of Kent
and Sussex ; here, deposition was continuous from Upper Jurassic times
onwards, but other areas show a break in the succession of deposits. The
rocks of south-east England are folded into the broad Wealden anticline
(see Figs. 97 and 98), so that the oldest beds of the Cretaceous, the Hastings
Sands, are exposed in the centre of this region ; their outcrop extends to
the coast at Hastings. The folding took place in early Tertiary times,
when the Alpine folds on the continent of Europe were being elevated.
North-west of Battle, Sussex, there are small inliers of Purbeck Beds,
representing the Jurassic core of the Wealden fold.

Around the outcrop of the Hastings Sands lies a tract of low land
formed by the Weald Clay, which is much used for brickmaking and contains thin beds of sandstone, such as the ripple-marked Horsham stone.
Around this again extends the outcrop of the Lower Greensand, which
comprises a variable series of sands and clays, in places 500 feet thick but
thinning out to the north under London. The name " greensand " is due
to the content (often small) of green grains of glauconite in the sands.
Overlying the Lower Greensand is the Gault, a thick clay deposit containing many fossils and worked for brickmaking (as at Dunton Green,
Sevenoaks, Kent), followed by the Upper Greensand. The latter is in
places a calcareous sandstone about 200 feet thick, but is impersistent and
thins out to the east and under London. Finally the thick Chalk formation
completes the succession, and its ridges form the North and South Downs,
encircling the Weald on three sides.[1]

The outcrop of the Chalk is in all some 600 miles long, extending from
Dorset and east Devon through Salisbury Plain and the Chiltern Hills into

[1] For a fuller description of the geology of the Weald see " The Wealden District,"
British Regional Geology (list on p. 238).

East Anglia and the Lincolnshire and Yorkshire Wolds, with branches forming the Downs of Surrey, Kent, and Sussex. The outcrop is 15 to 20 miles wide in the Chilterns and 5 to 7 miles wide in the Downs and Wolds. It narrows to less than a mile at the Hogs Back, near Guildford, where the beds dip steeply to the north (Fig. 67). The Gault, which everywhere underlies the Chalk, has an outcrop broadly parallel to that of the Chalk. If the latter is thought of as a thick layer folded about the anticlinal axis of the Weald and the synclinal axis of the London Basin (Fig. 98), the shape of its outcrop is readily understood. Another nearly east–west synclinal fold in the Chalk forms the Hampshire Basin, filled with Tertiary sediments (Fig. 94); the southern limb of this syncline dips steeply, and in the Isle of Wight and Dorset is sometimes vertical, and even overturned. The Chalk reaches its maximum thickness of about 1500 feet in the Isle of Wight, but is less than half that amount in Berkshire; the difference is largely due to the great thickness of Upper Chalk present in the Isle of Wight.

As a rock, the Chalk is a soft marine limestone, largely made up of minute particles of crystalline calcium carbonate, formerly thought to be chemically precipitated but now recognized as parts of the external skeletons (coccospheres) of calcareous algae. In addition the Chalk contains the remains of foraminifera such as *Globigerina* (small floating organisms, p. 36); and fossil shells of brachiopods, e.g. *Terebratula* (Fig. 96*g*), lamellibranchs, and sea-urchins (e.g. *Micraster*, Fig. 96*h*). It is an organic limestone, laid down in warm, moderately deep water on the continental shelf of the time, well away from the shore-line.

At the base of the Chalk there is the *chalk marl*, which is used extensively in the manufacture of Portland Cement. This rock (or a mixture of purer chalk and river

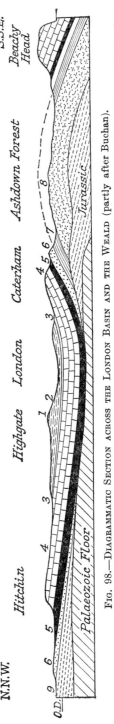

FIG. 98.—DIAGRAMMATIC SECTION ACROSS THE LONDON BASIN AND THE WEALD (partly after Buchan).

Showing the Palaeozoic floor beneath London. Length of section approximately 100 miles; vertical scale exaggerated about 20 times. (1) Bagshot Sands. (2) London Clay. (3) Woolwich and Reading Beds and Thanet Sand. (4) Chalk. (5) Gault and Upper Greensand (the latter is not continuous under London). (6) Lower Greensand. (7) Weald Clay. (8) Hastings Sands. (9) Jurassic rocks.

mud) is ground and dried, heated in a kiln until fusion begins, and then re-ground to a powder which has the property of setting hard on the addition of water. Two hard bands, called the Melbourne Rock and the Chalk Rock, each a few feet thick (Fig. 107), occur at the base of the Middle and Upper Chalk respectively; they contain shallow water fossils and represent slow deposition in shallower conditions which were temporarily present. Many flints are found in the Upper Chalk, fewer in the Middle Chalk, and none in the Lower Chalk. The flints may form layers along bedding planes or fill joints as irregular masses, and have grown in place as concretions; they represent solidified silica gel which, according to one theory, was deposited from solutions descending through the Chalk, the silica having been derived from the skeletons of sponges and radiolaria (siliceous organisms, p. 139) which were sparsely distributed through the mass of sediment. The Upper Chalk is a very important source of underground water in south-east England (see p. 276).

TERTIARY

At the end of the Cretaceous period there followed a shallowing of the sea in which the Chalk had been deposited, and parts of the floor were lifted above sea-level and denuded. Hence the Tertiary beds lie on an eroded surface; they are largely unconsolidated sands and clays. Flints contained in the eroded Chalk were broken and rounded into pebbles, which are found in the lower Eocene beds.

The Tertiary is notable for the appearance of mammals in great numbers, and of grasses and flowering plants; in the seas, too, which were warm at first, there was abundant life including many species of molluscs.[2] The great reptiles of the Mesozoic had become extinct. The subdivisions of the Tertiary were originally named according to the proportion of fossils in the rocks similar to modern forms, thus:

Pliocene	more	
Miocene	less	of recent[2] (forms)
Oligocene	few	
Eocene	dawn	

Orogenic movements, which formed the fold-mountains of the Alps, Pyrenees, Carpathians, Himalayas, and the Cordillera of North America began early in Eocene time and reached their climax in the Miocene. The sediments of an east–west trough (*Tethys*), which during the Mesozoic lay broadly in the region of the present Mediterranean, were folded to form the Alpine ranges (p. 193). The " outer ripples " of this orogeny are seen in the south of England in the folds of the London Basin, the Weald, and the Isle of Wight. There are no Miocene deposits in Britain, owing to the elevation of the area above the sea during that time, when the Alpine orogeny was at its maximum. During the Pliocene the climate gradually became colder, leading up to the glaciation of the Pleistocene.

[1] A mollusc is a soft-bodied animal protected by a hard shell or shells.
[2] Greek *kainos* = recent; used here as the termination " cene."

Eocene.

The sands and clays which occupy the two synclinal areas known as the London and Hampshire Basins (p. 229) are of this age. The London Basin begins near Marlborough in the west and opens out eastwards, as a plunging syncline ; the sequence of beds within it and their approximate thicknesses near London are as follows :

		Thickness.
Upper Eocene.	Bagshot Sands.	300 ft. (at Bagshot).
Lower Eocene {	London Clay.	up to 430 ft.
	Woolwich and Reading Beds.	about 50 ft.
	Thanet Sand.	up to 80 ft.

Between the London Clay and the Bagshot Sands there are transition beds alternating layers of sand and clay, which are often referred to as the Claygate Beds. In the Hampshire area the Bagshot Sands are thicker (about 1200 feet) and are subdivided into Lower Bagshot Sands, Bracklesham Beds, and Barton Beds.

The *Thanet Sands* are yellow marine sands containing few fossils, and with a layer of water-worn flints at their base, where they rest on an erosion

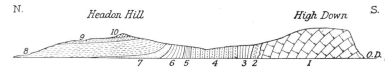

FIG. 99.—DIAGRAMMATIC SECTION ACROSS THE ISLE OF WIGHT, near Alum Bay.
(1) Chalk. (2) Woolwich and Reading Beds. (3) London Clay. (4) Lower Bagshot Sands and Clays. (5) Bracklesham Beds (clays with gypsum). (6) Barton Clays. (7) Upper Bagshot Sands. (8) Headon Beds. (9) Osborne and Bembridge Beds. (10) Plateau Gravel. Length of Section about 1¼ miles (after Bristow).

turface in the Chalk. The lower part contains some glauconite, and enough clay to make it useful as a moulding sand. The overlying *Woolwich and Reading Beds* are freshwater in character near Reading but become estuarine farther east. They are clays and sands which contain fossiliferous bands and pebble beds ; they are followed by the Blackheath Pebble Beds and the marine London Clay in the eastern part of the London Basin. The Thanet Sands mark the incoming of the Eocene sea, and the change from marine to estuarine conditions (Woolwich Beds) is interpreted as the retreat of the sea ; the whole sequence forms a sedimentary cycle. The succeeding Blackheath Pebble Beds and marine London Clay mark a second incursion of the sea. The *London Clay* is a blue or grey clay, weathering brown, approaching a true loam in parts (i.e. it contains a proportion of fine sand, see Fig. 42) ; it has fossils which resemble modern warm-water forms, and bands of calcareous concretions known as *septarian nodules*. Its full thickness is developed in the London area at Wimbledon Common and Hampstead Heath, where it is overlain by Bagshot Sands, and its existence under London has made possible the construction of the tube railways. The

London Clay and other Eocene clays supply much raw material for brick and tile manufacture.

The *Bagshot Sands* of the London Basin occur only to the west and south-west of London (apart from the two localities mentioned above), but are more thickly developed in the Hampshire Basin, where the different divisions, which include the Bracklesham Beds and Barton Clays, together reach a thickness of over 1200 feet. In the Isle of Wight an excellent coast section of the Tertiary strata and the Chalk is seen at Alum Bay,

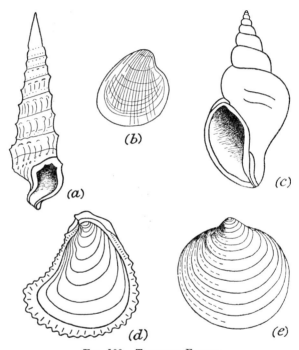

FIG. 100.—TERTIARY FOSSILS.

Gastropods: (*a*) *Cerithium* (Eoc.), (*c*) *Neptunea* (Plio.). Lamellibranchs: (*b*) *Cardita* (Eoc.), (*d*) *Ostrea* (an oyster) (Eoc.), (*e*) *Pectunculus* (Eoc.). All × ½. (After A. Morley Davies.)

where the beds are vertical and form part of the steep limb of the anticlinal fold which runs east and west across the island (Fig. 99).

While the Eocene deposits of south-east England were being formed, igneous activity was taking place in Scotland and farther afield. Volcanoes erupted in Mull, Skye, and Arran, and in Northern Ireland, where the great lava flows of Antrim were poured out. Similar basic lavas were erupted in Greenland, Iceland, and the Faroes—areas which are now separated but may once have formed parts of a great lava-field, perhaps a million square miles in extent. At various centres in the west of Scotland and Northern Ireland, igneous intrusions were emplaced, giving rise to the great ring dykes of Ardnamurchan and Mull, the plutonic rocks of Skye and other islands of the Hebrides, and the granites of Mourne and Carlingford. The Tertiary dyke-swarms associated with these areas came into existence : fractures which had been opened by the operation of crustal stresses were filled by rising basic magma.

Oligocene.

In the Hampshire Basin a series of estuarine marls, sands, and shelly limestones follow the Eocene beds in normal sequence. They are best seen in the Isle of Wight and are named after localities there ; they are, in ascending order, (1) Headon Beds, (2) Osborne Beds, (3) Bembridge Beds, (4) Hamstead Beds. Their combined thickness reaches 500 to 600 feet. They contain fossil plants of subtropical varieties, fossil shells (gastropods and lamellibranchs), and the remains of mammals. A bed of calcareous mudstone containing insect-remains is found near the base of the Bembridge marls in the Isle of Wight.

An outlier of sands and clays with bands of lignite occurs at Bovey Tracey, Devon, and is probably of Oligocene age ; the clays are used extensively in the manufacture of pottery, pipes, and sanitary ware. The Bovey deposits occupy a deep basin, 10 miles in length from south-east to north-west, which is probably aligned along the course of a fault.[1] A boring 652 feet deep at Heathfield failed to reach the base of the deposits.

Pliocene.

The beds of this system are found almost entirely in East Anglia, and comprise a series of unconsolidated shelly deposits called " crags," some of which contain gravels. They are shore deposits, and the sequence in ascending order is : (1) Coralline Crag, (2) Red Crag, (3) Norwich and later Crags, (4) Cromer Forest-bed. The last is a 20-foot bed of fresh-water clay and lignite, containing driftwood and the bones and teeth of mammals. The crags have a total thickness of 200 to 300 feet, of which the Norwich Crag forms more than half. Fossils indicate a gradual change throughout the series from warm water to arctic conditions—the beginning of the intense cold of the Glacial Epoch. The crags provide lime for agriculture, and phosphatic nodules in the Red Crag were formerly worked for phosphate.

QUATERNARY

Pleistocene.

Overlying the Pliocene in the east of England, and spread over older rocks elsewhere, are the boulder clays, sands, and gravels known collectively as *glacial drift*. The nature of these deposits has been discussed in Chapter 1, and it remains here to indicate something of their distribution. With the very cold climate which spread south over Britain and northern Europe during the Great Ice Age of Pleistocene times, ice accumulated in the mountain areas of Scotland and glaciers moved out over the lower ground and into the North Sea and Irish Sea.[2] Ireland also was covered by ice largely of local origin. Local glaciers formed on high ground in England,

---

[1] The fault can be traced further to the north-west through the Dartmoor granite. (F. G. H. Blyth, " The Lustleigh Fault," in *Geol. Mag.*, 94, 1957. p. 291.)

[2] North America and other lands were also undergoing glaciation at this time.

such as the Lake District and the Pennines, and in North Wales ; the ice eventually spread about as far south as London (Fig. 101). Under the ice-sheets were formed the boulder clays which cover a large part of northern, central, and eastern England, and the Midland Valley of Scotland. The Drift edition of the 1-inch maps of the Geological Survey (see page 241) shows the great extent of the drift over these areas.

Fig. 101.—Extent of Glaciation in the British Isles and Lines of Ice-flow (after Wills). Unglaciated areas are shown stippled.

Early in the glaciation of the country Scandinavian ice came across the North Sea, bringing boulders of distinctive rocks such as laurvikite and rhomb-porphyry, which are now found on the eastern coasts of England ; local ice was deflected by that from Scandinavia. Thus, the ice moving eastwards across Fife (see below) was turned northwards, some of it passing over the Orkneys and leaving there erratics and striæ which today are evidence of its former presence (see Fig. 101). On the coasts of Durham, patches of boulder clay containing characteristic Norwegian erratics and broken sea shells from the bed of the North Sea have been rammed into fissures in the Magnesian Limestone cliffs and there preserved from denudation.

The Midland Valley of Scotland is largely covered by stiff boulder clay, the thickness of which reaches 150 feet in places. Glaciers moving south off the Highlands and north from the Southern Uplands together travelled eastwards across this area, except for that part of it south-west of the River Clyde. Three distinct phases of glaciation have been distinguished here, represented by three types of boulder clay which succeed one another; these clays indicate advances of the ice, and are separated by sandy and peaty deposits which point to milder, " interglacial " periods when the ice was temporarily being melted. In Kincardineshire a black boulder clay containing marine shells is followed by a red clay, which derived its colour from the rocks of the Lower Old Red Sandstone, and this again by a grey boulder clay. Some of the glacial sands and gravels form kames and eskers, which have already been mentioned (p. 40) ; those representing the final retreat of the ice are the best preserved.

In northern England, boulder clay covers much of Northumberland and Durham ; the purple boulder clay of Hessle in south Yorkshire is a distinctive deposit. West of the Pennines, three glacial episodes can in places be recognized, corresponding to advances of the ice-front, with intervals of retreat when water from the melting ice deposited sands, gravels, and laminated clays. In the first advance, ice from the south-west of Scotland brought boulders of Criffel granite into the Vale of Eden and deflected the Lake District ice. The second or main glaciation saw the Scottish and local ice-sheets moving southward together, and northern ice also moving down the north-east coast of England. A less powerful re-advance of the Scottish ice later modified the relics left by its predecessors.

The drifts of the southern Midlands, a region lying to the south of the Pennines, record a complicated sequence of events, not yet completely unravelled. This area was invaded both by ice from the Welsh mountains and the Irish Sea basin to the north-west, and by ice moving south-west from east Yorkshire and the North Sea, approximately along the line of the Cretaceous outcrop. These glaciers left deposits known as the Western and Eastern Drifts respectively. The Western Drifts of the Cheshire plain, which extend as far as Birmingham and to Worcester in the south, contain much material derived from Triassic rocks, and also erratics from Scotland and the Lake District which travelled down over the Irish Sea. The Eastern Drifts include blue boulder clays containing fragments of Chalk and Jurassic rocks, with an admixture of Triassic material where outcrops of those rocks were crossed. Associated with these clays are a variety of water-laid deposits marking retreat stages of the glaciers.

In eastern England, which was invaded by ice from the North Sea and from Scandinavia, four glacial stages are thought to be represented, with interglacial periods between them. A lower boulder clay, called the Norwich Brick-earth (possibly formed by an ice-sheet melting out in water), is followed by sands and gravels which rest upon it. These indicate a milder interval, and they are succeeded by the Chalky-Jurassic Boulder Clay which, as its name implies, contains ground-up Chalk and Jurassic fragments derived from the rocks over which the ice moved. This deposit, with which glacial gravels and sands are associated, is separated by some geologists from the great Chalky Boulder Clay ; the latter is spread over large areas of Norfolk and Suffolk and parts of adjoining counties to the west. Overlying the Chalky Boulder Clay are gravels, brick-earths, and river alluvium, and finally a fourth clay, the reddish-brown boulder clay of Hunstanton.[1]

Changes in the surface drainage were produced by the glaciation, a striking example being the diversion of the River Severn into its present course below Shrewsbury. The Severn in its upper reaches flows northeastwards from the Welsh hills, and the river formerly drained north into the Irish Sea, joining the Dee on its way. But during the retreat of the Irish Sea ice which covered the Cheshire plain, melt-water was impounded between the ice-front and the high ground to the east and south, forming a glacial lake (Lake Lapworth) whose outlet was by a col at Ironbridge, where a gorge was cut by the overflow. After the ice had disappeared, the Severn was prevented by accumulations of drift from following its pre-glacial course, and became established in its present channel through the Ironbridge Gorge.

The south of England formed an area of unglaciated but frozen country, and the dry valleys or *coombes* in the Chalk downs of the south were cut by melt-water from winter snows, when the glacial conditions began to ameliorate. The frozen ground did not allow the melt-waters to percolate downwards, and they flowed over the surface, cutting the steep-sided coombes which are now a characteristic feature of the Chalk, as in the South Downs and in the Chiltern Hills near Ivinghoe.

The full sequence of events represented by the Pleistocene deposits of Britain still remains to be established ; the broad outline, however, is known, and can be compared with similar events on the continent of Europe.

Banded glacial clays known as varves (p. 41) were investigated by the Swedish geologist Baron de Geer, who, by counting the seasonal layers and correlating them from place to place, arrived at an estimate of the time taken for their deposition. In one engineering excavation, at Lake Ragunda, de Geer found a thickness of 24 metres of undisturbed varves lying above a deposit of moraine. From the number of laminæ he estimated that 7000 years had elapsed since the ice margin retreated past this region ; this, together with other counts near by, showed that a total of 9000 years have passed since Stockholm became free from ice. The method has also been applied to Scottish varves and to others in North America.

It has been explained in Chapter 1 that in excavating through drift nothing should be taken for granted, either as to its thickness or its manner of variation. Boulder clay frequently fills hollows and old river valleys in the pre-glacial topography, which bears no relation to the present surface. Thus, buried channels have been proved by borings to exist beneath the drift in the valleys of the rivers Clyde, Forth, and Tyne, and elsewhere ; the old course of the Mersey, now a drift-filled hollow, was explored by borings during the construction of the new Mersey Tunnel (see Chapter 15).

The pre-Glacial River Devon in Scotland, a tributary of the Forth,

[1] See West, R. G. and J. J. Donner, *Quart. Jour. Geol. Soc.*, 112, 1956, p. 69.

flowed in a valley which is now filled with late-Glacial clays and overlying post-Glacial sands and silts.[1] A few miles east of Stirling, borings through the buried valley to underlying Coal Measures proved the valley floor to a depth of 350 feet at one point ; a geophysical survey showed its extent.

Recent.

Recent deposits overlying the glacial drift are mainly alluvium and gravels laid down by rivers, together with blown sand, peat, and spring deposits. These have been formed since the ice retreated north from Britain about 10,000 years ago, as the climate ameliorated ; in places they contain the relics of early man, such as flint weapons, arrow-heads, spear-heads, knives, and scrapers. With the melting of the ice-sheets great quantities of water were released, and sea-levels rose everywhere. Isostatic compensation also began to take effect, as the ice load was removed, re-elevating the land which had been depressed (p. 167). In Scotland the rise was greater than in the south, and is marked by the 100-foot platform

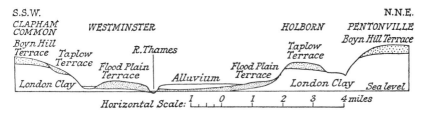

FIG. 102.—SECTION ACROSS THE LOWER THAMES VALLEY. Gravels shown stippled.

(Fig. 49, p. 158). The amount of the isostatic uplift was partly masked by the world-wide rise in sea level (*eustatic* change) due to melting of the ice, and the 100-foot platform (and other raised beaches) represent the difference between these two effects. At the maximum glaciation sea level was probably 300 feet lower than at present. It is believed to be still rising, at 1 to 2 mm. per year, because of melting ice-caps and glaciers at the present time (and see p. 160).

Alluvial deposits along the courses of rivers consist of sand, silt, and clay, with occasional seams of gravel, and in places attain a thickness of 20 to 30 feet. Some of the old gravel terrace deposits of the River Thames are shown in Fig. 102. Accumulations of blown sand occur at many localities around the coasts, as in East Anglia and Kent. The spits, bars, and other coastal accumulations have gradually been formed.

The fens of Cambridgeshire and adjoining counties are a flat expanse of silt and clay, with beds of peat at certain levels. The area was once a bay or estuary, of which the Wash is now a remnant, formed by the submergence of a broad valley which was hollowed out in soft Jurassic clays. This bay became silted up, mainly by material brought in by the sea, and layers of peat grew at times especially near the landward margin. The fen deposits are called *warp* (sandy silt), and *buttery clay* when smooth

[1] See Parthasarathy, A., and F. G. H. Blyth, *Proc. Geol. Assoc.*, 70, 1959, p. 33.

and clayey. They have accumulated as the sea level has slowly risen since Pleistocene times, with several oscillations of level. Slight emergence of the area resulted in an extension of the peat seawards. Submergence caused silts and clays to be deposited over the peat as the sea advanced. The deposits reach a thickness of about 60 feet, and rest on boulder clay. Much of the low-lying fenland is now protected from the sea by artificial embankments. The surface shrinkage of peat areas has already been discussed in connection with the fenland drainage (p. 21).

The pollens of former plants and trees are well preserved in the peats, and the results of pollen analysis [1] have made it possible to construct a picture of the changes in vegetation, and hence in climate, during the post-Glacial period. From such data, together with geological sections and archæological evidence, the history of this part of the North Sea area during the last 10,000 years has been worked out.

SELECTED REFERENCE LITERATURE

British Regional Geology, a series of small volumes published by H.M. Geological Survey, and comprising :

" Scotland : Northern Highlands." 3rd edition, 1960.
" The Grampian Highlands." 2nd edition, 1948.
" The Tertiary Volcanic Districts, Scotland." 3rd edition, 1961.
" The Midland Valley of Scotland." 2nd edition, 1948.
" The South of Scotland." 2nd edition, 1948.
" Northern England." 3rd edition, 1953.
" The Pennines and Adjacent Areas." 3rd edition, 1953.
" East Yorkshire and Lincolnshire." 1948.
" North Wales." 3rd edition, 1961.
" South Wales." 2nd edition, 1948.
" The Welsh Borderland." 2nd edition, 1948.
" Bristol and Gloucester District." 2nd edition, 1948.
" Central England." 2nd edition, 1947.
" East Anglia and Adjoining Areas." 4th edition, 1961.
" London and the Thames Valley." 3rd edition, 1960.
" The Wealden District." 4th edition, 1964.
" The Hampshire Basin and Adjoining Areas." 3rd edition, 1960.
" South-West England." 2nd edition, 1948.

Each of these booklets gives a description, with maps and sections, of the district covered, and a list of the 1-inch Geological Survey Maps dealing with the district, together with a Bibliography.

READ, H. H. " Geology." Oxford University Press. 1949.
TRUEMAN, SIR A. " Coalfields of Gt. Britain." 1957. Edward Arnold.
WELLS, A. K., AND KIRKCALDY, J. F. " Outline of Historical Geology." 5th edition, 1966. Murby, London.
British Association publication : " A view of Ireland : (2), Geology." Dublin. 1957.
CRAIG, G. Y. (Ed.) " The Geology of Scotland." 1965. Oliver & Boyd, Edinburgh.

---

[1] Godwin, H. " The History of the British Flora." Cambridge Univ. Press. 1956.

CHAPTER 12

GEOLOGICAL MAPS AND SECTIONS

The first geological map of England and Wales was made by a surveyor and civil engineer, William Smith. On the journeys which he frequently made, and during his work in canal construction, he saw that certain bands of rock could be traced across the country for considerable distances. These bands or layers, in the Cotswolds, he described as having the appearance of "superimposed slices of bread and butter." He began to record his observations and after a number of years was able to publish, in 1815, a "Coloured map of the Strata of England and Wales " on the scale of 5 miles to an inch. The substantial accuracy of this pioneer map is a tribute to the ability and industry of its maker. The science of geology remains one in which observation is of prime importance, and William Smith was, in his day, an able observer.

After this important publication, geological mapping was begun privately in the mining areas of Cornwall and Devon by Sir Henry de la Beche, who later was made the first Director of a Geological Survey for the whole country. This Survey, during more than a hundred years since its formation, has been responsible for producing and revising a geological map of the British Isles on the scale of 1 inch to a mile, with accompanying Memoirs. Among its many other publications may be mentioned the maps of areas of economic importance on the 6-inch scale (see Appendix), the series of Bulletins, and the Regional handbooks (list on p. 238).

Symbols. In reading a geological map the primary objects in view are to determine what rocks outcrop over the area represented and how they are arranged, i.e. to find out the local *succession* and *structure*. From this information inferences can be drawn as required. The outcrops of different kinds of rock are distinguished on a map by a scheme of colouring or shading, as was indicated in Chapter 9, and the structural attitude of strata is shown by dip arrows and other symbols.

On the colour-printed 1-inch and 6-inch maps of Great Britain,[1] standardized symbols are used to denote the sedimentary formations and bodies of igneous rock, as well as distinctive tints. Each of the big age-groups or *systems* into which strata are divided is represented by a small letter of the alphabet ; a numerical suffix denotes the different subdivisions of the system. Thus, all the beds of the Cretaceous system are lettered h, and a particular formation, e.g. the Chalk, is denoted by the symbol h^5. The geological systems, which have been described in the previous chapter, have the following notation [2] :

[1] These general remarks apply also to the maps of other countries.
[2] Another scheme is to number the different formations. Again, on the maps of the United States Geological Survey the initial letter of the name of a system is used to denote the rocks of that age, as J for Jurassic, O for Ordovician, etc.

239

Tertiary	i, j, k, l		Carboniferous	d
Cretaceous	h		Devonian	c
Jurassic	g		Silurian	
Trias	f		Ordovician	$\}\ b$
Permian	e		Cambrian	a

Various symbols are used for Pre-Cambrian rocks.

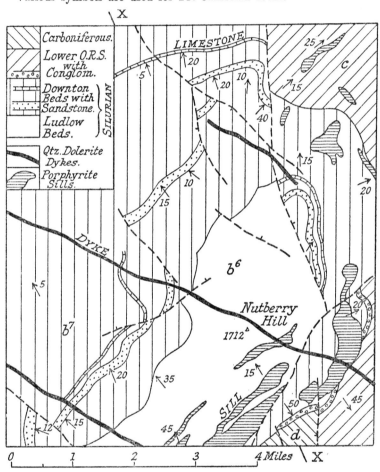

FIG. 103.—SIMPLIFIED GEOLOGICAL MAP OF THE COUNTRY SOUTH-EAST OF STRATHAVEN,
LANARK (based on part of sheet 23, Geol. Survey Scotland).
Topographical contours have been omitted. Heavy broken lines are faults.

A list of symbols and colours employed on a particular map is printed in
a column along one border, the strata being arranged in the column in order
of age, with the oldest at the bottom. The local names of the different beds
are given and in many cases thicknesses are indicated. Igneous rocks are
generally denoted by a capital letter, such as G (granite) or B (basalt), and

by a bright colour. Metamorphic rocks (see Chapter 7) are indicated by some other style of lettering.

The boundary between two outcrops is shown on the 1-inch map by a full line, except where its location on the ground is uncertain or where it is covered by superficial deposits, when a broken line is used. Superficial deposits, e.g. plateau and valley gravels, river alluvium, etc., are shown bounded by a thinner dotted line. Glacial deposits are also depicted by a dotted line on the *Drift Edition* of the 1-inch maps, but are omitted from the maps of the *Solid Edition*; the latter show the outcrops as they would appear if any cover of glacial drift were removed. Dip arrows, with the amount of dip in degrees, and signs for horizontal ($+$) and vertical beds ($\rightarrow$) are employed, together with any other special symbols that may be necessary for a particular map.

Succession of the Strata. Where a list of strata is given on the map, the beds are placed in their correct order of superposition, i.e. in their geological sequence; beds whose position in a sequence is uncertain are specially noted. Apart from such a column, the order and relative ages of the beds can usually be made out from an inspection of the map, the relation of each bed to those adjoining it in outcrop being studied, and inferences drawn according to one or other of the following criteria:

(1) A V-shaped outcrop in a valley. If the V points downstream the beds dip downstream (Fig. 59); once the direction of dip is determined the relative ages of the beds can be deduced. The older bed underlies the newer, assuming there is no inversion of the strata.

(2) Dip arrows: a dip arrow points towards younger beds; e.g. in Fig. 103, at the 35° dip near bottom of map, the Downton (vertical ruling) is younger than the Ludlow (plain). Inverted dips are sometimes shown by values greater than 90°, e.g. overturned beds dipping at 70° can be indicated by the value 110°.

(3) Stratum contours may be sketched on locally where an outcrop crosses topographic contours, and the direction of dip thereby found.

(4) Unconformity. Where the outcrop of a bed cuts across other outcrops on the map (cf. Fig. 69), the relationship is unconformable and the newer beds are those above the unconformity. Fig. 103 should also be read as an exercise and the order of the beds determined.

Superficial deposits of recent formation may cover or partly cover the underlying rocks, and are therefore the youngest of all (see alluvium in Fig. 97).

Igneous Rocks. Besides the sedimentary strata of an area, igneous rocks may be present. They may occur in large masses (*major intrusions*), or in smaller masses (*minor intrusions*) such as dykes and sills, the appearance of which on a map is characteristic. A dyke is a wall-like mass of igneous rock which fills a vertical or steeply inclined fissure in other rocks. Its outcrop is nearly parallel-sided, straight or gently curved, and it cuts across the outcrops of other beds (Fig. 103). A sill, on the other hand, is a flat sheet-like mass, intruded parallel to the bedding planes of strata, and so follows the boundaries of the strata in the course of its outcrop. Lava flows, which have been poured out at the earth's surface, assume irregular areas of outcrop, since they rest indiscriminately on all underlying rocks.

Faults and Folds. Faults are represented on a map by heavy lines; broken lines are used if the exact position of the fault is uncertain. The downthrow side of a normal fault is generally indicated by a short stroke placed against the fault line (see Fig. 103). Apart from this, the side of the downthrow can be estimated by reference to the relative ages of strata, where different formations lie on either side of the fault, since the *younger* beds occur on the side of the downthrow. (This will not apply to a wrench fault, where the movement is a horizontal one.)

The dip of a fault may often be estimated from the degree of curvature of its trace or outcrop. A vertical fault appears as a straight line on the map, while a fault inclined at a steep angle has a curved trace according to the topography it crosses. The lower its angle of inclination to the horizontal the more sinuous becomes the outcrop of the fault surface; this is well seen in the case of thrust planes which are nearly horizontal, e.g. the thrusts shown on the Assynt District map (Geol. Survey Scotland, 1-inch), the outcrops of these very flat surfaces of dislocation behaving almost like contour lines.

The effect of dip faults as seen on a map is to displace the outcrops of the beds broken by the fault (p. 188); in Fig. 103, the outcrop of the sandstone band (dotted) which runs from the south-west corner towards the top centre of the map is broken in this way. Strike faults, on the other hand, either repeat or conceal the outcrops of beds or part of a bed (p. 189). It should be remembered that the throw of a fault may not be constant along its length and therefore a diminishing displacement at successive points along the fault may indicate that it is dying out; in the figure, the north-westerly fault which shifts the sandstone near the top centre of the map hardly displaces the limestone band to the north of it at all. The student should practise estimating the amount and kind of movement of the faults shown in the figure.

Folded beds are traceable on a map when dip arrows are given (p. 182). Two dips pointing in opposite or nearly opposite directions indicate a syncline or an anticline according to whether they point together ($\longrightarrow \longleftarrow$) or apart ($\longleftarrow \longrightarrow$). The shape, also, of the outcrop of a plunging fold is sometimes characteristic, as explained in Chapter 10. Thus, given a " canoe-shaped " (roughly elliptical) outcrop or half of such a shape, the presence of a fold is at once suggested and confirmation may be sought from an inspection of dip arrows.[1] The axis of a plunging fold generally runs through the " nose " of the canoe-shaped outcrop (i.e. roughly parallel to the long axis of the " canoe "); it must be remembered that when the structure is plunging the strike lines are curved in plan, and the dips do not remain parallel but are radially arranged at right angles to the strike (Fig. 70). In Fig. 103, near the top, this is seen in the case of the sandstone band already referred to; the shape of its outcrop (although broken by faults), together

[1] This confirmation is necessary, since the outcrop may have other explanations.

with the dip arrows, indicates an asymmetrical anticline plunging to the north-north-east.

Folds which are overturned or isoclinal sometimes have characteristic outcrop forms, which can be seen on maps such as the Scottish 1-inch sheet No. 24 (Peebles) of the Geological Survey. One possibility is shown in Fig. 104, where limbs and axial planes of folds all dip east ; discussion of these and other complex folds is beyond the scope of this book.

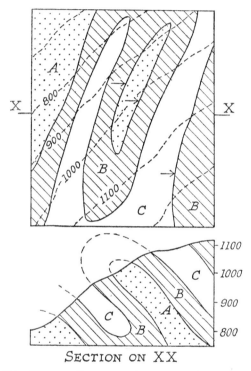

SECTION ON XX

FIG. 104.—MAP AND SECTION OF ISOCLINALLY FOLDED STRATA.

From an analysis of the directions of faults and joints and axes of folding in an area, the attitude of the stresses which operated to form them may sometimes be inferred ; for example a principle compression bisects the angle between pairs of wrench faults (Fig. 83, p. 195). Such structures, which are formed during rock deformation arising from crustal stresses, are part of a *tectonic* pattern. The term tectonic is used to denote the deformation of crustal rocks considered in relation to the forces and movements which caused it. (Greek : *tekton*, a builder).

Description of an Area. A short geological description of an area may be conveniently made under four main heads, as follows :

(1) *District.* A brief statement of the location of the area and its main topographical features.

(2) *Succession.* The rocks of the area are listed in the order of their geological age, generally in a column with the oldest at the bottom, and the nature of each is described ; e.g. in Fig. 103 the succession is b^6, b^7, c, d, in ascending order. Igneous rocks are listed separately.

(3) *Structure.* Under this head is stated the nature and direction of (a) the folding, and (b) the faulting seen in the rocks of the area. Jointing and cleavage if present are also described, and any significant minor structures. In the figure, for example, the main structure is an anticlinal fold trending north-north-east, with steeper dips on the south-east limb than on the north-west ; the fold is broken by a series of dip faults with a general north-westerly direction, and by a strike fault (across the south-eastern corner of the map) which conceals the outcrop of the junction between b^6 and b^7 on that limb of the fold. An important north-south fault occurs in the east of the area, and throws down the nose of the plunging anticline.

(4) *Economics.* Rocks which have an economic value are mentioned here, such as road metals and building materials ; water supply from underground sources (if any) in the area can also be indicated.

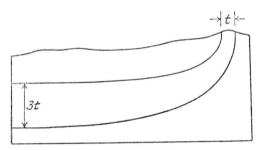

FIG. 105.—EFFECT OF EXAGGERATION OF VERTICAL SCALE.
Note the apparent change in thickness of a bed in passing from the vertical to the horizontal position. Vertical scale = 3 × horizontal.

Horizontal Sections. The relations of strata and their structure can often be usefully shown by means of a horizontal section. This should be drawn along a line which traverses the rocks in the dip direction, unless for special reasons some other line is desirable. It is constructed from the surface evidence, shown on the map, but evidence from borings or underground workings, when available, is used to supplement the surface indications. It must be remembered that the latter cannot, as a rule, be extrapolated downwards for any great distance. The horizontal scale of the section is the same as that of the map, or a simple multiple of it ; the vertical scale is generally exaggerated, for ease of handling where the topographical differences are not great, and is often three times the horizontal scale or more. This is especially the case with sections drawn for 1-inch maps ; true scale sections are more applicable to 6-inch maps.

In constructing such a section, the profile of the ground along it is first drawn. This is done by noting the positions where the line of section on the map intersects topographical contours, and plotting the corresponding heights up from a datum line on the section paper to the scale adopted. The points so obtained are then connected by a smooth line, due regard being paid to steep slopes, river valleys, and the heights of summits. Geological data are next marked on the profile; a simple way of transferring the information from map to section is to lay a strip of paper along the line on the map and mark off on it the positions of outcrops, faults, etc., which are traversed, with a note as to the amount of dip where available. Dip arrows which lie near to the line, if not actually on it, give valuable information. The strip of paper is then laid along the profile and the data on it marked in pencil on the section (Fig. 106a). The direction and amount of dip, and the exaggeration of the vertical scale (Fig. 105) must be taken into account in drawing each boundary on the section. Faults are shown by strong lines and are made vertical where their dip is uncertain. Structure lines linking up similar beds may then be added, together with suitable colouring or shading to represent the beds shown (Fig. 106b). The student should practise drawing his own section for the line shown on Fig. 103, or for some other line.

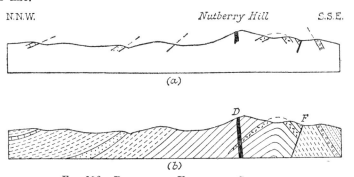

FIG. 106.—DRAWING OF HORIZONTAL SECTIONS.
(a) Outcrops and dips plotted for the line XX in Fig. 103. (b) Completed section.
(D) Dyke. (F) Reversed fault.

Vertical Sections. The strata penetrated in a vertical direction in sinking a well or bore-hole, or present in a cliff section, may be represented by means of a vertical section, in the special geological sense of the term. A column is used to represent the boring, and in it the geologica ldata are plotted to scale and indicated by shading or colouring. Thicknesses of beds passed through are measured down successively, starting from ground level, and are stated at one side of the column, while the distances of the different horizons below ground level are recorded at the other side (Fig. 107). The boundary of each formation is shown by a full line across the column, except when it is an unconformity, which is represented by a wavy line.

Vertical sections are used for comparing the strata present in different localities, e.g. in coalfields. In a district where a number of vertical sections are available, several of them lying approximately along a straight line can be selected and plotted at intervals proportional to their actual distances apart. By linking up the geological horizons shown in the sections, the skeleton of a continuous longitudinal section is obtained, which may be of use in depicting the underground structure of the intervening ground, e.g. changes in the thickness of a series of beds become apparent.

Measured cliff sections, either natural or in excavations, may be shown in the form of a column when the beds are regular ; broken or contorted beds are best shown by a sketch or photograph.

Sub-surface Contours and Isopachytes. In mining or other districts where a large amount of bore-hole data is available, it is possible to use this information to make contour maps of buried surfaces. The levels of a particular geological surface (or *horizon*) at a number of points are plotted, and contours are drawn by interpolation. This procedure is also useful in interpreting the results of trial bores in connection with engineering construction, as in the exploration of a dam site (see Chapter 14) ; it was used effectively in the case of the Vyrnwy dam.

Where bores have been put down to test the thickness of a mineral deposit, such as a coal-bearing sequence or an orebody, a map showing lines of equal thickness, called *isopachytes*, can be constructed from the bore-hole data. Such a map is useful in finding the volume of the deposit.

Field-mapping.

The making of a geological map involves much painstaking observation, which has then to be transferred to the map in symbols ; a trained eye is needed to appreciate the significance of many geological facts observed in the field. The

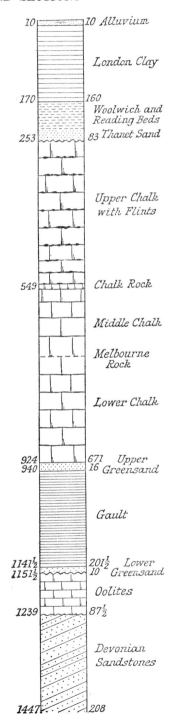

FIG. 107.—VERTICAL SECTION AT THE DEEP BORING AT RICHMOND, SURREY.
Thicknesses in feet on right of column, depths from surface on left. Unconformities shown by wavy lines across column.

necessary practice in observation can only be had out-of-doors in contact with the rocks themselves, and laboratory studies are supplementary to field work, which is of prime importance. The civil engineer may find himself engaged on construction in a district of great geological interest, or of lesser interest, but his work wherever it is gives him special opportunities of observing rock exposures and sections both at the surface and in excavations of all kinds. If his observations can be placed on a map, a permanent record is made of facts which might otherwise go unrecorded, since they are lost when the excavation of a dam is filled with concrete, or when the area of a reservoir is flooded, or the lining of a tunnel placed in position. The notes given here on field work and equipment can only serve as a starting-point, and methods must be modified as the work dictates ; but they will have served their purpose if they encourage the reader to make an attempt at recording geological data.

Equipment. An essential piece of equipment in geological field work is a well-balanced hammer, which should be heavy enough to enable a sharp blow to break open a hard rock for inspection. A square-section head tapering to a chisel edge at one end and weighing about 1 lb. is probably the most generally useful, though a more weighty instrument may be required under some conditions. That shown in Plate XIB is a 2-lb. hammer. A spare shaft is useful. A light hammer for " trimming " specimens is needed if these are to be collected.

For measuring directions such as strike, or the bearing of a rock-face (to be recorded on the map), a *compass* is required. This need not be of a prismatic type, although for sighting distant objects and for general usefulness the prismatic compass is very valuable. The dial should be large enough to carry graduations which will enable a bearing to be read to the nearest degree. A straight-edge attached to the compass and parallel to one diameter of it facilitates measurements ; some instruments are mounted in a metal case which has a built-in straight-edge. The line engraved on the glass cover of a prismatic compass also serves this purpose. If the graduated dial is attached to the magnetic needle and swings with it, direct bearings can be read off against a fixed zero. When the needle swings past a fixed dial, a reading in degrees east or west of magnetic north is obtained. The magnetic declination for the instrument should be found in the field by comparing its reading with the bearing of a known line, e.g. a line drawn on the map to a prominent land-mark. For a description of special instruments like the Brunton compass the reader is referred to books listed at the end of the chapter.

The *clinometer*, for measuring the dip of bedded rocks and inclinations of other surfaces, may be either a separate instrument or incorporated within the compass. It usually consists of a plummet which hangs vertically and gives a reading against a scale when the instrument is tilted to the slope of the strata. Another type uses a bubble tube mounted on one arm of a hinged scale (like a folding rule) to give the horizontal ; the other arm rests on the rock surface to be measured, and the angular separation of the two arms gives the amount of dip. A simple clinometer can be made out of a protractor mounted on a piece of three-ply wood or stiff board, with a short plumb-bob hung from the centre of the protractor circle.

A notebook is needed for recording observations supplementary to those put direct on to the map, and for sketches ; a pocket lens of magnification 8 or 10 is also useful for examining the constituents of rocks (see p. 64), and a haversack for carrying equipment and specimens is a standard item of equipment.

Lastly there is the question of the *map* and *map-case.* In a country where maps on the 6-inch (or similar) scale are available, these generally form the best basis for recording geological observations in the field. In special areas a 25-inch or still larger scale map may be needed. For convenience of carrying the map is cut into several parts, the border having first been removed ; sections from several sheets can then be put together as required. The map-slips may be conveniently housed between two pieces of cardboard hinged together. Sheets of the new 6 inch to a mile map of Great Britain measure 18×18 inches ; these can be cut into four sections, each 9×9 inches, and suitable boards would be about $9\frac{1}{2}$ inches square. If the boards are hinged together by adhesive tape along one edge, they form a simple case in which the map can be carried about and protected from rain, and also a support for writing on it. Rubber bands placed parallel to the outer edges of the covers hold the map, so that the case can be opened like a book, with the map inside it. More elaborate types of map-cases can be purchased, with a leather cover to the cardboard, a strap for carrying, and other refinements. A slightly soft pencil (HB or B) is the best for recording on the map in the field—observations are later inked in and the pencilling rubbed out—and a pocket scale graduated to read in feet on the same scale as the map is useful for measuring distances.

Methods of Mapping. Using a 6-inch or similar map, the object is to draw on it as accurately as possible the boundaries of the outcrops of rocks which are present in the area ; outcrops may be continuous, or displaced by faulting. Generally speaking, the boundaries and fault lines are not at once apparent, since the ground is covered with grass or other vegetation, and therefore all the evidence available must be recorded and pieced together ; an exception would be a bare rock-surface or fore-shore at low tide. A method which is sometimes useful is to follow a particular geological horizon across country, plotting its course on the map. A prominent lime-stone formation in a series of shales, for example, could be mapped in this way. More commonly, however, the method used is to plot on the map every rock exposure observed, small and large, and then to draw boundaries by inspection, each boundary enclosing all the exposures of a particular kind. This involves inspecting every part of the ground in order to extract from it the maximum possible amount of information. If necessary, pits can be dug to supplement scanty surface evidence, and fragments of rock in the soil noted.

Exposures of rock are indicated on the map by drawing in pencil a line to represent their size, shape, and position as closely as possible, by reference to near topography such as hedges, fences, etc. Cliff-sections, as in quarries, may need an explanatory note or sketch in the notebook. Where exposures are not plentiful, evidence from soil fragments may be used, the necessary notes being written on the map in abbreviated form. Topographical features which appear to have a geological significance, e.g. scarp slopes, are also sketched on the map by some system of hachuring (hill-shading) or trend lines ; they are useful in controlling the position of the boundary lines which are eventually drawn. Measurements of dip and strike are also recorded.

All these observations are inked in at the end of each day's field work. Two or three different coloured inks are used for the purpose ; exposures, for example, might be recorded in blue or brown, and hill-shading in green, black being reserved for dip arrows and final boundary lines. The nature of the rocks at each exposure is stated in some abbreviated form, in small lettering.

Stream sections on hillsides frequently yield valuable information and should be traversed and recorded carefully. Rocks are exposed in the bed and banks of a stream which elsewhere may be covered with soil or debris. Measurements of dip can be made here and distances paced, and from this information rough estimates of thickness for different beds can often be arrived at (see Fig. 58). Prospecting in unsurveyed areas overseas often begins with exploring stream sections.

Faults are generally not seen directly on the ground, though they may occasionally be visible in cliff and quarry sections. They may be suggested by breaks or displacements in topographical features, which will be shown on the map by hill-shading, e.g. the sudden termination of a ridge. Some indications of the presence of faulting are as follows :

(1) A line of springs or seeps not corresponding with a normal boundary between permeable and impermeable strata (cf. Fig. 117).

(2) Presence of fault-breccia (p. 187) or slickensides (p. 191).

(3) Sudden changes of dip or strike not attributable to folding.

(4) Displacement of topographical features and the formation of fault scarps.

(5) Juxtaposition of the outcrops of different rocks, the outcrops following one another in the strike direction (illustrated in Figs. 76, 109).

(6) The repetition or concealment of outcrop (strike faulting).

(7) The occurrence of inliers not attributable to other causes.

(8) Presence of closely spaced joints and shear-zones.[1]

Faults may also be deduced from borings, when the depths of a stratum in a group of borings are compared.

When as much evidence as possible has been accumulated and recorded on the map the boundary lines for the various outcrops are drawn in ; faults are shown by heavy broken lines, and the map is completed by colouring, a key to the colours being provided.

For a more exhaustive description of geological mapping the reader is referred to the first book listed overleaf.

---

[1] e.g., instances in igneous rocks are discussed in " The Lustleigh Fault in N.E. Dartmoor," by F. G. H. Blyth, *Geol. Mag.*, 94, 1957, p. 291.

G.E.—R

Traversing and Reconnaissance. The above remarks apply particularly to large-scale maps. To cover a large area more rapidly, without going into such detail, a 1-inch map may be used and the geology sketched on to it by reference to prominent topographical features and changes in topography, and checked by inspection at intervals. This may be called a geological reconnaissance, and it will be carried out by a series of traverses across country. The direction of a traverse will be chosen to give the maximum amount of information ; obviously, the geological " grain " of a country will be most easily seen if the rocks are traversed in the dip direction. Where no map is available a compass traverse can be made, straight distances between points being paced or timed, and the bearings of the lines measured in the forward and backward directions.

The use of aerial photographs in recent years has introduced a valuable new method of reconnaissance. From a series of overlapping photographs, taken in pairs for stereoscopic viewing, many physical details on the ground can be located ; this procedure may then serve as a basis for more detailed geological investigation. The method is most useful in inaccessible (e.g. densely wooded) country.

Augering. Evidence of the nature of surface rocks to a depth of some 20 feet can be obtained under certain conditions by use of the auger. This consists of a screw blade mounted on a length of steel piping, which is jointed in lengths of about 4 feet, and is screwed into the ground by turning on a T-piece attached to the upper end. It will penetrate soils and soft deposits such as clays, but not hard rocks. Augering in gravels or bouldery deposits is difficult. In ordinary use, the auger is screwed down for a short distance (6 to 12 inches), then pulled vertically out of the hole, and the sample adhering to the blades of the screw is examined and removed. This operation is repeated and a series of samples at frequent intervals is thus obtained. The nature of the material, the presence or absence of groundwater, or (in the case of a shallow superficial cover) the depth to bed-rock can be ascertained in this way. The complete apparatus weighs about 20 lbs. and is easily transported. Specially designed augers for obtaining larger samples of soft sediments are available.

SELECTED REFERENCES

GREENLY, E., AND WILLIAMS, H. " Methods in Geological Surveying." Murby, London. 1930.

BROWN, C. B., AND DEBENHAM, F. " Structure and Surface." Arnold & Co. 1929.

BLYTH, F. G. H. " Geological Maps & their Interpretation." 1965. Edward Arnold.

CHAPTER 13

THE GEOLOGY OF WATER SUPPLY

This chapter discusses the geological principles which govern the distribution of underground water in rocks, and its movement through them ; examples are given of supplies obtained from sources in Britain. The next chapter deals with the control exercised by geological factors on supplies which utilize surface waters from rivers and lakes.

Sources of Water. The chief source of water is *rainfall* ; together with other forms of precipitation, such as snow and dew, it is classified as *meteoric water*. In contrast with this, the water derived from magmas during their crystallization, or from lava flows (as steam), is called " plutonic " or *juvenile water* ; and that contained in the interstices of sedimentary materials when they were deposited, and not all driven out by processes of compaction and cementation, is known as *connate water*. For the present purpose only rainfall need be considered as the source upon which water supply depends.

Rainfall Statistics. Detailed records of rainfall in Britain have been kept since about 1860, when G. J. Symons began to organize the recording of rainfall data ; local records go back much farther. The statistics show that the average rainfall for the whole of England, taken over a period of thirty-five years (1881–1915), is 32·6 inches per year, and for the British Isles as a whole, 41·4 inches per year. The rainfall for a particular locality may vary considerably from the average for the whole country : thus Greenwich has an average of 24·5 inches per year, while a mountain station such as Borrowdale in Cumberland receives as much as 140 inches. Recently a new long period average, for the 35 years 1916–50, has been prepared : the average for England is 33·8, and for Great Britain 41·9 inches per year. For some localities the rainfall averages for 1916–50 are found to be 10 per cent or more greater than for 1881–1915. It follows that in areas where water resources are to be investigated, detailed rainfall data are needed if correct interpretations are to be made.

The average rainfall at any place varies from month to month (seasonal variation) ; the following figures give the monthly falls in inches at Greenwich, averaged over a period of 100 years (1820–1919) :

Jan.	1·81	Apl.	1·60	July	2·44	Oct.	2·67
Feb.	1·56	May	1·87	Aug.	2·38	Nov.	2·30
Mar.	1·59	June	1·98	Sept.	2·15	Dec.	2·02

For this particular locality, October is thus the wettest, and February and March the driest months. The higher rainfall of the summer months is largely lost in evaporation (p. 255).

Maximum intensities of rainfall generally occur over short periods of time, as in the case of thunderstorm rain. The greatest recorded fall in England in 24 hours is 9·56 inches at Bruton, Somerset, on June 28, 1917.

251

A fall of 9·00 inches on August 15, 1952, was recorded at Longstone Barrow, Exmoor, and led to disastrous floods at Lynmouth.

Measurements of rainfall are made by means of a gauge, which usually consists of a metal cylinder 18 inches long and 5 inches in diameter, containing an inner cylinder in which the rain is collected through a funnel. The

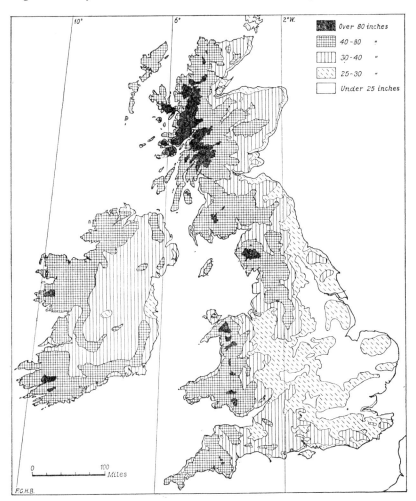

FIG. 108.—MEAN ANNUAL RAINFALL OF THE BRITISH ISLES.

apparatus is placed in level ground, away from trees and buildings to avoid condensation, and is partly buried to minimize evaporation in summer and freezing in winter; the top of the gauge should be 12 inches above the ground. The site should be sheltered from strong winds. Readings are booked daily, recording the rain of the previous 24 hours. Ten inches of snow may be taken as equivalent to 1 inch of rain. Where a greater capacity is required for weekly or monthly readings, as at less accessible moorland stations, a larger type of gauge (such as the " Bradford ") is used, in which the amount of water collected is measured by inserting a graduated rod.

The rainfall recorded in any given period may be shown on a map, on which are plotted the observations at a large number of stations, and lines of equal rainfall (*isohyetal* lines) are drawn at intervals by interpolation. Maps of this kind, together with rainfall statistics, are issued annually in the Meteorological Office publication known as *British Rainfall*. A map of the average annual rainfall in Great Britain is published by the Ordnance Survey, on a scale of 10 miles to 1 inch.

If an isohyetal map of Britain (Fig. 108) be compared with the geological map, it will be seen that in both cases the country may be divided into two broadly contrasted areas by a line drawn from about the mouth of the River Tyne to the Exe estuary. To the east of this line there is relatively low land formed by younger rocks, with lower rainfall ; to the west, older rocks outcrop and form higher ground, with a higher rainfall. Maximum rainfall tends to occur on the leeward side of high ground. Scotland's considerable rainfall largely accounts for the location there of important hydro-electric plants.

Accurate rainfall statistics are essential for any engineering scheme involving the supply of water, because the amount to be dealt with and its probable variations must be known as closely as possible. Although existing records may be drawn on for information, each scheme should possess its own local records, the collection of which is one of the first necessary pre-liminaries. Two gauges per 1000 acres of gathering ground are commonly employed.

In using rainfall statistics it is sometimes necessary to make allowance for very wet and very dry years, and in this connection the following ratios may be taken as a guide : the rainfall of the wettest year is from $1\frac{1}{4}$ to $1\frac{1}{2}$ times the mean yearly rainfall for a period of years ; and for the driest year, roughly $\frac{2}{3}$ of the mean. The average annual rainfall for two consecutive dry years is about $\frac{3}{4}$ of the mean for the period ; and for three consecutive dry years, $\frac{4}{5}$ the mean. An interesting comparison with these figures is provided by the drought of 1932–4 : for the 21 months ending July 31, 1934, the rainfall in England was 79 per cent of the normal, the " normal " being taken as the average for the 35 years from 1881 to 1915. And in three consecutive dry winters in 1941–2, 1942–3, 1943–4, the mean rainfall in England and Wales was 16·6 inches, or 85 per cent of the long-term average (for October to March).

Dispersal of Rainfall. Of the rain that falls on the earth's surface, part returns direct to the air as water vapour by evaporation and by transpiration from plants ; part flows away in streams and rivers ; and part enters the soil and subsoil and percolates to the rocks beneath. These quantities may be termed the *evaporation loss*, the *run-off*, and the *infiltration*, the last including *percolation* and *soil moisture*. In the tabulation below, shallow percolation which emerges after rainfall to join the surface drainage is separated from deep percolation. There is also a very small proportion of the rainfall which is utilized directly in domestic consumption and which is not shown here. Fig. 109 also illustrates these quantities.

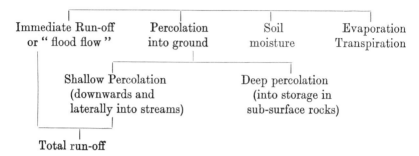

RAINFALL

Immediate Run-off or " flood flow "	Percolation into ground	Soil moisture	Evaporation Transpiration

Shallow Percolation (downwards and laterally into streams)

Deep percolation (into storage in sub-surface rocks)

Total run-off

The proportions of the three quantities, evaporation, run-off, and percolation, vary greatly ; seasonal variations occur, and the influence of geological and topographical factors is considerable. The amount of percolation can be estimated if the rainfall, run-off, and evaporation are known, from the equation :

$$R = E + F + P + S_m$$

where R = rainfall, E = evaporation plus transpiration, F = surface flow or run-off, P = percolation, and S_m = soil moisture. S_m is not easy to determine, and in the following discussion is omitted. The run-off from a catchment area may be measured by gauging the streams draining the area,[1] and evaporation measurements can be made (see discussion below) or an average value assumed.

Factors affecting Dispersal of Rainfall. 1. *Evaporation.* The amount of evaporation is controlled by the air temperature and humidity, by air currents, and by the temperature of the ground on which the rain falls. Measurements show that in England the maximum evaporation occurs in July, when about 15 per cent of the total annual evaporation takes place, and the minimum in January, with 2 per cent of the total. The total evaporation varies according to the district, and in many places is of the order of 17 inches or more (out of a rainfall of 25 inches and upwards).

Measurements of evaporation have been made with water in tanks, and with pans filled with soil and buried so as to be level with the ground surface ; evaporation has also been estimated from records of water levels, and of intake and outflow at reservoirs. Measurements from the tank at Camden Square, London, date from 1885 and give a value for the average annual evaporation there of 15·5 inches, of which nearly 87 per cent occurs in the

[1] For a discussion of the methods used see works on Engineering Hydrology (p. 279).

months from April to September. According to H. L. Penman (1948)[1] the evaporation loss from *continuously wet* bare soil is 0·9 times that from an open water surface exposed to the same weather conditions. Much detailed work has been done on the evaluation of evaporation and transpiration losses since the Rothamsted Station's Reports of 1907–09. Penman (1950) has shown that evaporation in Gt. Britain ranges from about 12 inches p.a. in the north to 21 inches in the south-west ; values of 17 or 18 inches hold for much of southern England.[2] As the rainfall increases broadly from east to west (Fig. 108), many different combinations throughout the range of

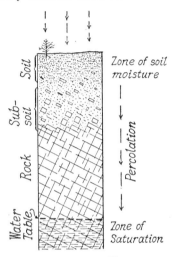

FIG. 109.—SOIL PROFILE, WITH HYDROLOGICAL TERMS.

rainfall and evaporation exist ; one extreme is the low rainfall and high evaporation in the south-east of the country, where percolation is in consequence very low. By contrast, some areas have high rainfall and low evaporation.

2. *Topography and Vegetation.* The gradient of the ground on which rain falls, and its cover of vegetation (or lack of cover), influence the proportion of the run-off and the chances of percolation. Steep hillsides give a high run-off value, especially if the rock surface is bare of vegetation. Conversely, for given conditions, run-off is least over level ground. Trees and plants take up much water in spring and summer, and the amount of rainfall available for infiltration is thereby reduced. A mantle of vegetation and leaves absorbs rain during a fall and tends to prevent flooding. In treeless country, cloudbursts (a high rate of precipitation, amounting to several inches per hour, for a short time) may cut deep gullies by the large run off

[1] Penman, H. L., " Natural Evaporation from Open Water, Bare Soil, and Grass," *Min. Proc. Roy. Soc.*, 193A, 1948, p. 120.

[2] Penman, H. L., " Evaporation over the British Isles," *Q. J. Roy. Met. Soc.*, 76, 1950, p. 372. (Reprinted in *Journ. I.W.E.*, 8, 1954, p. 415.)

See also : Lapworth, C. F., " Evaporation from a Reservoir near London." *Journ. I.W.E.*, 19, 1965, p. 163.

produced. Wash-outs of this kind in semi-arid regions, as in parts of South Africa, may do serious damage to lines of communication and to property. In the Exmoor floods of 1952, due to an exceptional local rainfall (p. 252), the River Lyn became a torrent, changing its course and sweeping away bridges and houses in its path. In places the valley sides were scoured clear of boulders and all movable material. More damage may be done in one severe storm than in many years of normal erosion.

3. *Nature of the Subsoil and Rock.* The geological character of the ground greatly affects the relative amounts of run-off and percolation. For example, a clay outcrop (such as the Gault) allows little percolation, and the run-off is correspondingly increased. On the other hand, a porous sandy soil, and porous or broken rock, will permit considerable percolation, as in parts of the Greensand outcrops. Even with a bare rock surface, such as an exposure of fresh and unweathered igneous rock, some water penetrates along joints and fissures (see examples on p. 273).

Residual deposits (p. 143) may play a large part in blocking the downward passage of rainwater in countries with hot, dry climates ; when once formed, they act as a " mackintosh " to the rocks below and hinder deep percolation, making water supply often a matter of great difficulty. Permafrost conditions (p. 4) also effectively hinder percolation.

From the factors briefly indicated above it will be seen that the proportions of evaporation, percolation, and run-off for a given area cannot be estimated in advance, but for any area the details must be investigated and deductions drawn from the local information available.

Percolation. The question of what proportion of the rainfall on a given area percolates into the underlying rocks has received much attention. The extent of percolation influences the amount of water which can be taken from wells without making too great a demand on the underground supplies, and this applies especially to areas where large numbers of wells abstract water from a single formation, as with the Chalk in various parts of its outcrop. Estimates of percolation which are reasonably accurate can be made for areas where conditions are relatively simple ; for example, the dry sandy tracts formed by the Bunter Sandstones in parts of Nottinghamshire and elsewhere have few surface streams, and an annual rainfall of about 30 inches can be considered as contributing some 20 inches to evaporation and 10 inches to percolation.

Measurements of percolation have been made at certain localities by means of percolation gauges. A section of the soil and sub-soil, either a cube or cylinder about 3 feet in depth (but sometimes larger), is enclosed in a metal container which is sunk nearly flush with the ground. From its base a drain leads off the percolating rainwater. Records obtained with such gauges at Rothamsted are published annually in *British Rainfall.* These records are consistent among themselves. Varying results can be obtained, however, since percolation is affected by the nature of the surface on which the rain falls, e.g. whether it is bare soil, or grass-covered, or supporting crops of different kinds. The setting up of a gauge also involves re-packing the excavated rock and soil into the gauge, and it is difficult to reproduce exactly the natural conditions before the ground was disturbed. A further criticism of percolation gauges is that they give data for only small areas ; variations in geology may be present in a formation throughout its extent, and these are not allowed for when local gauge data are assumed to apply to a whole outcrop.

Percolation is therefore often estimated by assuming a value for evaporation (and for soil-moisture, if available) and deducting this together with the flow of surface streams (expressed as inches of rain per annum) from the annual rainfall.

Careful observations extending over long periods have been made for areas of Chalk grass-land with no surface streams in south-east England. It has been shown that at Compton, West Sussex, the annual evaporation is nearly constant and almost independent of variations in rainfall ; it amounts to 17·4 inches (averaged over 50 years) out of an average annual rainfall of 37·6 inches.[1]   Again, by plotting values of average yearly rainfall (R) against percolation (P), for several stations on the Chalk of south-east England, the following formula has been derived :[2] $P = 0·9R - 13·5$ (inches). The data used in this instance are obtained from records of gauges, and from measurements of water levels in wells and the flow of springs. It will be seen that this formula, when applied to the Compton figures, gives a result in agreement with that found there independently. It appears, therefore, that for grassed Chalk areas in south-east England, where annual rainfall varies between 35 and 40 inches, evaporation accounts for between 17 and 17½ inches.

Water Resources of an Area. When it is required to assess the amount of water available from a catchment, for which the average rainfall has been determined, a preliminary estimate may be made as in the following example. Let the average rainfall be 30 inches per annum ; 1 inch of rain per year on 1 square mile of catchment is equivalent very nearly to 40,000 gallons per day. The rainfall available for percolation and run-off is the total rainfall less the evaporation loss (or, $P + F = R - E$, see p. 254). Suppose evaporation (E) is taken as 17 inches ; then

$$P + F = 30 - 17 = 13 \text{ inches per year,}$$

and

Quantity (galls/day) = 13 × area of catchment (sq. miles) × 40,000.

By assuming a value for run-off (based on stream gauging records), a figure for percolation can be arrived at. Not all the water percolating could be recovered from wells, but a large part of it might be available from suitably placed wells. Deductions must be made for the flow of any springs which have to be maintained. Where water available for storage is to be estimated, the run-off (F) would be reduced by making allowance for drought ; e.g. for two consecutive dry years the run-off would be reduced by ¼ of its estimated average value (p. 253). Run-off in mountain areas of more than

[1] D. Halton Thomson in *Journ. Inst. W.E.*, 1, 1947, p. 39. (See also *Trans. Inst. W.E.*, 36, 1931, p. 176 ; and 43, 1938, p. 154.)

[2] C. F. Lapworth, in *Journ. Inst. W.E.*, 2, 1948, p. 97 ; and *ibid.*, 17, 1963.

10,000 acres in extent may be taken very roughly as from $\frac{1}{10}$ to $\frac{1}{5}$ cusec per 1000 acres.

Domestic Water Consumption. The average rate of consumption for domestic purposes is now about 50 gallons per head per day in large towns, and between 20 and 30 gallons per head per day in rural districts. These figures do not include water used for industrial purposes, such as in factories and power plants, or for cattle (15–18 g.p.d. per head). There is a tendency for a continual rise in water consumption, and in some cities much higher quantities are now provided than those quoted above. It is necessary, in planning a supply, to allow for any such tendency and also for probable variations in the population of the district under consideration.

Groundwater. The part of rainwater which infiltrates at the surface and percolates down through the soil and sub-soil is stored in the " zone of saturation " (Fig. 109). This zone is present at a relatively small but variable depth. The water held in interstices, joints, and fractures in the rocks there is called *groundwater*. It is seen in wells and borings when they penetrate the zone of saturation, and under suitable conditions it emerges as springs (p. 265). It is slowly but constantly in motion through the rocks, as discussed below. A water-bearing formation is called an *aquifer*.[1]

Water from rivers may also, in some circumstances, enter the ground and add to the body of groundwater; such rivers are said to be *influent*. Other rivers are fed by groundwater emerging along parts of their course, and are called *effluent*; the contribution of groundwater to stream flow is known as the *base flow* of the stream. During a period of drought, when surface run-off is reduced to nil, the entire flow of such a river may be due to the base flow, and this is subject to determination from graphs of river discharge (hydrographs).

Porous and permeable rocks. We now consider the textures and structures which make it possible for water to be held in rocks and to move through them. A *porous* rock is one which contains interstices or pore-spaces, e.g. a sand or sandstone; in the zone of saturation groundwater fills the pores and is transmitted through them by hydraulic pressure, unless they are very small. When the pore-spaces are minute they act as capillary tubes, and hold the water which is in them; larger interstices allow easy movement of fluids. It is convenient, therefore, to distinguish between *micropores*, which are defined as less than ·005 mm. in size, and *macropores* (larger than ·005 mm.). According to which kind of porosity is mainly present, water may or may not be able to move readily through a rock-mass, although the latter may have a high porosity. The capacity of a rock for transmitting water is known as its *permeability*. Sands and gravels, which usually have much pore-space, are often highly permeable; clays, on the other hand, are practically impermeable because their pore-

---

[1] (Lat. " aqua," water, and " fero," to bear.) The term is used for a formation which yields water comparatively freely.

spaces are extremely small and the water in them is virtually stationary. Some permeability values are given on p. 262. Impermeable rocks, through which water can pass with difficulty if at all, include clays, shales, marls, unjointed igneous rocks, compact limestones, and residual deposits such as laterite. Permeability may vary in direction, and is sometimes greater parallel to bedding than across it.

Rocks with divisional openings. Groundwater can also travel through a rock along joints and fractures, fissures, and other structural planes ; even a non-porous rock may allow the passage of water in this way. Rocks through which groundwater moves by means of such structures may be called *pervious*. The importance of divisional planes in controlling the amount of water which may be obtained from a formation is often great, and it is vital, for instance, in the case of the Chalk.

Porosity. The *porosity* (p) of a rock is the percentage of void space that it contains, or $p = (voids \times 100)/total\ volume$. The following list is given as a guide to the range of porosity for different materials, but values vary widely, even for similar kinds of rock:

	Porosity %
Soils	greater than 50
Clays	45 or more
Loose sand and gravel	20 to 47
Sandstones	5 to 25
Limestones	5 to 25
Chalk	about 50
Dolomitic limestones	below 5
Granites (and other igneous rocks)	less than 1
Quartzites	about 0·5

Soils, which form the uppermost layers of the ground, are very porous and take up much water from rains. Some of this is used by plants and some is evaporated ; but if the soil becomes saturated, water is then available to percolate downwards into the sub-soil and rock below. *Clays*, though highly porous, are composed of very small particles and are microporous, so that little water is transmitted through them. A clay is therefore generally spoken of as impermeable, though strictly speaking the permeability is very low rather than nil. *Chalk* is another example of a highly porous but virtually impermeable rock ; it is, however, pervious in the mass when open joints are present (p. 276). Compact rocks such as *quartzites*, and holocrystalline *igneous rocks* like granites and gabbros, when fresh, and also dolerites and finer grained types, have generally a very low porosity.

Limestones vary greatly in the void space they contain : a number of oolitic limestones, for example, which were tested at the Building Research Station showed in some cases more than 20 per cent porosity. By impregnating the rocks with a coloured filler before sectioning, the pores can be made easily visible for microscopic examination in a thin slice, revealing both macropores and micropores. It was shown that the relative proportions of these two kinds of pores varied greatly with different limestones ;

in some cases nearly the whole of the porosity was due to micropores, in other cases they accounted for less than half the total pore-space. The passage of water through these rocks would be to a large extent governed by the kind of porosity present, e.g. flow would be enhanced if macropores formed the greater part of the total porosity.

Sands and Sandstones. The porosity of a sand depends on several factors, such as : (1) The grade sizes of the grains. A deposit containing mainly grains of one grade will possess a higher porosity than one consisting of a mixture of grades, since in the latter case the smaller grains will partly fill interstices between the larger and so reduce the pore space (Fig. 110c). This applies also to sandstones.

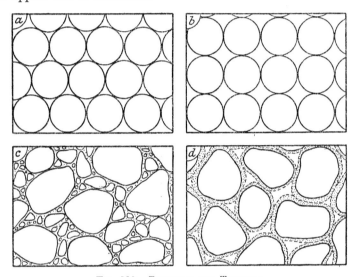

FIG. 110.—POROSITY AND TEXTURE.

(a) Close packing of spheres, porosity = 27 per cent. (b) Open packing of spheres, porosity = 47 per cent. (c) Poorly graded sand, porosity reduced by presence of small grains. (d) Well-graded sand (i.e. grains mainly of one size), porosity reduced by cement (stippled) between the grains.

(2) The amount and kind of packing which the grains have undergone. Figs. 110a and 110b show two kinds of packing for theoretical spherical grains, the pore spaces being inter-connected, though irregularly shaped.

(3) The amount of cement present. Interstices may be filled wholly or partly with mineral matter which binds the grains together, and in this way porosity may be considerably reduced (Fig. 110d).

It will be seen that many different possibilities arise from a combination of the three factors indicated above.

Flow of Water in a Granular Medium. The velocity of flow through a granular medium such as a sand has been the subject of numerous experiments, from which the flow is found to depend upon (a) the size of grain, (b) the porosity ratio, (c) the head under which flow takes place and the distance covered (i.e. the hydraulic gradient), and (d) the temperature of the water, which affects its viscosity. The formula derived by Darcy (1856) is :

$$V = k \cdot \frac{h}{l},$$

where V = the velocity of percolation, h = the difference of head under which flow occurs, over a distance l, and k = a constant depending on the nature of the material, determined experimentally in the field. By introducing common salt (NaCl) into a well and taking samples from other wells at timed intervals, the average velocity of percolation from one well to another may be calculated from the sample with the highest chlorine content. Dyes and electrolytes are also used for studying the movement of groundwater (see p. 276). The hydraulic gradient being known from the water levels in the wells, and the velocity found as above, k can be calculated from the Darcy formula.

The constant k is really a measure of the permeability of the material, and corresponds to the permeability factor P, in modern usage. P may be determined in the laboratory from samples, which are placed in a cylinder, to one end of which water is supplied under a known head ; the rate of percolation is found by measurement from an outlet at the other end of the cylinder. The permeability is then calculated from a formula such as $P = qlt/Tah$, where q is the quantity of water passing through the sample in time T ; l the length of the sample, and a its cross-section ; h the head, and t the temperature correction.

The value of this permeability coefficient equals the rate of flow in gallons per day through 1 square foot of cross-section of the material under a hydraulic gradient of 1 in 1, at a temperature of 60° F. The same value gives the quantity of water in gallons per day passing through 1 mile of a water-bearing bed (measured at right angles to the direction of percolation) for each foot of thickness of the bed and for each foot per mile of hydraulic gradient.[1]

The range of velocity met with in natural granular materials is indicated in the following table (after Tolman) :

Material	Grain size mm.	Average velocity, feet per day, at 1 per cent hydraulic gradient
Silt, fine sand . .	0·005 to 0·25	0·065
Medium sand, sandstone .	0·25 to 0·5	1·16
Coarse sand, sandy gravel	0·5 to 2·0	6·33
Gravel	2·0 to 10	30·0
Max. vel. in gravel . .	1·85 (effective diam.)	110·0

The Darcy formula can also be expressed in terms of the quantity (Q) of water passing through a rock in unit time, thus :

$$Q = P.I.A,$$

where P is the permeability coefficient, I the hydraulic gradient, and A the cross-sectional area through which the water moves. If Q is measured in gallons per day, A in square feet, and I is made equal to 1 (i.e. 100 per cent gradient), then P is expressed in standard units. Approximate values for P, in gallons per day through 1 square foot of cross-sectional area at a hydraulic gradient of 1 in 1, are as follows :

[1] See Tolman, p. 208, in book list on p. 279.

Sediment	Average Permeability Coefficient
Very fine sand	50
Fine sand	300
Medium sand	600
Coarse sand	1500
Gravel (fine)	5000
Coarse gravel	15,000 or more

It should be noted that these are average values; the range in each instance extends from a fraction of the average up to several times its amount.

Water-table. The zone of saturation (page 258) is bounded by an upper surface which is called the saturation level or *water-table*. In general, this surface has a shape which is roughly parallel to that of the topographical surface above it, being higher under hills and lower beneath valleys (Fig. 111), and it falls to sea-level at a coastline. Its position may be found

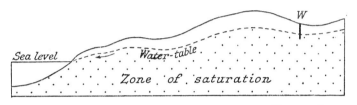

FIG. 111.—WATER-TABLE AND ZONE OF SATURATION IN UNIFORM ROCKS.
W = water-table well.

by measuring the depth to water levels in wells (as at W); water enters an unlined well below the water-table and stands at the level obtaining there. Alternatively, the depth of the water-table below the surface can sometimes be found by resistivity measurements (p. 327). In non-uniform rocks the ideal conditions shown in the figure will be modified.

If enough data from wells and borings are available and are plotted on a map, contours for the water-table may be drawn by interpolation. This has been done, e.g. for large areas of the Chalk in south-east England [1] and for the sandstone aquifers of the Trias. Such a contoured hydrographic map (Fig. 112) shows the shape of the water-table, with its " watersheds " generally (but not always) beneath surface watersheds and its hollows below topographical valleys, and indicates the direction of flow of the groundwater, from higher to lower levels at right angles to the contours. Below surface streams there is in general a flow of groundwater parallel to the valley. Where the water-table intersects a valley (Fig. 113, *s'*) and groundwater emerges and feeds a stream, the contours of the water-table have the shape of a V pointing upstream; this condition is common in temperate climates. If the water-table beneath a valley is low, as in arid climates, water from the river can enter the ground during a wet season and add to the groundwater.

[1] The water-table in the Chalk is not a continuous surface as for a porous rock like sandstone, but a discontinuous surface connecting water levels in fissures and joints.

The zone between the ground surface and the water-table periodically holds a certain amount of water, known as *vadose water*, which moves downwards and goes to feed the permanently saturated zone below. At greater depths in the earth's crust, where stresses are high, interstices and fissures in the rocks tend to close and the movement of groundwater is inhibited.

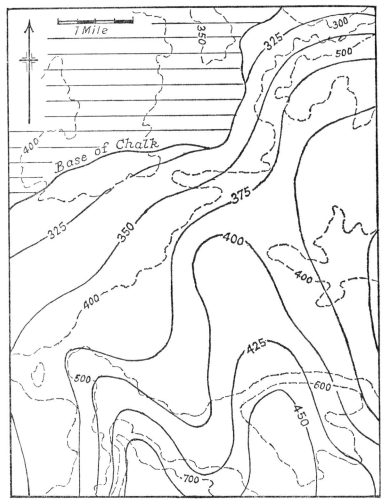

FIG. 112.—WATER CONTOUR MAP FOR PART OF THE CHALK.

Gault shown by horizontal ruling, topographic contours by broken lines. Groundwater flow is easier where water contours are widely spaced than where they are closer.

Rain usually causes a temporary rise in the water-table below the region where the fall occurs, and increases the flow in the aquifer. This is shown in Fig. 113, where an aquifer lies above impermeable beds, and the water-table emerges at the junction between the two ; the normal water-table (1), below which the rock is permanently saturated, is raised temporarily to (2), and the gradient of the water-table down to the junction of the beds is increased. A spring consequently emerges at s, and flows until the limiting gradient (1) is restored. The amount of the rise varies, but is usually greater beneath an upland area than below a valley. There is a time lag, which may amount to several weeks, between a rise in the water-table (as observed in wells) and the rainfall which produced it, owing to the time taken by percolation. Near an escarpment (Fig. 113), groundwater flow is quicker because of the steeper gradient of the water-table there. Where the travel of the groundwater is mainly by fissures and joints the time lag is less ; in one instance in the Chalk of northern France, it amounted to 2 weeks (and see p. 276 for rate of flow).

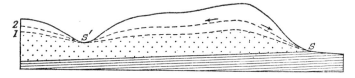

FIG. 113.—RISE OF WATER-TABLE AFTER RAIN.
Spring (s) emerges at junction of permeable and impervious beds. Valley spring shown at s'. 1 = normal water-table, 2 = water-table after heavy rain.

Perched Water-table. Where a local impervious layer, such as a seam of clay or layer of silt, occurs in a permeable deposit above the main water-table, a relatively small body of groundwater will be held up by the impervious layer, and a *perched water-table* thus formed (Fig. 114). Small supplies may be derived from perched groundwater of this kind, but where they are of shallow depth below the surface they are more liable to contamination than a supply obtained from a deeper well. If a boring meets a body of perched water, and is then continued through the impervious

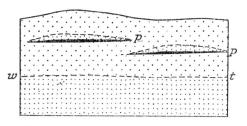

FIG. 114.—PERCHED WATER-TABLES (p) AT CLAY SEAMS IN PERMEABLE SEDIMENTS.
wt = main water-table.

layer which supports it, the water-level in the bore-hole may fall rapidly as the perched water drains away to lower levels.

Water-table at a Coastline. Where a permeable formation meets the coast, the fresh groundwater within it rests on sea-water which penetrates the rocks below sea-level. The boundary between the two waters is a parabolic one (Fig. 115) ; the fresh water rests on the heavier salt water and there is very little diffusion between them. This has been demonstrated a number of times in excavations made in connection with engineering works, since attention was first drawn to the matter when some borings were made near Amsterdam about 1889. The shape of the fresh and salt water contact has also been confirmed with models. If ρ = the density of sea-water, then, in Fig. 115, a column h of salt water is balanced by a column $h + t$ of fresh water, or

$$\rho h = (h + t) \times 1$$
and $$h = t/(\rho - 1).$$
If $\rho = 1 \cdot 025$, then $h = 40t$.

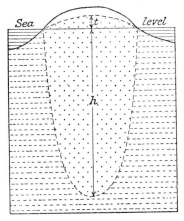

FIG. 115.—FRESH AND SALT-WATER CONTACT AT AN ISLAND.

In permeable rocks near a coast the water-table rises and falls with the daily fluctuations of the tides. This produces corresponding changes of level in adjacent wells, which are consequently known as *ebbing wells*. If pumping from such wells is too heavy, salt water will be drawn in and the supply thus contaminated ; this has happened, e.g., along the Mersey estuary, in the Wirral peninsula, the Humber, and the Thames estuary.

Springs. Groundwater which flows out at the surface constitutes a *spring* ; it is to be distinguished from a *seep*, where water oozes out of the ground over an area, but both indicate the outcropping of the water-table. Springs may be grouped as follows :

1. Stratum springs.
2. Valley springs.
3. Fault springs.
4. Springs from solution channels.
5. Artesian springs.
6. Deep-seated springs.

The springs of the last group are associated with vulcanicity and deep fractures, and yield juvenile water, not rainwater ; they will not be further discussed here. (See " hot springs," p. 93.)

1. *Stratum springs* arise when the downward passage of groundwater in a permeable deposit is hindered by an underlying impervious layer. The groundwater emerges as a spring (or line of springs) at the contact of the two formations (Fig. 113), i.e. at the base of the permeable formation, and hence it may also be referred to as a *contact spring*. The springs issuing from the base of the Lower Greensand where it rests upon the Weald Clay, as at Leith Hill and near Sevenoaks in Kent, and the Greensand on red marls in E. Devon, are examples. The impervious layer may be igneous rock, which holds up the groundwater in a cover of sediment, such as old river gravels. Springs of this group show, in general, an increased discharge after a rainy

season; they are frequently found at the foot of an escarpment. During severe frost, small stratum springs may become temporarily frozen.

Another kind of stratum spring may arise at the junction of two formations where permeable beds dip beneath an impermeable cover. This may be called an *overflow spring*, since the groundwater literally overflows at the edge of the impervious stratum (as in Fig. 120, at the point where the horizontal broken line meets the ground surface). The springs at Ewell, Surrey, are an example : they rise where Tertiary clays overlie the water-bearing Chalk, which dips towards London. Springs may also emerge along the outcrop of an unconformity, where the rocks below it are impermeable.

Pockets of weathered igneous rocks (e.g. granite), which have a high porosity, may discharge excess water after rainfall by springs at their margins. Such areas of porous, weathered rock may be of considerable importance in arid areas where fresh water supplies are scanty, as in Western Australia.

2. *Valley springs* are due to the emergence of the water-table where the topography falls below its level ; water then flows out at the surface, as at *s′* in Fig. 113, and feeds surface streams. In an exceptionally dry year, the water-table may be lowered below valley level and the springs then dry up.

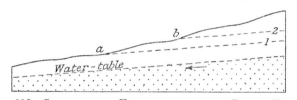

FIG. 116.—Section along Valley to illustrate Bourne Flow.
Rise of water-table to level (1) produces flow at *a* ; further rise to (2) causes flow at *b*, higher up the valley.

Bournes constitute a special case of valley springs, and have a seasonal flow which depends on the winter rainfall. Rise of the water-table above the normal level causes springs to break out in previously dry valleys (Fig. 116). These give rise to the streams known as bournes (or lavants), which flow for a few months and then dry up again until the next wet season. Continued rise in the water-table results in the bourne emerging at successively higher points in the valley. Bournes occur chiefly on Chalk areas in England, and many villages are named after them, e.g. Winterbourne Stoke in Dorset, or Hurstbourne, Hants. One of the most famous is the Croydon bourne, which rises at Wapses Lodge, near Caterham, and flows towards Croydon ; the time at which this stream will rise can be predicted from observations of the water level in local wells. It was studied in detail towards the end of last century by Baldwin Latham, who showed that it only appeared when the rainfall of the last three months of a year exceeded 10 inches.[1] Some bournes appear at intervals of a few years, when there occurs an unusually large rise in the water-table ; such flows were called " woebournes " in the past and were looked upon as a bad omen.

[1] *Trans. Croydon Nat. Hist. Soc.*, 1904.

3. *Fault Springs.* When a permeable formation is brought against impermeable rocks by faulting, groundwater in the permeable bed may escape along the fault and appear at the surface as springs (Fig. 117). A line of springs of this kind is frequently useful in mapping a fault (see p. 249). One well-known fault spring supplies water to the village of Boxwell in Gloucestershire ; here the Fullers Earth (a hard blue marl, locally 70 feet thick), which normally underlies the Great Oolite (133 feet thick), is faulted against the latter and water from the Great Oolite is thrown out at the surface along the line of fault, which in this case is open to the passage of water. Sometimes, however, water is prevented from moving along a fault surface, as when the fracture is sealed by a band of impervious crushed rock

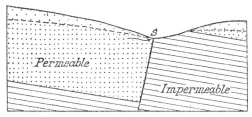

FIG. 117.—FAULT SPRING (*s*) due to downthrow of impervious beds against water-bearing beds. Water-table shown by broken line.

or clay (also called *gouge*). A fault, therefore, may or may not act as a channel for the movement of groundwater.

Water from the Holwell spring at Horsted Keynes in Sussex is used for public supply ; at this locality the Tunbridge Wells Sands are faulted against the Ashdown Sands. As the two sandy formations have different permeabilities, the movement of water across the fault is restricted and a large spring flow emerges.

4. *Springs from solution channels.* In limestone districts where there is much underground water in circulation (see p. 3), streams flow along bedding planes in channels enlarged by solution, and may emerge as springs in valleys, to feed surface streams. Plentiful examples of springs of this kind are found in the Carboniferous Limestone districts of the Mendips and the Pennines. The springs at Bedhampton, Hants, have a very large flow which ranges from about 18 to over 30m. gallons per day according to the season. The water is derived from the Chalk, and supplies are taken by the Portsmouth Water Company.

5. *Artesian springs.* These are of infrequent occurrence ; they arise, for example, where water is confined in permeable rocks under artesian head (see p. 272) beneath a cover of boulder clay. If this cover is locally broken, as by fracturing, the artesian water below emerges as a spring. Instances are known in Lincolnshire and Yorkshire, where boulder clay overlies the Chalk, which is the aquifer.

Wells. The commonest way of recovering groundwater is to sink a well and lift water from it. A shallow well is defined as one less than 100 feet deep ; it is usually lined with brick, concrete, or other material, and the upper part of the lining can be made water-tight to prevent the ingress of impure surface waters. Generally speaking, such a well will provide only a small supply suitable for local requirements, e.g. for single houses or farms. The water drawn on is located comparatively near the surface, in the upper part of the zone of saturation (see Fig. 111), and is more liable to contamination from various sources than water from a greater depth; refuse pits and cesspools near shallow wells, if properly constructed and placed on the downhill side of the well, need not contaminate the water supply. The passage of water through the rocks commonly effects a filtering and purifying action, and the longer the travel the purer the water.[1] It is often an advantage to have near the surface an impervious layer of rock through which the well is sunk into water-bearing rocks below ; the impervious layer prevents pollution from surface sources. It must also be remembered that a shallow well may dry up completely after a period of drought ; seasonal fluctuations in level are to be expected. Variations in level of over 100 feet may occur in wells in the Chalk.

In open-textured sands and gravels, a well may take the form of a per-forated pipe a few inches in diameter, with a pointed shoe, which is driven into the ground. It is called a *tube well*. If the water is raised by an ordinary hand pump at the surface, the depth to which the tube is driven should not exceed 25 feet. This kind of well is suitable for temporary supplies, and though not much used in England is common in America.

Where the cost of construction is not prohibitive, a deep well or boring, suitably placed, will in general provide a more copious and reliable supply. Sizes vary from 4 inches to about 3 feet in diameter for borings and from 3 feet upwards in the case of wells. A description of the construction of such wells and bores is beyond the scope of this book. Location is important, if an optimum supply is to be obtained, and the well site should be selected after a study of the geological and other factors bearing on the case. In porous water-bearing strata, like the Bunter Sandstones of the Midlands, a good supply may be expected once the boring has penetrated the water-table (see instances cited on p. 275). An increase in the diameter of the bore will produce a corresponding increase in the volume of water available, the presence or absence of joints in the rock being a secondary consideration. On the other hand, in microporous rocks like the Chalk (and some oolites), where the movement of groundwater is virtually confined to the joints and other divisional planes, the success or otherwise of a boring for water will depend on whether an open joint or system of joints is struck. In rocks of this kind, two otherwise similar borings, even close together, may give very different yields, one copious and the other practically nil, according to whether or not the line of the bore crosses joints or fissures along which water is circulating ; hence an increased supply is not necessarily obtained by duplicating a boring under such conditions.

Horizontal galleries radiating from the bottom of deep wells, and prefer-

---

[1] In its passage through a rock mass, groundwater will slowly dissolve any soluble matter ; water from limestone, for example, is hard on this account (see p. 274).

ably crossing lines of groundwater flow, are constructed by some water companies, the object being to tap more fissures and so increase the supply. The driving of galleries in the Chalk was advocated in 1870 by G. V. Lucas, but earlier instances are on record. Groups of wells are often connected underground by means of short headings between the wells.

Cone of Depression. When water is pumped from a well or boring, the surface of the water-table immediately around the well is lowered, and it assumes roughly the form of an inverted cone (Fig. 118). This is known as the *cone of depression* or *cone of exhaustion*. The slopes of the cone are flatter in highly permeable or " open " materials, like gravel, and steeper in less permeable kinds of rock. When a cone is developed, the pressure gradient thus established produces the necessary flow towards the bore-hole to balance the amount of water which is being extracted. The greater the draught on the well, the wider is the extent of the cone of depression.

When a well has been drilled and a cone of depression established, on pumping the well after a rest period the immediate effect is to steepen the gradient of the water-table towards the well (2, Fig. 118), and water has to be lifted from this level, which is called the *pumping level*. When pumping ceases each day, the water level will return to a temporary *rest level* (1) and ultimately, if left undisturbed, to the original level of the water-table.

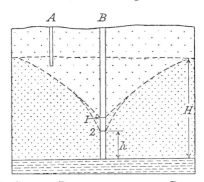

FIG. 118.—CONE OF DEPRESSION AROUND A PUMPED WELL.

1 = daily rest level, 2 = pumping level. The shallow well A has been rendered dry by pumping from B (upper dotted line is the original water-table).

The depth of pumping level below the water-table is the *drawdown*. Most wells are pumped and rested alternately ; if the rest level falls slowly it is a sign of over-pumping, i.e. more water is being taken out than flows in from the aquifer. When this occurs the cone of exhaustion gradually extends, and shallow wells falling within its area become dried up (*A*, Fig. 118). A supply may sometimes be increased by deepening a well, within the limits imposed by the thickness of the aquifer.

A new deep well should not be sunk so near to an existing well as to interfere with its supply, i.e. the probable size of the cone of depression around the new well should be taken into account. Some large wells in the Chalk, for example, have cones extending to a radius of about a mile, and this figure may be exceeded in such rocks as the Triassic sandstones. The base of the cone of depression around a pumped well is known as the circle of influence of the well.

The relation between the yield of a well which has been drilled through permeable rock down to an impervious stratum, and the dimensions of its cone of exhaustion for a free water-table is given by the equation :

$$Q = \pi P(H^2 - h^2) \div 2 \cdot 3 \log_{10} R/r.$$

where Q = quantity pumped in gallons per day,

   P = permeability coefficient (see p. 261),

   H = height in feet of water-table above base of aquifer,

H — h = drawdown (Fig. 118),

   R = radius of cone of depression at water-table,

   r = radius of well.

If R is not known, it may be taken as 1000 feet as a first approximation ; the value of log R/r has much less effect on Q than the other variables. Values of P for different geological deposits are given on p. 262. This formula was originally derived by Dupuit (1863) and is useful for estimating yield for different values of drawdown, for the particular conditions given. It was modified by Theim (1906), who considered two observation wells (within the cone of depression) from which a field measurement of permeability could be made. Other formulæ apply to confined aquifers. For a discussion of the hydraulics of wells the reader is referred to works on Hydrology such as those listed on p. 279.

Estimation of Yield from Drawdown. Methods recently developed in the U.S.A., and applied in Britain and elsewhere, enable information about the yield of a new well, and the permeability of the rocks penetrated by it, to be obtained from a short pumping test. Successive increases in the rate of pumping give different values of drawdown, and these are recorded during the test. From this information the probable yield of the well can be estimated ; the procedure is much quicker than the long-established method of sinking a well and carrying out a full-scale pumping test for 14 or 15 days. The theoretical basis of the new methods, and the results obtained in experiments carried out by the Geological Survey in this country, have been discussed in a series of papers by Dr. J. Ineson.[1]

Groundwater Lowering. The principle of the cone of depression can be usefully applied in certain kinds of excavation to bring about a temporary lowering of the water-table. It may be necessary, for example, to keep dry an excavation such as a trench or foundation, in water-bearing sands or alluvium, where the water-table is only a few feet below the surface and groundwater flows readily into the trench or pit. One method is to drive into the ground a series of tube wells at intervals along the side of the excavation, the group of tubes (or filter wells) being connected by a suitable main to a pump (Fig. 119). Each tube has a pointed shoe for driving into the ground, and groundwater enters the tubes through perforations. When the wells are driven to the necessary depth, and pumping is started, the cones of depression which are in due course established around each tube,

[1] In *Jour. Inst. Water Eng.*, 6, 1952, p. 33 ; *ibid.*, 7, 1953, p. 215 ; *ibid.*, 13, 1959.

together form a zone from which the groundwater has been extracted and in which dry excavation can be carried out (Plate XIIIB). Gravel-filled wells are also used ; the gravel is placed in the annular space between the unlined wall of the well and a central perforated casing, and acts as a filter. Groundwater entering the well at any level can then be pumped out.

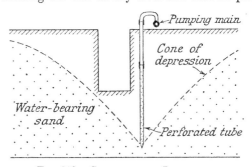

FIG. 119.—GROUNDWATER LOWERING.
Dry excavation can be carried out in the cones of depression formed by pumping a series of tube wells.

The groundwater lowering technique was used by Wentworth-Shields in the construction of the George V dock at Southampton, to avoid possible trouble from water-bearing sands in the excavations.

Confined Aquifers and Artesian Water. The foregoing pages have been concerned with conditions where a free water-table is present. We now consider *confined aquifers*, i.e. aquifers which are covered by overlying impermeable strata. Groundwater is then held in them under pressure, giving rise to *artesian* conditions ; such water rises towards the surface when tapped by a well or boring. Where the pressure is sufficient the water flows out at the surface and constitutes a *flowing well*. This was originally

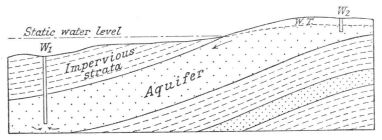

FIG. 120.—ARTESIAN WATER STORAGE.
W_1 = artesian well. W_2 = water-table well. W.T. = water-table.

the case in the old Province of Artois in northern France, and the wells were called " artesian " after the name of the province. Deep wells in the central London area formerly overflowed, but owing to heavy pumping there the water does not now reach the surface (see p. 277). A flowing well has the great advantage that the cost of pumping is reduced or eliminated. The term " artesian " is generally extended to those wells or borings in which the water rises in the bore-hole, indicating that it is under pressure, although it may not come right to the surface ; i.e. it is a non-flowing artesian well.

Artesian conditions depend entirely on the geological structure of the water-bearing formation or aquifer, the essential requirement being an inclined permeable layer covered by an impervious layer (Fig. 120). Rainfall collects over the gathering ground and sinks into the aquifer and is stored there under pressure, since it cannot rise past the impervious cover. If the aquifer is tapped by a well, as at W_1, water will rise in the well, but owing to the frictional resistance to flow offered by the aquifer the height to which it rises is lower than the static water level, the difference being the head lost in friction. Good examples of this kind of artesian storage are provided by the Bunter Sandstones which dip beneath the Keuper Marl in Nottinghamshire ; and by the Lower Greensand below the Gault in Cambridgeshire, and the Lincolnshire Limestone (p. 275). A structure such as that shown is called an *artesian slope*. Other examples of such structures are shown in Fig. 121.

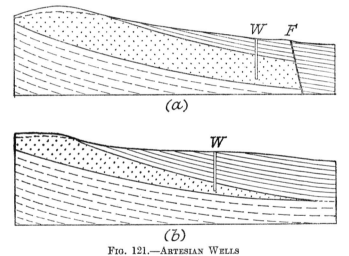

FIG. 121.—ARTESIAN WELLS

n (a) faulted aquifer, (b) gravel lens or thinning aquifer. Impervious beds, full or broken lines ; aquifers, dotted. F = fault. W = well.

Small aquifers are sometimes provided by tapering gravel lenses in boulder clay (cf. Fig. 121b). Water circulating along joints in crystalline igneous rocks may also be found to rise under artesian pressure in bore-holes which meet water-bearing joints.

When the aquifer has the form of a syncline, an *artesian basin* results; the Chalk of the London Basin (Fig. 98) is a well-known instance; it is covered by the porous Thanet Sands and by the overlying impervious London Clay, and is underlain by the Gault clay. Rainwater enters the Chalk at the gathering grounds in the Chilterns and the North Downs, where the formation comes to the surface, and percolates towards the lower parts of the basin ; thence much of the underground water originally moved eastwards to the sea, in the general direction of the plunge of the structure.

The Hampshire Basin (p. 229) also yields artesian supplies, and the Paris Basin has a similar artesian function, the Chalk again being the aquifer. Artesian water has also been obtained from deep bores which penetrate the Lower Greensand below the Chalk and Gault ; at Slough, Buckinghamshire, one such bore, 900 feet deep, yielded a supply of 100,000 gallons per hour overflowing at the surface. Much larger artesian systems are found in other countries, for example the Dakota Sandstone syncline on the flank of the Black Hills in the western United States ; in this structure a gently dipping eastern limb underlies a wide belt of country, and supplies artesian water to many wells drilled through overlying shales to the water-bearing sandstone. The great artesian basin of Queensland, Australia, extends over some 600,000 square miles west of its intake on the Great Divide, and furnishes water to many deep wells in arid country, with an aggregate yield of some 500m. gallons per day.

Underground Water Supplies from British Strata. Some of the more important formations from which supplies are obtained are described below ; the list is not intended to be a complete statement of underground resources.

Pre-Cambrian and Igneous. These rocks are on the whole compact, with a very low porosity (generally less than 1 per cent), but they are much jointed. They frequently yield water from springs, which are fed by water passing along joints and fractures ; an example is the Pewtriss spring, which issues from the thrust-plane below the Pre-Cambrian on the northern side of Hereford Beacon, in the Malvern Hills, and gives about 50,000 gallons per day of very pure water (maximum yield = 77 gallons per minute, minimum = 8 gallons per minute). Many houses and farms take their water from springs rising in the metamorphic and igneous rocks of the Pre-Cambrian, as in the Scottish Highlands, where supplies of this kind are commonly available. Most dwellings were originally built near a source of water, before modern piped supplies were installed.

Igneous rocks (not necessarily of Pre-Cambrian age) also have low porosity, are jointed, and may yield water from springs ; the town of St. Austell, Cornwall, obtains 600,000 gallons per day from springs emerging from granite, and Camborne similarly uses water from springs.

Small but reliable supplies from granitic rocks in districts of low rainfall in Africa have been described by F. Dixey (see book reference on p. 279) as being obtained both from joints and from pockets of weathered rock near the surface. In the latter case the water is held in interstices, and is recovered from wells constructed so as to have a large surface of infiltration.

Older Palæozoic. Rocks of this age are mainly well-compacted sediments, often hard and cleaved. Occasional springs arise at junctions or fractures ; limestones, in particular, throw out lines of springs along their outcrop, e.g. the Cambrian limestone of the north-west Highlands, or the Wenlock Limestone (see p. 209). Older Palæozoic rocks on the whole are of restricted use for underground water supply, but on the other hand they provide valuable upland sites for impounding reservoirs in Britain as discussed in Chapter 14.

Populations of considerable size in Cumberland and the Southern Uplands derive supplies of drinking water from natural and artificial lakes, as well as from springs ; such waters are usually soft. The cleaved Ordovician and Silurian rocks of North Wales also yield much water from springs, which may be led into pipes and distributed by gravity.

Newer Palæozoic. The rocks of the Old Red Sandstone give limited supplies of water. Many domestic wells are located in them, and in Edinburgh, Upper Old Red Sandstone water is used for brewing. Conglomerates in the Old Red Sandstone of east Somerset yield water from springs, for example at their junction with overlying Carboniferous shales. In the less permeable Devonian rocks of west Somerset and Devon, springs issuing from fissures are often reliable for small supplies. Springs are thrown out at the boundaries of the Middle Devonian Limestones of South Devon, and these rocks also yield water from wells.

In the Carboniferous Limestone plentiful water occupies fissures and is hard ; [1] it is used in many places, e.g. the city of Bristol takes water from the Cheddar springs. The lead mines of Derbyshire and the hematite mines of west Cumberland tap much water in the limestone, as do the lead mines of the Halkyn district of North Wales. Drainage of water from the Halkyn mines was needed to make deeper working possible (p. 314). In the Pennines, much water in the limestone flows away by underground streams, but these can provide useful supplies when tapped.

The Millstone Grits contain relatively pure water, but often have a low porosity and yield only small quantities unless they are well fissured. In many places the grits are porous near the surface, where the cement between the grains has been weathered out, but much less permeable at greater depth, and water is best obtained from fractures and fissures. Water from many springs on the outcrop of the Millstone Grit, together with surface run-off, is impounded in reservoirs in the Pennines.

The Coal Measure Sandstones hold much water, but it is largely contaminated ; it is serviceable, however, for industrial purposes, e.g. for replenishing canals, and supplies can be pumped from disused mines. In South Wales the thick Pennant Sandstones of the Middle Coal Measures locally yield large supplies of water. Above the productive Coal Measures of the Midlands there is a group of sandstones called the Enville Series (formerly classed as Permian) which are valuable aquifers ; the city of Coventry obtains a regular supply from wells sunk in these beds, in addition to taking water from the Rivers Severn and Avon.

Permian rocks, apart from the Magnesian Limestone, are comparatively unimportant for water supply, but Permian conglomerates in Somerset and Devon provide local sources. Much water is taken from wells in the Mag-

---

[1] *Hardness* of water is due to dissolved impurities ; a pure water is *soft*. The chief salts in solution which cause hardness are the carbonates and sulphates of calcium and magnesium. Carbonates produce " temporary hardness," which can be removed by boiling and by other means, and sulphates " permanent hardness," which can be removed by chemical treatment. Hardness is expressed in parts per million (by weight) ; formerly the expression degree of hardness was used for 1 part in 100,000 (equivalent to 10 p.p.m.).

nesian Limestone ; the hardness of this water is considerable, averaging 450 p.p.m. from the Upper Limestone, and 300 p.p.m. from the Lower Limestone. Hard water of this kind can be improved by the use of softening plant, before it is put into supply.

Mesozoic. These rocks contain the largest aquifers in Britain. The sandstones of the Triassic system form a big group of water-bearing rocks, and it is estimated that about one-third of the rain falling on their outcrop can be recovered. The Bunter formation forms the most important aquifer of the Midlands. The Lower Bunter Sandstone and the succeeding Pebble Beds are highly permeable and yield water readily ; here especially the diameter of a borehole is an important factor in the yield (see p. 268). The Upper Mottled Sandstone is a somewhat softer rock ; it contains thin bands of marl and gives a permanently hard water (from 120 to 350 p.p.m.) because of its content of sulphates. In the Birmingham area, where the Upper Mottled Sandstone reaches a thickness of over 300 feet, this formation together with the Pebble Beds below it constitute a source of abundant water both for public supplies and for industrial uses. Nottingham, Wolverhampton and other towns in Staffordshire, as well as many smaller places, take water from the Bunter. As an example of the yield of wells in Bunter Sandstone the case of Nottingham may be quoted, where copious supplies of 1·5 to 2·8 million gallons per day have been obtained from each of several wells. The Bunter rocks thin out from north-west to south-east across the Midlands.

The Lower Keuper Sandstone which overlies the Bunter is one of the best water-bearing formations of the country (see p. 222) ; in Warwickshire and Worcestershire its thickness reaches 400 feet or more, but, like the Bunter, it thins considerably towards the south-east under a cover of Keuper Marl. The lower part of the formation is a better aquifer than the upper, because of its coarser grain. (The old name " waterstones " for the upper part of the Keuper Sandstone was used because of a banding in the stone which resembled " watered silk ".) Artesian supplies are obtained from this aquifer where it is covered by the impervious Keuper Marl, e.g. the 600-feet deep boring at Stratford-on-Avon brewery originally gave 1800 gallons per hour at 50 feet above ground level : this supply is now somewhat reduced. The quality of Keuper Sandstone water is good, but it is commonly harder than Bunter water, with 250 to 450 p.p.m. and sometimes considerably more. The sulphate which is present makes the water very suitable for brewing.

In the Jurassic system the limestones yield water, generally hard, from both pores and joints ; the towns of Bedford and Swindon, for example, take supplies from wells in the Great Oolite, but the nature of this and other Jurassic limestone formations varies considerably, as does the quality and amount of water available. In Northamptonshire and Yorkshire the oolites pass into sands, which give good water in many cases, e.g. from wells in the Northampton Sands and from springs which issue at their contact with the Upper Lias clays. Another formation which is locally important for supplies of underground water is the Lincolnshire Limestone, a well-jointed oolitic limestone which reaches a thickness of 100 feet or more to the south of Lincoln but thins out rapidly to the north. Where the Lincolnshire Limestone is covered by clays to the east of its outcrop, artesian wells tapping the aquifer yield plentiful water. The Jurassic rocks generally do not give large supplies, but, as indicated above, provide water for many small towns and villages situated on or near their outcrop.

The Cretaceous system contains the largest and probably best known aquifer in Britain, the Chalk ; the Upper and Lower Greensands are also water-bearing in part, and the sands of the Wealden Series (Tunbridge Wells Sands and Ashdown Beds) yield local supplies of soft water. The permeable sands of the Lower Greensand hold good and plentiful water which is soft and contains some iron (due to the presence of the mineral glauconite) ; it is much drawn on in Bedfordshire and Cambridgeshire (p. 272). Water from the Upper Greensand is also soft ; the " malmstone " is a prominent water-bearing horizon in this formation, as at Selborne, Hants ; many springs rise at the base of the Upper Greensand, as in East Devon. The Spilsby Sandstone of Lincolnshire (probably Lower Cretaceous, Wealden), only about 80 feet thick, provides water for a number of towns, including Skegness ; where it is covered by impermeable beds the water in it is under artesian pressure.

The artesian reservoir formed by the Chalk below London has been briefly described above ; the Chalk formation also supplies water to many towns and villages situated on its outcrop, the extent of which was indicated on pages 228-9 (and see Fig. 94). It is a porous rock, but the pores are very small and hold their water by capillarity (p. 259) ; the Chalk is, however, pervious on account of fissures, which are estimated to represent between 2 and 4 per cent of its bulk. While, therefore, the pore-contained water is almost entirely retained, water moves freely through the system of joints and fissures which traverse the rock, and drains into wells from them. Experiments on the rate of travel of water through fissures in the Chalk showed that a pink dye (fluorescein) which was put into the water at swallow holes at North Mimms, Hertfordshire, took 70 hours to reach the Chadwell spring 9½ miles away, an average of 17,200 feet per day.[1] The difference in water levels between these two points is about 100 feet, giving a gradient of some 10 feet per mile ; the flow was to the north-east along the strike, not in the dip direction.

At many localities the Upper Chalk is the best aquifer, because of the presence of open fissures, the yield being smaller for the Middle and Lower Chalk. This is especially the case in the south-east of England ; but in the Chilterns the Middle and Lower divisions of the Chalk have large out-crops over which much rainfall infiltrates, and they then yield larger supplies. Yields of the order of 40,000 gallons per hour or more are fre-quently obtained from Chalk wells, and in some cases 2 million gallons per day is exceeded. Where the beds are folded anticlinally, fissures tend to be opened out on the crest of the fold and the rock is thus more pervious and the yield greater. Chalk water is hard, and does not undergo a natural

[1] Metropolitan Water Board, 32nd Annual Report, 1937.

filtration as would be the case in passing through a sand; hardness to the extent of 250–350 p.p.m. is commonly found, and may exceed 400 p.p.m.

London Wells. In the London area there are a large number of deep wells, which are sunk through Tertiary deposits into the underlying Chalk. It was estimated that, in 1936, over 20 million gallons per day of water from the Chalk was taken for public and industrial supplies from wells in the County of London alone, a small area.[1] The amount has increased since that date. If a larger area is considered, say within a radius of 25 miles from London, the daily quantity of underground water extracted probably exceeds 250 million gallons ; as much again is taken from river sources, principally from the Thames and Lea. Most of the underground supply is derived from the Chalk, and the above figures give some idea of the importance of this formation as an aquifer in the London area, quite apart from its wider extent.

From the well records it is known that water levels in the Chalk under London have fallen steadily and are still falling, the water pumped out being in excess of replenishment from the surrounding parts of the aquifer. The average fall in level of the water-table for the 100 years preceding 1920 was 2 feet per year ; at the beginning of that period water levels (which defined the pressure surface in the aquifer) were well above the top of the Chalk in the central part of the syncline, and upward pressure was exerted on the base of the London Clay. In the years from 1920 to 1940 the fall was more rapid in certain parts of the area ; in the north-west the rate of fall was 3 feet or more per year, and in the central part of the London Basin it averaged 5 feet per year up to about 1940. The rate was reduced some-what during the 1939–45 war, but from 1945 onwards it was resumed ; and many new industries needing water were sited in the area, particularly along the Thames estuary. As a result of the lowered pressure in the artesian system, water levels in some areas of the London syncline are now below the top of the Chalk, and the upper part of the Chalk in those areas is empty of water. One such " water hollow " has existed beneath Putney and Richmond for many years ; another has developed under the Lea valley on the border of Essex.

Another consequence of the lowered water levels has been the beginning of contamination through the entry of estuarine water from the Thames into the underground system. From Deptford to the Plumstead Marshes the Chalk is brought to the surface (with only a thin cover of alluvial deposits) by minor folding and faulting which is superimposed on the broad structure of the London Basin. Along this tract, some 10 miles in length, water from the river can enter the Chalk through the permeable alluvium, in the absence of an impermeable cover, owing to the reduced pressure and lower water levels in the aquifer. Formerly, fresh water from the Chalk used to emerge in places as springs in the river bed at low tide ;[2] but with

[1] " Underground Water Supply of the County of London," by Dr. Stevenson Buchan, *Trans. Inst. Water Eng.*, 43, 1938, p. 129.

[2] W. Whitaker and J. C. Thresh in " The Water Supply of Essex," *Mem. Geol. Surv*, 1916, p. 54.

the fall of water levels and the consequent reduction in pressure in the aquifer, the flow has become reversed, and estuarine water now enters the Chalk through the superficial deposits. This has resulted in the underground water locally becoming somewhat saline, and as more salt water was drawn in (with the continued overpumping of the aquifer) the increased salinity has spread for several miles north of the river.

Various remedies to offset the deterioration of the groundwater conditions in the London area have been proposed, and some have been put in hand : (i) It has been suggested that industrial users could take water from alternative sources, instead of from the Chalk, when the quality of the water used is not of first importance ; e.g. from near-surface gravel deposits, or from the Thames (as is done by some users).

(ii) Restrictions on the sinking of new wells, and on increased rates of abstraction from the aquifer at existing wells, came into force with the Water Acts of 1945 and 1948. These restrictions resulted in a measure of slowing down of the process of deterioration.

(iii) The putting back of water into the Chalk through wells, the water being taken mainly from the River Lea in East London. This was done for several years up to 1914, and the fall in water levels was *locally* reduced there. Recently, experiments in re-charging the Chalk aquifer below East London have been resumed by the Metropolitan Water Board, and are continuing.[1] River water is used for the replenishment after suitable treatment to remove impurities, and is taken from the R. Lea during periods of excess flow in the winter months. From October 1953 for 5 months, filtered and chlorinated river water was recharged into the Chalk at the rate of 6m. gallons per day, through wells in the Lea Valley, and also in subsequent years. In the summer months it has been possible to abstract more water for supply than if there had been no recharge. At the same time the fall in water levels has been locally arrested. Thus the recharge water has, in effect, been stored in the Thanet Sand and Upper Chalk below the Lea Valley, for use in the peak demand period of the summer, and at an economic cost. It is necessary to guard against the clogging of the water-bearing joints and fissures in the Chalk by ingoing silt and mud. Much sediment is in suspension in river water in times of flood, and treatment by filtration or settlement is then needed to prevent the sediment from entering the underground system.

Tertiary. The sands that lie above the Chalk contain water which is drawn upon locally to a limited extent. Water in the Thanet Sands may escape downwards into the Chalk ; alternatively, Chalk water may be drawn from borings into the Thanet Sands where the rocks are saturated. The character of the Lower London Tertiaries (Thanet Sands and Woolwich Beds) varies throughout their outcrop from east to west. Where they consist largely of sands, as in southern Essex, they sometimes yield useful water supplies ; thus Chelmsford takes 5000 gallons per hour for public supply from a 9-inch borehole which penetrates 110 feet of the sandy deposits.

[1] E. S. Boniface, " Some experiments in artificial recharge in the lower Lea valley." *Proc. Inst. C.E.,* **14,** 1959.

The Bagshot Sands yield supplies for houses and villages, and in the syncline of the Hampshire Basin they provide also for small industrial requirements, and occasionally for public supplies as at Cowes, Isle of Wight. Difficulty is commonly experienced in these sands through the silting up of boreholes, and gravel or other filters are employed.

The Pliocene Crag deposits of East Anglia give water in varying quantity, sometimes several hundred gallons per hour, and occasionally enough to supply a small town. Small supplies are also derived from Glacial sands and gravels which overlie the Crags.

Recent deposits such as alluvium, river gravels, and coastal deposits contain water which may be tapped by shallow wells, but precautions should be taken to ensure that it is free from organic matter before it is used for domestic purposes ; the yield will, in general, be small, except where water pumped from a well in alluvium is quickly replaced by water drawn in from a near-by river. Gravels sometimes occur in lenticular layers in boulder clay and give rise to perched water-tables. Shallow supplies may often be obtained from old river terrace gravels.

SELECTED REFERENCES

British Rainfall. Annual volume of the British Rainfall Organization. Meteorological Office, London.

BUCHAN, S. "The Water Supply of the County of London from Underground Sources." *Mem. Geol. Survey*, London, 1938.

DAPPLES, E. C. " Basic Geology for Science and Engineering," Chap. 9. Wiley & Sons, 1959.

DIXEY, F. "Handbook of Water Supply." Murby. 1950. 2nd edition.

EDMUNDS, F. H. " Outlines of Water Supply in England and Wales." *Trans. Inst. Water Engrs.*, 46, 1941, p. 15.

MEINZER, O. E. (editor). "Hydrology." McGraw-Hill Book Co., 1942.

THRESH, J. C., AND BEALE, J. F. " The Examination of Waters and Water Supplies." Churchill, London. 1951 (6th ed., revised by E. Windle Taylor).

TOLMAN, C. F. " Groundwater." McGraw-Hill Book Co. 1937, reprinted 1957.

Symposium : Conservation of Water Resources, *Inst. C. E.*, Lond. 1963., (especially Paper 10).

BUTLER, S. S. "Engineering Hydrology." 1957. Prentice Hall.

WISLER, C. O., and BRATER, E. F. " Hydrology," 2nd edition, 1959. Wiley & Sons.

NOTE.—The lists of Wells published by the Geological Survey as " War-time Pamphlets " are being revised and re-issued under the title *Water Supply Papers* (see Appendix); each Paper contains data for a 1-inch New Series sheet, e.g. Dartford, NS 271 (1965).

Technical Papers are now published by the Water Resources Board (constituted in 1963), with reference to both underground and surface water resources in Gt. Britain.

Chapter 14

THE GEOLOGY OF RESERVOIR AND DAM SITES

Public water supplies from surface sources include water taken locally from rivers and lakes, and also that stored in impounding reservoirs generally situated at some distance from the area of supply. Thus a town which lies on a large river frequently takes its water from that source. The water is filtered and, if necessary, purified both chemically and bacteriologically before being used ; modern methods of purification [1] make it possible to take water from the lower reaches of rivers, which are more liable to contamination than the upper reaches.

London has for many years taken the bulk of its water for public supplies from the Thames above Teddington ; though, as stated above (p. 277), equally large quantities for industrial, private, and public supplies are derived from underground sources. Southampton, originally supplied from wells in the Chalk, has added to its resources by taking water from the River Itchen. Bournemouth also draws a dual supply from the Chalk and the River Avon, and Darlington uses water from the River Tees ; further examples of a similar kind might be given. These river sources are readily accessible and often less costly to obtain than well supplies involving an expensive drilling programme ; on the other hand the cost of purifying river water before it is put into public supply is usually greater than the expense involved in treating well water.

Distinct from river supplies, upland surface sources provide water for some of the largest cities in Britain, the water being stored in impounding reservoirs and conveyed to the towns by pipe-line or aqueduct. Thus, Glasgow takes a supply from Loch Katrine, Edinburgh from the Talla reservoir in the Pentland Hills, Manchester from Thirlmere and Hawes Water in the Lake District, Birmingham from the Elan Valley reservoirs in Central Wales, and Liverpool from Lake Vyrnwy in N. Wales. There are also many smaller schemes, e.g. Torquay and Plymouth obtain supplies from reservoirs situated on the granite area of Dartmoor at Tottiford, Fernworthy, and Burrator.

In Scotland, since 1945, many dams have been constructed for impounding water for hydroelectric generation, together with tunnels for conveying water (reference on p. 302), apart from numerous earlier schemes.

Where the run-off is utilized in this way (as distinct from the percolation fraction of the rainfall) and the water is impounded, geological factors have an important bearing on the choice of site for both the reservoir and the dam ; the reservoir should be of maximum water-retaining efficiency and the dam must be securely founded.

Preliminary Geological Investigations. Geological advice is now taken in connection with most large civil engineering undertakings, and is generally essential where a reservoir site of any size has to be chosen.

---

[1] See, for example, " Symposium on the Sterilization of Water (part C)," *Jour. Inst. Water Eng.*, 4, 1950, p. 502.

PLATE XIII

Photo by H.M. Geological Survey.

(A) FLOWING ARTESIAN WELLS TAPPING WATER-BEARING CHALK AT BERE REGIS, DORSET. THE TUBE-WELLS ARE ABOUT 90 FT. DEEP AND SUPPLY WATER TO WATER-CRESS BEDS.

(B) GROUNDWATER LOWERING : TUBE-WELLS AND PUMPING MAIN IN POSITION (LEFT) ALONG A LINE OF TRENCH IN WATER-BEARING SAND.

PLATE XIV

Photo by J. C. Waddington.

DAM FOUNDATION TRENCH IN GRANITE, FERNWORTHY RESERVOIR, SOUTH DEVON. TIMBER FLUME CARRIES STREAM DIVERSION ACROSS THE TRENCH. NEARLY HORIZONTAL SHEET-JOINTING IS SEEN IN CENTRE OF PHOTO.

When the geological conditions are straightforward they can often be handled by the engineer himself, but he should have enough knowledge of geology to be able to recognize likely difficulties and to know when to call in expert advice. A thorough geological investigation should be made *before* the works are begun, and observations should continue during their progress because additional data become available, and geological prediction may be required to guide the excavation programme, as construction proceeds.

A geological exploration of this kind generally costs little compared with the total cost of the scheme ; in a number of cases in recent years it has amounted to between $\frac{1}{4}$ and 1 per cent of the whole. This relatively small amount represents a valuable insurance against expensive difficulties, otherwise unforeseen, which might arise during construction but which it may be possible to predict from a study of the geological factors involved.

Factors governing Choice of Reservoir Site. Non-geological factors such as distance from the town to be supplied, altitude of site, area of catchment and amount of rainfall, will not be further discussed here though they have a fundamental bearing on the cost of a scheme and the suitability of a site. The geological considerations can be put under three heads :

(1) Geology of the catchment area. This affects the proportions of run-off and percolation, as indicated in the previous chapter (p. 256). Enough information may be available from existing maps, such as the 1-inch maps in Great Britain, though if necessary it must be supplemented by observations made at first hand.

(2) Geology of the reservoir area (i.e. the area to be flooded). The special requirement here is that there should be no danger of serious leakage when the ground is under pressure from the full head of water in the reservoir. Geological mapping on a large scale (e.g. 6 inches to a mile) is generally needed to collect and assemble the required data. The position of the water-table can also be investigated, if necessary, and the possible silting up of the site taken into account.

(3) Geology of the dam site. A secure foundation for the dam is essential and, to avoid taking conditions for granted, the nature of the subsurface geology at the site can be explored by trial bores or other means, and a large-scale map prepared, e.g. on a scale of 25 inches to the mile. The dam will in most cases involve the excavation of a trench, whether the structure is of concrete, masonry, or earth with a core wall, and the geological conditions in the trench area should be known as closely as possible. The ideal dam would have the whole length of its foundation in sound water-tight rock, and preferably in one kind of rock—conditions which are seldom realized in practice. Percolation below the dam when the reservoir is full, and the position of the body of impounded water relative to the water-table, are matters which have also to be considered. Each site must be investigated on its own merits, since no two are alike. The following discussion necessarily concerns general principles, not all of which may apply to any particular case. They are illustrated in the succeeding descriptions of a number of schemes, but should be supplemented

by further reading. A short bibliography of the subject is provided at the end of the chapter, in addition to references given in footnotes.

GEOLOGY OF RESERVOIR AREA

Superficial Deposits. At many sites suitable for impounding reservoirs, layers of superficial deposits such as peat, alluvium, or glacial drift are present, lying above the solid rocks, and need close investigation. Peat is best avoided if possible ; its thickness is often difficult to estimate, except from many bore-holes, and if much is present its removal is generally necessary. The organic acids and colouring matter of the peat adversely affect the purity of the water. The removal of peat may be a costly process, as was found at the Alwen Reservoir supplying Birkenhead ;[1] or impractical, as at the Silent Valley Reservoir site, Belfast ; in the latter case the peat, which was 30 feet thick in places, was successfully treated by covering it with a layer of clean sand 2 to 3 feet thick. Alluvium does not constitute such a difficulty, though if trenches have to be cut through it the question of timbering may arise, and also the water content of the alluvium may be troublesome during construction (see page 285).

Glacial deposits may be a help if they are impervious, e.g. boulder clay ; an ideal reservoir site would be on an impervious series of rocks or a thick deposit of boulder clay ; and the ends of a dam may be run into boulder clay. On the other hand, if the deposit contains sands and gravels (e.g. moraine) these porous materials may lead to serious leakage, especially if they occur near the sides of the reservoir or at its downstream end, where the water level will eventually stand at its greatest height above the original surface. Under these circumstances it may be necessary to trench through the permeable deposits for the construction of a cut-off, or use some other method of treatment. It must be remembered that the shape of the rock surface beneath a cover of drift bears no relation to surface topography, and that in glaciated country there may be buried hollows and channels filled with the drift. (See also p. 286.)

An instance of this occurred at the site of the Pollaphuca Reservoir on the headwaters of the River Liffey, about 17 miles south-west of Dublin. It was known that a large pre-Glacial valley filled with drift lay below the site, with its deepest part about half a mile to the north of the present river. The depth (132 feet below surface) and extent of the buried valley were proved by trial borings. Much of the drift fill consisted of boulder clay and fine sand, with impersistent lenses of permeable gravel, as revealed by trial pits. After permeability tests had been carried out, it was concluded that serious leakage from the reservoir through the buried valley was unlikely to occur.[2]

Permeable and Soluble Rocks. With regard to the solid geology at the site, i.e. the rocks below any cover of superficial deposits, difficulties

---

[1] *Proc. Inst. C.E.*, Vol. 206, 1917–18.

[2] V. D. Harty, " Site Investigation for Reservoirs and Dams," *Trans. Inst. C.E. of Ireland*, LXXII, 1946, p. 161.

may arise from the presence of highly permeable rocks which are likely to reduce the water-tightness of the reservoir. Limestones and other soluble rocks are the worst offenders in this respect, since solution channels may be present which carry away large quantities of water. In the case of the Hales Bar Dam on the Tennessee River, U.S.A., the presence of large cavities in the limestone formation at the site necessitated an expensive grouting programme, and leakage was finally stopped only by the injection of hot liquid asphalt through a series of holes drilled in the rock.[1] (See also p. 297, Great Falls Reservoir.) Beds of gypsum are even more soluble than limestone ; the failure of the Macmillan Reservoir in the U.S.A. was due to water escaping through a gypsum layer which became widened by solution. Underground flow of water through a band of porous grit produced serious leakage at the Broomhead Reservoir [2] of the Sheffield Waterworks. Leakage through fissures may also occur, but cases are known where the fissures have become sealed by silting up from within the reservoir.[3]

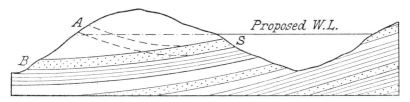

FIG. 122.—LEAKAGE FROM A RESERVOIR THROUGH POROUS STRATUM.

S = outcrop of porous bed in area to be flooded. Possible synclinal structure, with no leakage, shown at A ; alternatively, B shows outcrop of porous bed at lower level in adjacent valley.

Rocks which are not likely to allow the passage of much water include shales and slates, schists, gneisses, and crystalline igneous rocks such as granite, except where well-developed joint systems are present in them.

Structural Features. Simple geological structures and impermeable rocks provide straightforward conditions, as where the strata are not highly folded or faulted. Such conditions are seldom realized in practice, because topographical and other considerations partly govern the choice. A general dip upstream rather than downstream is to be preferred. Porous beds outcropping on valley slopes which are ultimately to be submerged should be investigated, to see if they would form possible conduits for the underground flow of water away from the reservoir (Fig. 122). This figure clearly points to the need for examining the geology immediately outside the reservoir area. Beds dipping *towards* the reservoir area may help to contribute flow from springs.

A porous bed may be sealed off by concreting a trench cut along its outcrop, or by grouting ; both methods were employed in the case of the Broomhead Reservoir (*loc. cit.*).

[1] *Eng. News Record*, Vol. 96, 1926, p. 798.

[2] Swales, J. K., on " The Broomhead Reservoir," *Water and Water Eng.*, London, Vol. 36, 1934, p. 565.

[3] Strange, in *Proc. Inst. C.E.*, London, cxxxii, 1898, p. 137.

Faults may be troublesome if open to the passage of water ; either they are potential outlets for the escape of water from the reservoir, or for the emergence of springs in excavations during construction. In the former case they may be treated by grouting or by trenching along the line of fracture, the trench being filled with clay puddle or concrete ; in the latter, a pit can be sunk at the spring and the water pumped out.

Landslides are an indication of unstable conditions, and ground which has been subject to them should be avoided if possible. Leakage of water through a porous bed (as at *B*, Fig. 122) may give rise to landslides on slopes away from the reservoir some time after it has been filled, unless preventive measures are put in hand.

Position of Water-table. In general, when natural conditions of equilibrium are changed, as by the presence of a large body of impounded water, the effects of seepage and disturbance of ground-water flow must be considered. Water from the reservoir will sink into the ground, and its movement then depends on the position of the water-table and on the

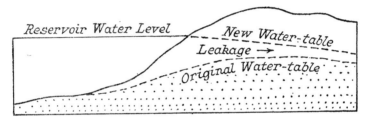

FIG. 123.—DIAGRAM TO ILLUSTRATE POSSIBLE LEAKAGE FROM A RESERVOIR.

nature of the rocks (see above). In many places the water-table lies close below the surface in a valley, rising on either side (see Fig. 113). If the water-level in the reservoir does not exceed that of the water-table under any adjacent ground (such as a local watershed) there should be no serious loss by seepage. If it does exceed the level of the water-table at some point, as in Fig. 123, leakage will occur and its amount will depend on the permeability of the rocks present. Where these are fine-grained sediments, the leakage should not be great, but the presence of open-textured or much-jointed rocks may result in considerable seepage losses. Care should be taken to ensure that perched water-tables are not mistaken for the main water-table.

Silting up of Reservoir. Streams flowing into the reservoir when it is completed will deposit their sediment there, and if the amount of detritus is considerable it may lead to the silting up of the artificial lake in a comparatively small number of years. The time taken will depend much on the nature of the catchment ; a good cover of trees, for instance, helps to reduce silting. As silting goes on, water storage capacity is gradually reduced and the efficiency of the reservoir impaired. Where this appears likely to happen, the possibility of making provision for washing out the silt through passages in the dam, or dealing with it in other ways, should be considered. Much sediment is brought in at times of flood : at some sites it may be possible to construct a by-pass for flood waters around the reservoir, or silt-traps on streams feeding the reservoir.

GEOLOGY OF SITE FOR DAM

Trial Borings. In selecting the site for a dam the general considerations are those of safety and economy. If a large-scale geological map of the area where the dam is to be founded can be made, the mapping will probably elucidate the main structures, including faults, in the rocks, but additional information is generally sought from borings. Rotary boring yields a core, which is a record of the rocks passed through, and is to be preferred to percussion drilling. Trial bores are also used to explore sub-surface conditions and in doubtful or critical areas shafts may be sunk to obtain detail. Large bores 36 inches in diameter, which allow of the direct inspection of the rock, have been employed in America, e.g. in exploring cavernous limestone at the site of the Norris Dam, Tennessee, and at the Kentucky Dam. Such bores are useful where water entering the bore-hole can be controlled. The placing of bore-holes should not be haphazard, but planned to give the maximum amount of information having regard to the known geological structures of the site. It is desirable that any extensive boring programme should be in the charge of an engineer with some know-ledge of geology, and a regular inspection made by a geologist, so that items of evidence which may be very important, although small in them-selves, shall not be missed. During the progress of drilling, any sudden loss of water in the drill-holes should be recorded, as it may point to the presence of open fissures in the rock.

Superficial Deposits. The rocks on which the dam is to be built will often have some cover of superficial deposits such as drift or alluvium as already indicated ; these materials, together with any broken rock, will be removed over the area of the foundation, so that the dam is securely founded on sound rock. The nature of the cover which is going to be cut through will influence the methods to be employed in its excavation, and should therefore be investigated, special attention being paid to its porosity and water content. If the dam trench is a deep one, it may be important to estimate the behaviour of the superficial deposits during construction ; support for the sides of the excavation and volume of pumping if the material is water-bearing are two main considerations. Running sand and silt which was encountered in part of the cut-off trench for the Silent Valley Dam (an earth dam) near Belfast,[1] necessitated the use of compressed air in the excavations and of special cast-iron cylindrical linings in that section of the trench (Plate XV).

Contours of Rock Surface. The shape of the solid rock surface at the site may be determined by trial bores, as already indicated, or some-times by a preliminary geophysical survey (Chapter 16). If borings are

[1] " Construction of the Silent Valley Reservoir, Belfast Water Supply," by G. McIldowie, *Proc. Inst. C.E.*, Vol. 239, 1935, p. 465.

used, the number of borings should be adequate (Fig. 124), and suitable spacing considered. A contour map of the buried surface can, if necessary, be constructed, based on the bore-hole data. An extensive boring programme is specially needed in a drift-covered area, since glacial deposits are of such an irregular nature that large topographical hollows and old river valleys may be present in the sub-drift surface. If these are met with during construction without having been anticipated, considerable difficulties and additional expense may be involved, since excavation must be taken down through the drift to solid rock. In numerous cases on record, buried valleys filled with drift have been met in dam foundations and have necessitated locally deeper excavations in the trench. The fill of these buried valleys may be glacial sands or gravels carrying water, or boulder clay, and the nature of the deposits is liable to vary considerably in a short distance. In making trial bores through boulder clay, very large boulders add considerably to the difficulty of boring and have sometimes in the past been mistaken for solid rock ; bores should be continued for 20 feet or more in such cases to ensure that the rock floor has in fact been reached.

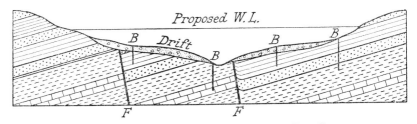

FIG. 124.—SPACING OF TRIAL BORINGS AT A DAM SITE.
A few borings as shown (B) do not reveal the faults or the structure of porous bed (dotted).

Conditions in the Foundation. Under this heading fall questions such as the nature and condition (fresh or decayed) of the rocks on which the dam is to be founded ; their strength, which must be enough to take the weight of the dam without crushing or shearing ; structural features such as the dip of strata, spacing of bedding planes, presence of folds, faults, joints, and zones of crushed rock ; and the permeability of the rock and the nature of the water circulation through it, which govern the important question of leakage below the dam.

While small dams can be successfully constructed on beds of weaker materials such as clay, hard rocks like granite, sandstone, or gneiss are generally needed to take the load of a large structure. Formations in which hard and soft layers alternate are not generally good, because the penetration of water may weaken the softer layers and lead to movement along them. Alternations of sandstones and shales may also lead to slipping during excavation of the trench. The bearing power of different rocks varies widely, and even two rocks called by the same name may have quite different degrees of strength. If there is any doubt about the capacity of the material to carry the necessary load, it should be tested for crushing strength.

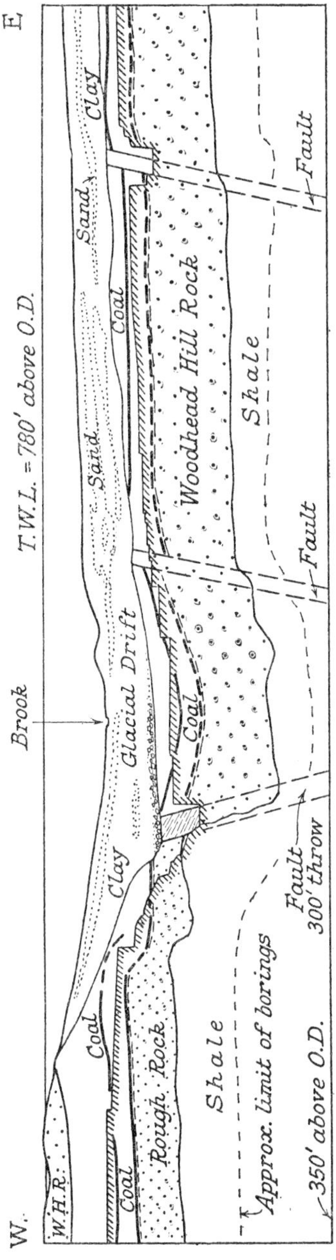

The best conditions arise when a dam can be built on one uniform formation ; if more than one kind of rock is present in the foundation, different bearing strengths may lead to unequal settlement of the structure.

Granite. This rock, when unweathered, provides a strong foundation for any engineering structure. But it is commonly a much jointed rock and may contain fracture zones, and these structures allow the percolation of water through the mass. It is necessary, therefore, to seal the joints by some system of grouting. Further, runs of soft rock may occur in granite, such as weathered zones, or belts of decomposition (often vertical or inclined) along which the granite has been altered by hydrothermal fluids to kaolin (p. 151). In a foundation, such soft zones need to be excavated to a greater depth and special measures taken to seal them off. (See also examples on pp. 294 and 301.)

Lavas. Rocks such as basalt and andesite flows have considerable strength, but are commonly much jointed and often very pervious ; the upper parts of the flows may be vesicular and therefore porous. If a dam to be built on lavas is located *above* the water-table, impounded water may leak away to lower levels. It is therefore important to find the position of the water-table and assess the value of the site from that point of view. A number of dams have been successfully built on lavas, e.g. Boulder Dam (p. 295).

Fig. 125.—Geological Section in Coal Measures along Western Part of Cut-off Trench at Water Grove Reservoir, Rochdale, Lancs. W.H.R. = Woodhead Hill Rock (a sandstone). Base of excavation shown by hatched line. Cementation of the lower part of the sandstone, which was much fissured, was carried out from over 200 drill-holes (after N. G. Elliot in *Trans. Inst. Water Engineers*, XL, 1935). Length of Section about 1800 feet.

Gneisses and schists. In these metamorphic rocks additional structures such as foliation and schistosity are present, often together with crumpling and folding. Such structures may have made the rocks more readily susceptible to weathering, and thus correspondingly weaker under load. Deeply weathered soils in gneisses and schists have been found at certain localities, as at the Tooma Dam site of the Snowy Mountains scheme, New South Wales. Deep weathering is especially prevalent in sub-tropical climates, as in parts of Rhodesia and in Malaya.

Some metamorphic rocks, on the other hand, such as quartzites, are normally strong and provide good foundation conditions.

Sandstones. An important consideration here, again, is the presence of open joints in a foundation. If many joints are present a large grouting programme may be involved, in order to secure the foundation against excessive leakage, and to reduce uplift pressure on the dam. Usually a good bond between concrete and sandstone is possible when concrete is to be placed on the rock.

Limestones. Rocks of this group are liable to be particularly troublesome because of their solubility. Solution cavities are to be expected to be present in limestone, especially beneath a valley, where much water circulation has gone on. Sometimes very deep cavities have been formed and extensive grouting is needed to effect a seal to further percolation of water. Any cavities which may be left open become further enlarged by solution in course of time, after the completion of the reservoir.

The Kentucky Dam provides an instructive example of such conditions. Grouting with cement was undertaken before excavation for the dam began, but was only partly successful. Excavation of the trench eventually revealed the presence of silt-filled cavities : had these been left untreated, washing out of the silt by water under the pressure of a full reservoir would have rendered serious leakage likely. A very deep solution channel extended under the line of the dam ; its filling of clay, silt, and limestone blocks was mined out through large-diameter core borings, and a concrete cut-off constructed across the channel.[1]

Shales. Foundation conditions in shale and other argillaceous sediments are discussed below (p. 289).

Structures. Given a suitable kind of rock at the dam site, beds which dip gently upstream and strike across the valley provide probably the best foundation conditions among sedimentary rocks, as the resultant of the weight of the dam and water pressure will then act nearly at right angles to the bedding planes of the strata. This condition is seen in Fig. 126 illustrating the Vyrnwy Dam (p. 292). Bedded rocks are strongest in compression when the load is applied perpendicularly to bedding. The weakness of laminated rocks like schists in resisting shearing stresses parallel to their foliation is illustrated by the failure of the St. Francis Dam, California.[2] One abutment of this structure was built against schists, the foliation direc-

[1] *Proc. Amer. Soc. C.E.*, 69, 1943 ; and Berkey Volume, p. 35 (see p. 302).

[2] *Economic Geol.*, Vol. 23, 1928, p. 553, for full description of geology of the site, by **F. L. Ransome.**

tion of which was parallel to the wall of the gorge across which the dam was placed. Concrete was poured against the smooth schist faces and adhered, but the rock failed along foliation planes when it came under the influence of the water pressure of a full reservoir.

Zones of fracture and strong joint systems are often lines of weakness and also channels for the circulation of water. The presence of sharp local folding (in contrast to broad and gentle fold-structures) may represent weak points in a formation, as in the case of the Howden Dam of the Derwent Valley Water Board, where the dam trench was cut down through small broken folds in the Yoredale Series.[1]

The presence of faults does not necessarily condemn a dam site, but it is important that the geological history of the faulting should be investigated. Except under special circumstances a dam should not be built across a fault known to have been active in recent times. If necessary, special joints can be incorporated in the design of a dam, which allow sections of the structure to move slightly relative to one another, so as to provide for possible small movements on a fault. This was done in the case of the Morris Dam, California, which was built across a geologically old fault.[2] Again, the proximity of a dam to a known zone of active faulting does not necessarily imply that the structure is seriously endangered ; the large concrete dam at Crystal Springs, near San Mateo, California, was not injured by severe movement on the San Andreas fault, which runs about 900 feet to the west of the dam, in the San Francisco earthquake of 1906 (see p. 162). Smaller earth dams built actually across the fault suffered displacements up to 12 feet but remained standing. The earth dam at Water Grove Reservoir (near Rochdale, Lancs.) was built across a fault with a throw of 300 feet in Coal Measure shales and sandstones (Fig. 125). This fault zone was filled with broken rock and clay which rendered it mpervious.

Dam Sites on Weak Formations. The special conditions which arise where a foundation is to be in shale or clay, and which involve special treatment, have been discussed by W. J. Mead,[3] and others. The bearing strength of such materials is relatively low, and decreases as the water content increases. Thus shales which may appear sufficiently strong in the dry condition in natural exposures or excavations may weaken considerably when wetted. Their capacity to carry a load is increased when the shale is restrained on all sides, but if support is removed (as during excavation) deformation may result, the material tending to flow away from the loaded area. One method of construction employed is to " float " a structure on shale by first removing a mass equivalent to the load of the structure.

Shales which have been disturbed may be traversed by shear zones, along which deep weathering has taken place locally, giving rise to zones of wet, plastic clay. If the presence of such zones is suspected they should

---

[1] *Proc. Inst. C.E.*, Vol. 206, 1917–18, Pt. II, Fig. 3.
[2] *Eng. News Record*, Vol. 121, 1938, p. 184.
[3] Report of 2nd Congress on Large Dams, Washington, 1938.

be looked for carefully during the geological investigation prior to beginning construction. In a spillway structure at the Fort Peck Dam, built on soft shales, resistance to sliding was increased by using reinforced concrete dowels, 30 feet long, placed in borings in the shale foundation and tied into the concrete floor of the structure.

Where sandstone bands are interbedded with shales, soft layers may occur below the sandstones, since the latter are channels for the movement of groundwater, and the adjacent shale becomes softened.

The correct preparation of a shale foundation for the placing of concrete upon it is an important matter. After the excavation of overlying alluvium (if present) and of weathered rock, the fresh shale surface thus exposed will tend to dry and shrinkage cracks may develop. This should be minimized by reducing as far as possible the time between the preparation of the surface and placing the concrete. A waterproof coating can also be used to protect the prepared surface, such as a coating of asphalt, which gives a good bond between the shale and the concrete. In grouting the open joints which are present in some shales, the grout pressures should be kept at a low enough value—not more than the load of the rock and structure above the level of grouting—as excess pressure may lift or deform the mass.

In the case of earth dams or embankments built on alluvium, the permeability of the latter should be estimated by field tests. Compaction of alluvial sands, silts, and clays may occur when under load ; a compaction of 8 per cent of the thickness of a sand was measured in tests at the Fort Peck site. As compaction takes place, water contained in the sediment escapes, and provision for this should be made. Soil mechanics tests can be carried out on alluvial sediments to determine their properties.

Percolation beneath the Dam. The permeable or impermeable nature of the foundation rock is a matter of considerable importance, for it governs the amount of percolation beneath the dam, and this percolation is both a source of leakage from the reservoir and also in some cases a possible cause of upward pressure on the base of the structure. Where the foundation rock is permeable, it may be possible to reduce percolation to a large extent by making the path of the percolating water as long as possible, thereby reducing the hydraulic gradient between the upstream and downstream faces of the dam. This can be done by constructing along the length of the foundation a cut-off trench, filled with impervious material to a designed depth and situated near the upstream face of the dam. The percolation path is thus deflected downwards and increased in length by this impervious barrier. The desired ratio of the depth of water in the reservoir (at the upstream face of the dam) to the length of the percolation path is taken at some value between 1 : 5 and 1 : 20, according to the nature of the rocks at the site, a higher ratio being used for fine-grained sediments than for coarse. Another form of cut-off consists of sheet piling, or of a vertical zone of grouted rock. The latter is useful in the case of jointed rocks, such as granite, liquid cement being pumped under pressure into holes drilled in the foundation. This procedure was adopted at the Fernworthy dam, S. Devon (see p. 294). Where a dam is to be built on very porous sediments, a horizontal concrete apron can be constructed, extending for some distance upstream and downstream from the dam.[1] This device also has the effect of increasing the length of the percolation path under the structure.

Where joints and bedding planes in the rocks below the dam remain open, water entering them will exert an upward pressure on the base of the structure. The pressure may be relieved by building into the base of the dam drains which carry any water up and out through the downstream face. This was first done in the case of the Vrynwy Dam (1896), and has since been made a feature of many later structures. The drains are usually placed near the water face and inspection passages which run the length of the dam are provided in some cases. Tests which have been made show that by this means uplift pressure is greatly reduced, sometimes to zero, on the downstream side of the line of drains.

Spillways and Prevention of Scour. It is necessary that adequate provision should be made for the discharge of flood waters by suitable spillways. Lack of proper provision in this respect has resulted in a number of dam failures in the past; the Dolgarrog disaster in 1925 was partly due to inadequate spillway. Rainfall records are important here, as providing data of former heavy storms in the past. The scouring action of flood waters passing over the spillway of a dam can also be allowed for in the design by the provision of a concrete apron at the toe or by some other means; the object is to prevent the removal of rock from the walls and floor of the valley at the downstream face of the dam by heavy discharges, which might lead to a weakening of the structure.

Local Stone for Construction. Where it is possible to use local materials for the dam a considerable saving in cost is effected. This applies equally to stone quarried near the site for masonry, or to gravel or crushed stone to be used as aggregate for concrete. Transport costs are reduced or eliminated, against which must be set the cost of the local quarrying. The geological exploration of a site and the country surrounding it should show what suitable materials are available and where they are located.

GEOLOGY OF EXISTING SITES

The following short descriptions of the geological conditions at a number of dam sites, in addition to those already mentioned in passing, illustrate the principles discussed above.

The Vyrnwy Reservoir. Constructed towards the end of last century for the Liverpool water supply, the Vyrnwy Dam was the first big masonry dam to be built in Britain. The reservoir, which has a capacity of 12,000 million gallons, is situated in the uplands of North Wales at a height of some 700 feet above the sea, and the site is of considerable geological interest.

[1] See, for example, the description of the Mohammed Ali barrages, which stand on the sediments of the Nile delta near its southern apex, in *Civil Engineering*, Vol. XXXV, p. 344 (London, December, 1940).

Inspection showed the presence of an old glacial lake basin, whose rock floor was covered with alluvium and peat to an unknown depth. To explore the rock floor, the engineer, G. F. Deacon, put down nearly 200 bore-holes ; from the information they gave he was able to make a contour map, and also a model of the buried surface. The contours showed the presence of a buried rock bar at one point across the valley, at a depth of 40 to 45 feet below ground level ; this was the barrier of the original glacial lake, now silted up, and upstream and downstream of it the solid rock was deeper. The dam was therefore sited at this point, the most economical position (Fig. 126), since it corresponded also with a narrow part of the valley.

Excavation confirmed the shape and glaciated nature of the rock floor, which was covered with striae running parallel to the length of the valley ; the upper 6 or 7 feet of rock were in bad condition and were removed at the site of the dam, the final surface being washed with jets of water and

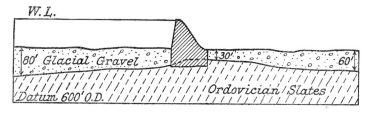

FIG. 126.—GEOLOGICAL SECTION ALONG VALLEY AT SITE OF VYRNWY DAM, N. WALES
to show buried rock ridge (after H. Lapworth).

scraped with wire brushes. The foundation rocks were Ordovician slates whose bedding planes dipped west (upstream) and were crossed by the cleavage. No springs issued from the beds exposed in the dam foundations, but it was thought possible that when the reservoir was completed, with a 144 feet head of water on one side of the dam, springs might issue under pressure. Rubble-filled drains were therefore built into the base of the dam, at intervals along the major bedding planes, and carried up through the dam like inverted funnels to above back-water level. A discharge of 2 gallons per minute from these drains occurred when the reservoir was full, an amount which, though small, would otherwise have caused a small upward pressure on the base of the dam.

Building stone for the structure was quarried about a mile from the site. In his account of the work [1] the engineer comments on the large quantity of stone rejected due to its bad quarrying properties, 700,000 tons being tipped as waste in obtaining the necessary rock for the masonry.

Caban Goch Dam, Rhayader. A group of reservoirs in the Elan valley, Central Wales, which were completed in 1904, supply water to Birmingham by an aqueduct 73 miles long. About 3 miles west of Rhayader the River Elan, after flowing through a broad alluvial valley, originally entered the 700-feet deep, steep-sided Caban Goch gorge, cut in massive

[1] G. F. Deacon in *Proc. Inst. C.E.*, Vol. cxxvi, 1896, p. 24.

conglomerates and shales of Lower Silurian (Llandovery) age. The conglomerates, which are well-cemented hard rocks, provided a good foundation
and abutments for the Caban Goch Dam, 122 feet high, which is built
across this gorge; the dam trench at one point went down 83 feet below
surface. Associated with the conglomerates are shales which are cleaved,
and the whole series dips at 20–30° to the north-west (i.e. upstream); a
strike fault runs along the Rhayader valley. The local rock was quarried
and some of it was used in construction.

Some two miles farther upstream, the Craig Goch Dam was built at a
narrow point in the valley, and was founded on massive fine-grained grits
which overlie the conglomerates mentioned above. A third dam was also
constructed at about the same time. With the building of the Claerwan
Dam, which is curved in plan and 180 feet high above the river bed, a fourth
(and large capacity) reservoir was completed in the Elan valley, and opened
in 1952.[1]

Treig Dam. The Lochaber power scheme, one of the larger water-
power units in Great Britain, involved the construction of two dams to
raise the levels of Loch Laggan and Loch Treig, the latter forming the
principal storage reservoir, and a short tunnel connecting the two lochs,
both of which now contribute water to the Ben Nevis tunnel (p. 314).
Special care was taken to reduce leakage past the dams to a minimum.

Treig dam is situated at the northern end of Loch Treig, where the valley
is narrow. It is founded on mica-schist, which was exposed at the west
end of the dam but covered on the eastern side by sands and gravels forming
a raised beach. On account of the presence of these deposits the dam was
built with an impervious concrete core-wall, which was keyed into the bed-
rock and formed a watertight seal up to crest level. The site was cleared
of soil and vegetation, and in excavating the trench for the dam a deep
depression in the bed-rock at one point made it necessary to go down to a
depth of 100 feet below ground surface. When the trench was excavated,
the foundation rock of the core-wall was drilled and grouted. At another
point, running sand was encountered and was dealt with by sinking a cast
iron cylinder, built up in segments, through the sand to underlying gravel;
the cylinder was then used as a sump from which water was pumped out.

Owing to the steep slopes and high rainfall of the catchment, large run-
off values occur and it was necessary to provide spillway accommodation
for big flood discharges. This was done by using the top of the core-wall
as a spillway 300 feet wide. The downstream rubble-filled face of the dam
was protected by a concrete apron, with special provision to reduce scour
of the river-bed below the dam.[2]

Laggan Dam. The Laggan dam is located at a constriction in the
Spean valley, nearly 5 miles downstream of Loch Laggan, and is 700 feet
long and 130 feet high above river level. A granite mass intrusive into
the Highland schists provides a secure foundation. Exposures of granite

---

[1] See *Proc. Inst. C.E.*, 1953–4, 2, p. 249.

[2] "The Second Stage Development of the Lochaber Water-Power Scheme," by
A. H. Naylor. *Journ. Inst. Civ. Eng.*, vol. 5, 1936–7, London.

occur on the valley slopes, but the river bed at the site was filled to a depth of 35 feet with large and small boulders, a deposit which prevented normal exploration of the bed-rock by trial borings. When the site was cleared of boulders, the granite was found to be traversed by a number of vertical joint planes parallel to the valley, as a result of which the foundation was in the form of large steps with smooth vertical faces and irregular top surfaces. Apparently sound granite on the valley slopes was found to be underlain by clay seams, up to an inch thick, running roughly parallel with the surface slopes of the valley. Since the Spean valley had been occupied by glaciers during the Pleistocene glaciation (p. 233), the clay seams were thought to have been produced by the shearing of the granite by forces due to glacial action, acting at the narrow part of the valley.

The foundation was carried down about 5 feet into sound rock, and at the upstream face of the dam was carried down a further 10 feet in a narrow trench in order to make the foundation as impervious as possible. Holes were drilled to cross the joints in the rock and were grouted under pressure. The vertical rock faces were also tied to the concrete of the dam by steel dowels. The rock was hosed and brushed clean, and coated with cement grout and mortar immediately before the concrete was placed. Granite was used for aggregate, and sand was obtained from nearby raised beach deposits.[1]

Fernworthy Dam. This gravity dam, which impounds water on the South Teign river for the supply of Torquay, has a maximum height of 137 feet from foundations to crest level. It is situated on the granite of north Dartmoor, and is a mass concrete structure faced with granite quarried locally. The following notes indicate some of the precautions taken in dealing with the foundation conditions. Preliminary trial holes sunk across the valley showed that a sound granite foundation probably existed at a depth of some 25 feet below surface. But one hole near the river entered a soft vein of micaceous hematite ; this vein, 10 feet wide, was eventually found to traverse the dam site in a nearly east-north-east direction, roughly parallel to the river at this point, and to dip steeply north. The south wall of the vein was in sound rock, coated with schorl and quartz, but the granite of the north wall was much broken and partly decomposed. The vein was probably a fault infilling, and was excavated to a depth of 82 feet below ground level, where its width was from 4 to 6 feet and diminishing downwards.

Precautions taken to secure the sealing of the soft vein included the construction of a cut-off trench and a curtain of steel piling. Grouting was also employed in holes drilled on either side of the soft rock. Possible leakage through open joints in the granite below foundation level was minimized by cementation through $1\frac{1}{4}$-inch diameter holes drilled in the bed-rock to depths of 70 to 100 feet. A series of $2\frac{1}{2}$-inch percussion drill holes 25 feet deep, and spaced at intervals along the length of the dam trench, were also grouted, forming a " screen " of grouted rock.

[1] A. H. Naylor, *ibid.*

Special care was taken in placing the concrete in the foundation, and water discharged by joints was taken through wrought-iron pipes which were left embedded in the concrete ; these pipes altogether discharged 16,000 gallons per hour on the downstream side. A view of the dam trench is given in Plate XIV. To eliminate possible water pressure under the heel of the dam a system of drains was built into the base of the structure, the water passing through them being gauged by a V-notch. An inspection tunnel runs throughout the length of the dam.[1]

Boulder Dam. The geology of the Boulder Dam site in Black Canyon, on the Colorado River, received extensive investigation for siting this high arched structure, which stands 728 feet above river level. Downstream of Boulder Canyon the Colorado has cut a narrow gorge 900 feet deep, known as Black Canyon, through a pile of Tertiary andesitic lavas, with some intrusive basalts and associated sedimentary formations. At the dam site, a layer of hard red breccia between 350 and 400 feet thick forms the floor and part of the walls of the canyon ; this rock, known as the Dam Breccia because it provides the foundation for the structure, contains large fragments of volcanic rocks, originally of pyroclastic origin, and is tough and well cemented. Numerous faults break the thick volcanic series but do not appear to have moved since the river began to cut its gorge ; they are not major lines of weakness. Geological opinion held that the rocks were strong enough to carry the exceptional load and abutment thrusts of the dam, and this was vindicated by later experience.

Four diversion tunnels, to take the flow of the river during the construction of the dam, were driven under good tunnelling conditions, with little timbering, and the contract for them was completed ahead of time. It was found that faults which were crossed in the tunnels did not allow the passage of any large amount of water, and few showed any crushed or soft rock. In such a large project the satisfactory location of spillways was of great importance ; good foundations for these were available in the rocks on both sides of the canyon.

During the geological exploration of the site, borings made in the river bed showed that the river flowed over a considerable thickness (more than 100 feet) of sand and gravel, or " river fill," beneath which the Dam Breccia was present in all the borings. The expectation that the canyon did not follow a fault zone was confirmed when these deposits were excavated, but an unexpected feature revealed was the presence of an inner gorge, 70 to 80 feet deep, buried beneath the river fill. Its shape showed that the whole depth of the fill was moved during heavy floods and scouring action took place on the sides of the gorge, a deduction which was confirmed by the finding of a sawn plank buried under 50 feet of sediment. The river carries a large amount of matter in suspension, and it is thought that the silting up of the reservoir is likely to be complete in about 200 years' time.[2]

---

[1] J. Kennard and J. J. Lee, in *Journ. Inst. Water Eng.*, I, 1947, p. 11.
[2] C. P. Berkey, " Geology of Boulder and Norris Dam Sites," *Civil Engineering* (New York), Vol. 5, 1935.

After the completion of Boulder Dam in 1935 the reservoir gradually filled during the succeeding three years, forming a large lake with an area of 229 square miles and constituting a water load estimated at 42×10^9 tons. This load is believed to have produced the many small local earthquakes which have since been recorded from the area ; the heaviest occurred in May 1939, about 9 months after the maximum water load was developed. Pre-Cambrian rocks are faulted against the Tertiary lavas and sediments of the area, and it is thought that activity on the faults was being renewed on a small scale under the weight of the new lake.[1]

Coulee Dam. With a volume two and a half times that of Boulder Dam, this great concrete gravity dam, 550 feet high, is built across the gorge of the Columbia River in the north-west of the United States. It impounds water in the main reservoir of the Grand Coulee scheme, and from it water is pumped to a second reservoir, situated 300 feet above the river in the dry canyon known as the Grand Coulee (p. 42), whence a supply is available for the irrigation of a large area of reclaimed land in the Columbia River basin. The power available at the main dam is used partly for pumping water to the upper reservoir and partly for hydro-electric generation; the latter operation began early in 1941, and water first flowed over the dam in June 1942, when the filled reservoir extended 151 miles upstream.[2]

The geology of the whole site is of great interest and provides a good example of the utility of glacial features and glacial deposits. The dam is founded on granite, part of a batholithic intrusion, which is covered at the site by river silts and gravels to a thickness varying from 50 to 300 feet. The granite was sound and was suitable for carrying the heavy load of the dam. Difficulty was experienced, however, in excavating the foundations, because the granite was traversed by horizontal sheet-jointing, and the frequency of the joints did not diminish as the excavation went deeper. It was eventually realized that residual stresses in the rock were being released by the unloading consequent on excavation, and horizontal " lift-seams " were developed in relief of the stresses. At the suggestion of the geologist, Dr. C. P. Berkey, excavation was stopped and the dam built—thus replacing the load—and the " lift-seams " were grouted. The foundation has proved to be safe and impervious. For exploring the foundations, before excavating the site, many trial bores were made by diamond drill apparatus. Some of the bores were 36 inches in diameter, allowing the foundation rock to be inspected from within the bore-hole. Glacial gravels obtained a mile from the site were used for aggregate for the concrete of the dam.

The Grand Coulee itself is a great canyon over 40 miles long, from 2 to 3 miles wide, and more than 600 feet deep, eroded in a plateau to the south of the dam. It was cut by the Columbia at a time when the river's normal westerly course was blocked by glaciers advancing from the north ; the lake which formed behind this ice dam filled the valley and then overflowed

[1] D. S. Carder in *Bull. Seism. Soc. Amer.*, 35, No. 4, Oct. 1945, p. 175.

[2] *The Engineer*, August 28, 1942, Vol. 174, p. 168.

PLATE XV

CUT-OFF TRENCH AT SILENT VALLEY RESERVOIR, BELFAST.   CONCRETE IN POSITION
IN MIDDLE DISTANCE ;   CAST IRON CYLINDERS IN FOREGROUND FORM THE
LINING WHERE THE TRENCH ENTERS QUICKSAND.

PLATE XVI

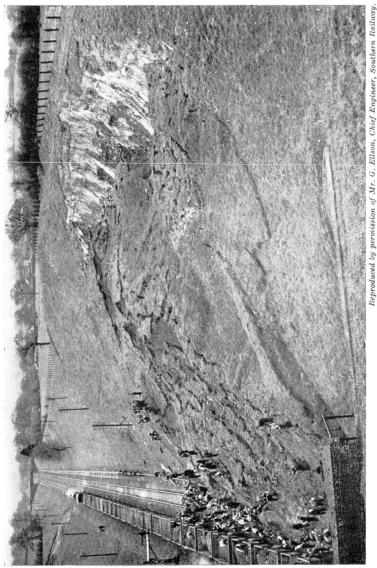

Reproduced by permission of Mr. G. Ellson, Chief Engineer, Southern Railway.

ROTATIONAL SLIP IN THE WEALD CLAY, NEAR SEVENOAKS, KENT. Water content of the clay slope had increased over many years before the slip occurred.

southwards across basalt lava flows which here lie above the granite. The river thus established a new course, and made the Grand Coulee before recession of the ice allowed it to re-excavate its old gorge. In the now abandoned glacial channel, two low dams have been built to form a storage reservoir about 24 miles long ; the water-retaining properties of the rocks at this site were particularly important because all the water has to be pumped into storage. The floor of the canyon is covered with silts, the nature of which is such that they are believed to be an effective seal against leakage.[1] But at places along the west side of the canyon the rock walls are covered by scree, and the possibility of leakage occurring there made this section of the walls the only one requiring special investigation.

Correction of Leakage at Great Falls Reservoir. The Great Falls dam, Tennessee, is situated just below the junction of a tributary with the Coney Fork River. The course of the tributary before it joins the Coney Fork is in the form of a loop, which bends back and passes within about 600 feet of the main river on the *downstream* side of the dam, where the river flows through a gorge. A narrow ridge is thus formed between the tributary and the river, and through the rocks of this ridge leakage developed from the reservoir when water was impounded by the dam. Over a period of 20 years (up to 1945) the leakage increased from 23 to 450 cubic feet per second. Most of it was through a limestone formation about 50 feet thick, and it grew in volume as fillings of clay became washed out from solution channels in the limestone ; the channels themselves were made larger by solution.

After experimental work with trial holes, grouting with hot asphalt was applied through a series of $3\frac{1}{2}$-inch diameter holes drilled to the limestone along a line parallel to the river cliff. These holes were first spaced 40 feet apart, but later at smaller intervals. Correction of the leakage was 80 per cent effective opposite holes spaced at 40 feet, 95 per cent effective opposite holes 20 feet apart, and almost 100 per cent where the holes had a spacing of 10 feet. Cement-grouted drill holes were placed on either side of those grouted with asphalt, in an attempt to encase the asphalt filling. The result of this treatment was to reduce the leakage of 450 cusecs to about 2 per cent of that volume.[2]

The Sasumua Dam, Kenya. This earth dam, with a maximum height of 110 feet, was completed in 1956 as part of the water-supply scheme for Nairobi, Kenya. It is situated 40 miles north-north-west of the city, in one of several valleys which drain south-east off the volcanic rocks of the Aberdare Forest. The mean annual rainfall of the Sasumua catchment is between 40 and 50 inches per year.

At the dam site, two series of lavas and tuffs, representing two episodes of vulcanicity, lie nearly horizontally one on the other. Deep weathering has reduced the upper part of each series to residual clay, grading into partly decomposed rock. The upper of the two weathered zones at the dam site has a varying thickness, up to 70 feet, and rests on about 60 feet

[1] C. P. Berkey, " Foundation Conditions for Grand Coulee and Bonneville Projects," *Civil Engineering* (New York), Feb. 1935, Vol. 5, No. 2.

[2] *Proc. Amer. Soc. C.E.*, 76, Jan. 1950, p. 101.

of sound rock ; this in turn lies on the weathered zone of the lower series. The site was explored by over 100 bore-holes. The weathered portion of the Upper Volcanic Series consists of relatively impervious material, and is called Sasumua " clay." It was used as a fill for the greater part of the earth dam, and was found to possess unusual properties which were of considerable engineering value during construction.

The abnormal properties of the Sasumua clay were : (i) a plasticity index much lower than that of a normal clay of similar liquid limit (ii) a higher angle of internal friction and higher permeability than for a normal clay of equal liquid limit ; (iii) variable results for the Atterburg tests and mechanical analysis, depending largely on the chemical which was used as a dispersing agent. Because of these features, the mineral composition of the clay was investigated and found to be as follows :

Halloysite, 58·9 ; kaolinite, 3·9 ; gibbsite, 9·1 ; goethite, 15·9 ; quartz, 6·4 ; other constituents, 5·8 (per cent). The halloysite crystals had the form of small tubes about ½ micron in length. Particle size measurements combined with the mineralogical data indicated that most of the clay fraction of the weathered lavas is present as clusters of clay mineral particles ; these clusters in effect form porous grains with rough surfaces. As a result, the " clay " has a low plasticity index, and has engineering properties which are characteristic of relatively coarse-grained soils.[1] Water is contained in the voids of the clusters as well as between them, giving a high value of liquid limit because the material consists largely of these porous aggregates of minute halloysite crystals.

The behaviour of the dam after construction, in respect of (i) compaction of the clay fill, and (ii) seepage from the reservoir, was very satisfactory. Other earth dams made of similar material (weathered volcanic rocks) had been built in Java (Tjipanoendjang, 1927) and in Australia (the Silvan Dam, 1931). Samples of the materials from these localities, when investigated at the time of the building of the Sasumua Dam, also showed a high content of halloysite (76·4 per cent, and 80–90 per cent respectively). The mineral was present as minute spongy aggregates, as at Sasumua. It appears, therefore, that such " clays," derived from the weathering of lavas and tuffs, can be as good as normal clays of high quality, with a low liquid limit, for the construction of earth dams.[2]

The Kariba Dam.[3] The construction of the Kariba Dam, on the Zambesi River some 250 miles downstream of the Victoria Falls, has produced the world's largest artificial lake, 175 miles long when full, with a surface area approaching 2000 square miles. After the sealing of the dam

---

[1] Among the engineering properties, optimum moisture content was found to be lower than the plastic limit for the clay, which had therefore to be dried before being used in order to comply with specifications. The angle of internal friction (34°, average) was found to be practically independent of the water content.

[2] Condensed from the paper by Prof. K. Terzaghi, " Design and performance of the Sasumua Dam," *Proc. Inst. C.E.*, London, 1958, vol. 9, p. 369.

[3] The author is indebted to the late Dr. Francis Jones, geologist to the Kariba Scheme, for this account. See also J. L. Kuill and K. S. Jones, *Geotechnique*, 15, no. 1, 1965.

in December 1958 the great lake began to form, taking several years to fill. The Zambesi, after emerging from its sinuous gorge below the Falls, traverses a wide valley eroded in sedimentary rocks, which is constricted at its eastern end by the Kariba gorge. The latter is cut through a fault-block of Pre-Cambrian gneisses. Upstream of it the ground rises gently for several miles on either side of the river to a well-defined escarpment or to a ridge where the gneisses form high ground (Fig. 127). The geological succession as related to Kariba can be simplified as follows :

Upper Karroo Beds . . (Sandstones of Triassic age)
Escarpment Grit . . . (Conglomerate and grit, Triassic)
Madumabisa Mudstones . (Argillaceous group of Permian age)
   (unconformity)
Quartzite . . . . (late Pre-Cambrian)
   (unconformity)
Gneisses, amphibolites, and
   schists . . . . (Pre-Cambrian).
      (Many pegmatites are intruded into the gneisses.)

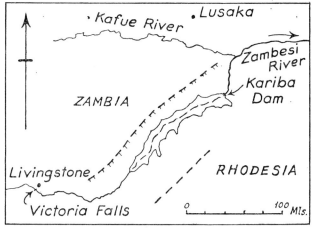

FIG. 127.—LOCATION MAP FOR THE KARIBA DAM ON ZAMBESI RIVER.
The escarpment which forms boundary of the Zambesi valley is indicated.

The bed of the Zambesi, where it enters the Pre-Cambrian fault-block or horst, is approximately 1200 feet above sea-level ; construction of the dam has raised the water-level to about 1600 feet. For a distance of several miles along one part of the rim of the reservoir ground-level is about 100 feet above eventual water-level ; this stretch was therefore carefully examined for water-tightness. The general structure of the reservoir area, which is that of a broad syncline, and the position of the mudstones, which provide an impervious floor to the reservoir, help to minimize leakage. The gneisses which form part of the high outer rim of the valley, and which close it near the dam site, are relatively impervious.

The dam itself is sited about three miles down the gorge, which is here less than ¼ mile wide, with sides rising steeply more than 600 feet above the river bed. Gneiss forms the floor and sides of the gorge on both north and south banks, but on the south side about 300 feet above the river the gneiss is unconformably overlain by quartzite. The latter is highly jointed and generally less sound than the gneiss. Small local faults are present, but movement on them took place in the geological past. The rocks in the foundation of the dam and in the abutments are strong. The site was determined not only by geological factors, but also on grounds of economy, problems of access, and the siting of quarries.

The Kariba gneiss consists of felspar, quartz, and biotite, though it is by no means uniform in texture or composition. It commonly shows strong foliation which is sometimes fine-grained, but especially at depth the banding often becomes coarse and intricately contorted. This was encountered in the diversion tunnel, approximately at river-level. In many places the rock is an augen-gneiss, in which the " eyes " are largely microcline felspar. At higher levels the coarseness diminishes and the mica content increases. Where the mica becomes a dominant mineral the rock is schistose rather than gneissose, and consequently somewhat weaker. The power house, surge chambers, and access tunnels were excavated in mica-rich gneiss, and considerable difficulties were met during construction ; regions of close jointing and small faults were encountered, but no wide crush zones. In addition, as is inevitable in the region, pockets of deep weathering occur where the schistose rock has partly disintegrated ; these, whenever encountered, slowed down the work, but they were not extensive in depth.

On the other hand, the condition of the gneiss just below the quartzite was often poor, and this was attributed to weathering in pre-quartzite times. An interesting fact which emerged from the " Rains-period " of 1958, which caused an abnormal rise in the Zambesi and the flooding of the works, was that very little surface water percolated through jointed, faulted, and weathered gneiss into the tunnels and large excavations below.

Materials for aggregate came from near-by sources. The main quarry was sited about two miles from the river, in rock which was noticeably foliated but passed downwards into what was virtually igneous rock, approaching granodiorite. The latter, on crushing, had little or no tendency to break into flat pieces, and was of good quality. For the coffer dams, small quarries on the north bank upstream of the main dam provided gneiss, often biotite-rich. Fine aggregate was mostly obtained from the river sand at the mouth of the Sanyati tributary. The bulk of this sand consisted of quartz, but other minerals present showed that some of it had been derived from weathered gneiss. Good quality cement was manufactured from a limestone at Chilongu, Zambia.

The generation of electricity at Kariba will supply power to Rhodesia and to mines in the copper belt on the Rhodesia-Congo border.

The Roseires Dam. This dam on the Blue Nile 500 kms. from Khartoum, and completed in 1966, is founded on a complex of metamorphic

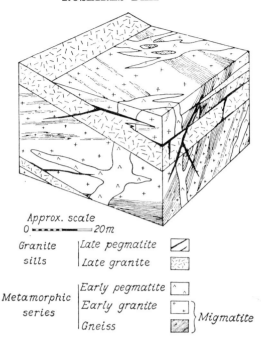

Approx. scale
0 ▄▄▄▄▄▄▄▄ 20m

Granite   Late pegmatite
sills   Late granite

Metamorphic   Early pegmatite
series   Early granite   } Migmatite
          Gneiss

FIG. 128.—RELATIONSHIPS OF THE ROCKS AT THE ROSEIRES SITE, SUDAN. *Below.*
Section through a concrete buttress foundation; dotted areas indicate weathered rock:
g=muscovite-gneiss, bg=biotite-gneiss, gr=early granite, mig=migmatite, s=late
granite sill, p=pegmatite.

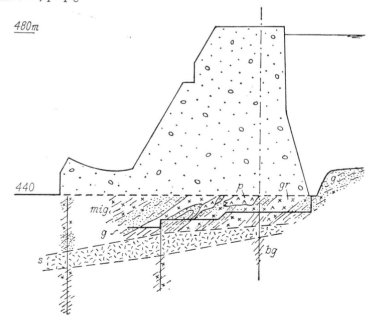

and granitic rocks which form a low rise in the bed-rock surface. The rise coincides with the course of the river in the Damazin rapids area ; with distance from the river the bed-rock is covered by an increasing depth of over-burden (sands, gravels, and silts). The rocks at the Roseires site are illustrated in Fig. 128 (top) ; they include younger granite and pegmatite sills intrusive into an older metamorphic assemblage, and were explored by extensive diamond core drilling. All the cores were recorded in detail, as well as the geology in the excavations. The central section of the dam is of concrete buttress type. The granite sills, which were sound fresh rock, were important in providing a strong foundation; Fig. 128 (lower) shows one buttress founded on a major sill, after excavation of overlying weathered material (shown by stippling).

The most important feature of the site, from an engineering standpoint, was the degree of weathering which had affected the various rocks. The gneisses were badly or completely weathered, and could be mechanically excavated ; the younger granite sills were fresh or only slightly weathered. In some places unweathered rock was underlain by extremely altered material. In investigating the site, four grades of rock-condition were defined for interpreting borehole data : I. fresh rock ; II. slightly weathered rock ; III. moderately or highly weathered rock ; IV. completely weathered rock. Neither grade III or IV rock was suitable as a foundation for the concrete dam, but grade I rock formed a satisfactory foundation material up to the maximum height of the buttresses and grade II rock was assessed in relation to the eventual height of the dam above it.[1]

SELECTED REFERENCES

BERKEY, C. P., AND SANBORN, J. F. " Engineering Geology of the Catskill Water Supply." *Trans. Amer. Soc. C.E.*, 86, 1923.

BRYAN, KIRK. " Geology of Reservoir and Dam Sites." *U.S. Geol. Surv. Water Supply Paper* 597 (*A*), 1928.

FULTON, A. A. and DICKENSON, L. H. " Hydroelectric dams built in Scotland since 1945," *Proc. I.C.E.*, 29, Dec. 1964.

LEGGET, R. F. " Geology and Engineering." Chapters 6, 13 and 14, 2nd edition, 1962. McGraw-Hill Book Co.

NOTE.—This book contains many references to literature on geology in engineering construction.

WALTERS, R. C. S. " The Nation's Water Supply." Nicholson & Watson, London, 1936.

RICHEY, J. E. " Elements of Engineering Geology." 1964. Pitman.

See also the section on Geology in Dam Construction, in the Berkey Volume : Application of Geology to Engineering Practice, *Geol. Soc. Amer.*, 1950.

---

[1] Knill J. L. and Jones, K. S., in *Geotechnique*, vol. 15, no. 1, 1965.

CHAPTER 15

THE GEOLOGY OF CUTTINGS AND TUNNELS

CUTTINGS

A cutting is a permanently open excavation. The nature of the rocks through which it is made will govern questions of construction such as the slope of the sides, drainage, need for retaining walls, method and rate of excavation, and to a great extent its cost. Thus, vertical sides are possible in massive-bedded hard strata, horizontal or gently dipping, with few joints, or in strong igneous rocks. In other sedimentary rocks it is necessary to take into account the relation between their structure and the direction of the cutting.

Cuttings in Hard Rocks. In firm horizontal strata, an excavation may be completed with the likelihood of only small slips occurring, such as are due to frost action on the walls of the cutting. In dipping strata it is an advantage when possible to make the cutting along a line at right angles to the strike of the beds (Fig. 129a), thus minimizing the chances of

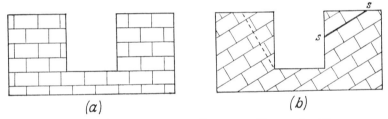

FIG. 129.—SECTIONS ACROSS A CUTTING IN MASSIVE STRATA.
(a) Cutting is in the direction of dip (or in horizontal strata). (b) Cutting is along the strike, in dipping beds. *ss* = possible surface of sliding.

falls of rock occurring. When this is not possible and the cut runs in the strike direction (or obliquely), one wall (*s* in Fig. 129b) will be less stable than the other, owing to the dip of the rocks into the excavation. Whether or not rock-slides will take place here along the bedding planes depends on the nature of the strata and the frequency of cross-joints, and ground-water—conditions which must be determined from an inspection of the rocks at the locality. Alternating hard and soft beds are treacherous under these conditions, especially when the weaker layers become softened by the percolation of groundwater along them.

The sides of the cutting can be sloped to a safe angle (dotted line in figure) instead of being left vertical. This involves a greater volume of excavation and hence increased cost. Where the acquisition of a wider strip of land is difficult or expensive, the cost of retaining the sides of the cutting with stonework or concrete (thus keeping the rock face at a steep angle) must be balanced against the cost of the extra excavation and purchase of land for a wider cutting.

Possible values for stable slopes in rock formations of different kinds are given below, but the figures should be taken as approximate only and subject to revision in any particular case according to the existing conditions.

Rock Formation	Slope of sides
Massive strata, horizontal, few joints,	Vertical or 1 in $\frac{1}{4}$
Massive strata, horizontal, jointed . . .	1 in $\frac{1}{4}$ to 1 in 1
Dry gravels and sands	1 in $1\frac{1}{2}$
Marls, shales, and firm dry loams . . .	1 in $1\frac{1}{2}$ to 1 in 2
Clays, soft clays, silts, alluvium, etc. . .	slope depending on depth of cutting and water content.

Cuttings in Soft Rocks. When a cutting is made in relatively soft materials [1] such as clays and sands, a wider excavation with greater surface area is generally involved. Should this be considered impossible for economic reasons, steeper sides with special arrangements for strengthening and drainage may be used ; but where it is possible to employ the flatter and more stable slopes, they are less likely to give trouble afterwards. The water content of the softer rocks is specially important and adequate provision should be made for the removal of excess water by longitudinal drains and, if necessary, by channel drains packed with rubble on the side slopes.

Surface water (run-off) from sloping ground above a clay cutting may run down over its sides, soaking into the clay and in time rendering it so plastic that the mass becomes unstable and slips. To prevent this, ditches have been made along the tops of cuttings to intercept and remove the surface water. Engineering opinion has been put forward against leaving the ditches open, since it is found that deep cracks develop in the bottom of such a ditch in dry weather, and these subsequently allow a deeper penetration of rainwater and reduce the strength of the clay. Shallow ditches filled with ashes, or pipe drains along the top of a cutting, are often effective [2] and avoid the above danger, since the clay in the ditch is not directly exposed to the atmosphere. Longitudinal drains of this kind were used for stabilizing cliffs of London Clay east of Herne Bay, where much slipping had occurred ; porous pipes were laid in a trench along the top of the cliff, and covered with brick hardcore and clinker.[3] (See also p. 306).

Slips in Clay Cuttings. A type of slip which commonly occurs in clay soils, in cuttings as well as in natural sections, is shown in Fig. 130. Movement takes place on a curved shear surface which is concave towards the slip ; the mass moves with a backward rotation on a horizontal axis parallel to the length of the cutting. It has been called " shearing slide " (Terzaghi) and " slump " (Sharpe, *loc. cit.*), but is now more commonly

---

[1] Known as " soils " to the engineer (see p. 324).

[2] Seaton, T. H., in *Journ. Inst. C.E.*, No. 6, 1937–8, p. 461.

[3] " Cliff-stabilization Works in London Clay," by J. Duvivier, *Journ. Inst. C.E.*, Vol. 14, 1939–40.

referred to as a rotational slide (or slip). It may be initiated in some cases by the formation of cracks several feet deep in the clay ground at the back of the slip, when natural support of the ground has been removed by the excavation or by denuding agencies; these cracks when traced should be filled to prevent further drying out and to stop ingress of water. An example of this type of movement is the slip in a railway cutting in the Weald Clay, near Sevenoaks, shown in Plate XVI.

Field observations have shown that when a slip occurs in a bank of clay, an almost vertical tension crack is formed near the top of the bank and a mass of clay slips outward and downward along an approximately cylindrical arc. Now it is not possible for the tension crack to remain open at a depth where the weight of overlaying clay is greater than the compression strength of the clay; for the sides of the crack would merely yield

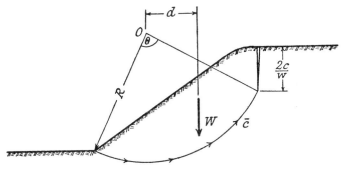

Fig. 130.—Mechanics of a Slip in a Clay Bank (after Terzaghi, *Jour. I.C.E.*, 1939).

until they were supporting each other, and the crack would therefore close. When the slip is about to take place the full shear strength is mobilized along the arc (Fig. 130); by taking moments about the centre O we have

$$\bar{c}R^2\theta = Wd,$$

in which $\bar{c}$ is the average shear strength of the clay along the arc; R the radius and θ the angle subtended at the centre; W the weight of the slipping portion, and d the lever arm of this weight about the centre O.

A second kind of movement, referred to under Flows on p. 23, is due to continuous deformation of a plastic mass. It arises in soft clays with such a high water content that they become plastic and begin to distort under the weight of the superincumbent material; heavy loads such as buildings near a cutting may also transmit pressures and help to cause flow. Associated with such flow movements there is often a rise of the floor of the cutting: the waterlogged clay transmits an upward pressure which becomes effective in causing movement where the weight of the excavated material has been removed. This is found to occur in both large and small excavations: it caused considerable trouble and extra expense in the construction of the Panama Canal about 1915; and in a 20-foot deep railway cutting at Botley, Hants, a similar occurrence on a smaller scale continued for some weeks in 1936, the tracks being pushed up $1\frac{1}{2}$ to 2 feet daily by the deformation of the clay.[1] The material that has moved in such a " landslide " must be excavated, and the new slopes strengthened or retained if necessary, and drained, thus adding considerably to construction or maintenance costs.

Very old landslips, which have flowed over an earlier surface and have since become grassed over, may be present and give deep soils with abnormal properties. A recent instance of this was found on the Atherfield Clay outcrop below the greensand ridge in Surrey, where old (or " fossil ") mudflows affected the lay-out of a new road.

Surface slips in clay are shallow movements occurring on clay slopes; they reduce the steepness of a slope and render it more stable, the thickness of material involved being generally less than 20 feet. The slip in the Oxford Clay at the mouth of the Bincombe railway tunnel near Weymouth, which blocked the line in 1936, is an example. More recently instances have been described from valleys near Shotton, Co. Durham, where natural slopes in boulder clay were involved. One slope, at about 29 degrees to the horizontal, had been undercut by the stream in Blunts Dene, and the average inclination became too great for the weathered surface layers of the clay to remain stable. They slid down, with a rapid movement, locally blocking the valley. The ratio of the thickness of the slipped material to the length of slope was about ·05, and in other instances ·04.[2]

Prevention and Treatment of Slips. In water-bearing, porous, and unconsolidated materials which may be liable to slips when excavated, the first essential is to reduce the water content or prevent its increase, by means of ditches, tile drains, or pumping from tube or other wells. The ingress of surface water should be prevented by diverting the run-off as already indicated. The side slopes of cuttings should be low enough to ensure stability of the material. Tests for the water content and other properties of a sediment can now be made, by the methods of Soil Mechanics, upon samples taken in advance of and during construction, and the behaviour of the soil predicted from them.

When a slip has occurred, it may generally be stabilized by proper drainage and the provision of support; a trench cut through it down to the surface of sliding (if present) will enable the necessary drains to be laid and will release water in the slipped mass. Treatment of ground liable to slips by burning a mixture of coal and earth on its surface is not recommended,[3] since it results in the formation of a hard surface layer which is pervious to water, leading to an increase in the water content of the soil.

An example of the successful stabilization of a clay slope which was subject to repeated slipping is provided by the works carried out at Herne Bay, Kent, in 1938 (reference at bottom of p. 304). Slips in the London Clay, which here forms cliffs about 100 feet high, took the form of mud-flows which developed along hollows down the cliff-face. These mud-runs

---

[1] Ellson, G., in discussion on paper by Seaton, *loc. cit.*, pp. 481-2.
[2] A. W. Skempton, in *Trans. Yorks. Geol. Soc.*, 1950.
[3] Seaton, *loc. cit.*, p. 467.

occurred in the surface layers of the clay, which had become softened through increased water content. Saturation of the clay probably took place by rain falling direct on the surface (much of which was bare of grass or other vegetation) and entering cracks, thus wetting the material to a depth of several feet ; and also by percolation of water through local superficial deposits of sand and gravel at the top of the cliffs. Since absorption of water was the primary cause of the trouble, the remedy consisted in intercepting this water as far as possible. On the basis of bore-hole data obtained during a survey of a length of one-third mile of cliff, a drainage system was designed and installed. This consisted of a longitudinal interceptor drain along the cliff top, and primary drains down the slopes, built at the base of the slipped material in each hollow, with herring-bone laterals. After the completion of the works the slopes were seeded for grass, and have been

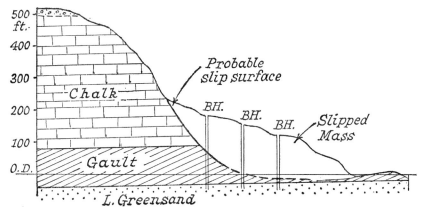

FIG. 131.—DIAGRAMMATIC SECTION THROUGH LANDSLIDE AT
FOLKESTONE WARREN, KENT.
BH = bore-hole.

unaffected by further slipping. There is a small discharge from the drains during normal weather, which rises after heavy rain to some 600 gallons per hour for 3 acres of cliff.

The severe winter of 1947–8 provided a test which demonstrated the efficacy of the system, the drained area presenting a striking contrast to the adjoining unstabilized cliffs to the east, where many new slips were promoted. The tidal surge of January 31, 1953 (p. 31), caused some damage at the base of the cliffs, but the main clay slope remained stable.

The Folkestone Warren Landslide. On the south coast of Kent a large landslide extends over a distance of 2 miles at the Warren, between Folkestone and Dover. The Chalk cliffs here reach a height of about 500 feet, and exert a high pressure (some 28 tons per sq. ft.) on the underlying Gault. The main line of the Southern Region of British Railways runs at the foot of the cliffs and crosses the landslip area. Since the line was constructed, over 100 years ago, many falls of cliff have occurred, the early ones due to erosion by the sea ; in 1915 a large fall took place and thousands of tons of Chalk blocked the railway. In 1935, very extensive slipping occurred and the line was wrecked, the whole cutting through which a train was passing being carried forward and the sea-wall at the base of the cliffs being moved bodily seawards. Further extensive slides moved in 1940. The engineers responsible for the upkeep of the railway were faced with two possibilities : either to re-locate the stretch of line farther back from the coast—a difficult and expensive procedure ; or to try and stabilize the existing ground. The latter was decided upon.

The area is situated on the northern limb of the Wealden anticline (see Fig. 97), where the Cretaceous formations dip at a small angle north or north-north-east. Underlying the Gault clay is the Lower Greensand, and borings entering this gave artesian flows. The underside of the clay was therefore wetted by groundwater in the Greensand ; and water moving down through the Chalk weakened the upper part of the clay by promoting an increased water content.

The large slides occurred with a rotary movement on curved surfaces which flattened out somewhat on entering the Gault (Fig. 131). When movement occurred the clay was pushed up as " islands " on the foreshore, where the lower limit of the Gault outcrop is exposed at low tide. Borings in existing slides, also, indicated that the thickness of the Gault is very much reduced underneath a slipped mass : instead of a thickness of 100 to 120 feet, there was in places only 30 to 40 feet of the clay present. Horizontal drainage headings also intersected slip planes, which were dipping seawards.

The mechanism of the slides would therefore appear to be as follows : the Gault becomes wetted and softened both by percolating water from above and by water from the Greensand below ; it thus forms a weak layer which is partly squeezed out, when slides occur, under the weight of the overlying mass of Chalk.[1]

Remedial measures which have been carried out comprise the building of a new sea-wall of heavy section, strengthened by buttresses, in front of the old wall ; the area behind the new wall has been filled in with Chalk and a covering material. These measures have resulted in adding a considerable load to the foreshore. In addition, the provision of drainage headings to discharge percolating water, and the removal of Chalk from the unstable area behind the sea-wall, have lessened the tendency to slide. The conditions at Folkestone Warren illustrate the behaviour of a stiff clay, under load, when its water content is increased.

Influence of Faults in Cuttings. The presence of faults may add considerably to the difficulty and expense of excavation, since broken rocks are more costly to deal with than sound rocks, and faulting may involve different types of rock which necessitate different methods of excavation. Faults are most prominent in the harder rocks, which yield to stresses by fracturing, in contrast to soft rocks which yield by deformation. In some cases where a fault runs parallel to the wall of a cutting, the rock up to the fault can be removed, and the fault surface left as the finished slope. The

[1] A. H. Toms, in *Proc. 3rd Int. Conf. on Soil Mechanics*, 1953, Zurich.

following description illustrates some features which may be encountered in faulted ground.

The short Cofton tunnel, 440 yards in length, on the L.M.S. Railway near Birmingham, was constructed in 1841 through a low ridge of gently folded Keuper Sandstone. The work of opening out the tunnel to make a wide cutting, whose maximum depth was 70 feet, was carried out in 1926–9.[1] No records of the strata passed through in the old tunnel were available, but the new 6-inch map of the Geological Survey showed that the line of the tunnel was crossed at a very acute angle by the Longbridge fault, which was known to have a throw of 200 to 300 feet at a point $\frac{1}{4}$ mile north of the tunnel. In the approach cuttings, interbedded soft and hard Triassic sandstones with marl bands were exposed, and the slopes had in places been repaired where the weathering of the softer beds had undercut the harder. Some small faults, which had led to minor slips, were also visible, but the precise structure in the tunnel area was not known.

The first part of the excavation removed glacial drift which covered the northern part of the tunnel area, and revealed the broken nature of the ground beneath. Much water flowing from joints thus exposed had to be pumped away. Further excavation showed that the Longbridge " fault " was in reality a zone of faulting, with a series of parallel fractures and associated minor faults, many showing slickensided surfaces and dipping at low angles. Records of geological data were kept from the beginning of the work, and a detailed geological survey was made of the ground covered by the widening.[2] At one stage of the work it was deduced from observation and measurement of the strata that hidden faulting with a throw of about 80 feet was present, and this later proved correct when the rocks were excavated.

As the work progressed, serious slips developed, masses of rock moving down into the cutting on the slickensided fault planes, which were lubricated with water and in some cases covered with wet clay " gouge." The possibility of similar slips arising in one particular section led to the construction of a concrete retaining wall,[3] 128 yards long ; eventually the badly fractured nature of the rock which had been revealed, and experience of the slips that had already occurred, led to the abandonment of the original excavation programme and the substitution of an alternative scheme. Flatter slopes than those originally planned were adopted over parts of the cutting, and the 550,000 cubic yards of total excavation exceeded the original estimate by 120,000 cubic yards (or nearly 28 per cent).

Three types of slip associated with faulting, called " hanging-wall slip " (Fig. 132), " footwall slip," and " trough slip," are discussed in the description of the work (loc. cit., p. 183), and the opinion is expressed that the tunnel was originally constructed instead of a cutting because of the

---

[1] " The Opening-Out of Cofton Tunnel, London Midland and Scottish Railway," by R. T. McCallum, Proc. Inst. C.E., Vol. 231, 1930–1, p. 161.

[2] The results of this survey are given in Summary of Progress, Geol. Surv. Gt. Brit., 1929, Pt. ii.

[3] The aggregate used for the concrete of this wall was the Rowley Regis dolerite.

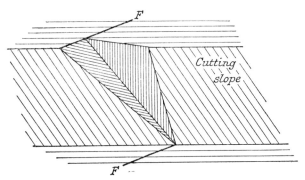

FIG. 132.—SLIDE ASSOCIATED WITH FAULT CROSSING A CUTTING OBLIQUELY
(after McCallum).   FF = trace of fault surface.

realization of the troubles that would ensue if an open cut were carried
through the ridge.   The railway crosses the ridge at its lowest point, the
depression being due to the zone of faulting which traverses the ridge there.
" If the railway had been sited either 200 yards west, or 300 yards east,
of its actual position, little or no trouble due to the Longbridge fault would
have been encountered, for the line would have crossed the fault clear of
the fractured zone in the Lower Keuper Sandstone."

Tectonic shear-zones have recently been discussed in detail by Prof. A.
W. Skempton (reference on p. 320).

TUNNELS

A main use of geology in connection with tunnelling is to enable a
proper estimate of the cost to be made ; the excavation programme and
type of blasting to be employed, timbering and the lining of the tunnel,
all depend on the nature of the rock in which construction is to be carried
out.   Excavation in broken rock, for example, may cost twice as much
as in sound rock, for the same size of tunnel.   The quantity of groundwater
that has to be pumped during the work is a further factor which influences
costs.   It is important that the distribution of underground water should
be known as far as possible for the original conditions, before these are
disturbed by the engineering works.

In general, old and massive rocks are best for tunnelling and drilling.
Difficulties in tunnelling increase in the younger rocks of the geological
column (the construction of tube railways in the London Clay is a notable
exception to the general rule), and are greatest in quicksands, sands, clays,
and glacial drift at the top of the column.   The water-bearing capacity
of the rocks also as a rule increases as their geological age decreases.

Geological Exploration.   It is desirable that an attempt should be
made at predicting the geological conditions likely to be encountered in
any given work of construction.   The line of the tunnel and the neighbouring
ground is geologically surveyed, and sub-surface data obtained by exploratory borings.   Careful control of such trial boring operations is necessary
in order to extract the maximum amount of information from the ground.

The cost of tunnelling, in general, is least when construction is carried out in sound rock, and in *one* kind of rock throughout. Straightforward geological conditions, such as simply dipping strata, allow costs to be estimated closely ; more uncertainties arise in connection with folded and faulted beds. Geological structures such as faults and joints should be mapped along the line of the tunnel. Strongly developed joint systems are potential channels for groundwater circulation and should be recorded. Badly faulted ground is to be avoided if possible ; if unavoidable, it may require special timbering or other treatment, and a prediction of where faults are likely to be met underground is therefore of the greatest importance.

Again, hard rocks when excavated may stand with little support (some tunnels are unlined throughout), because they are strong enough to withstand the lateral pressures exerted by surrounding rocks ; but if soft (e.g. clayey) bands are present there may be a tendency to slipping on these weaker layers, and suitable support for the walls of the excavation will be necessary. Interbedded hard and soft rocks, such as sandstones and shales, may give rise to many difficulties ; groundwater percolating through the sandstones soaks into the shales and softens them, and in this way promotes slipping, especially when the beds dip into the excavation.

The relationship between the direction of tunnelling and the strike of the beds, and its effect on the way in which the rocks break during excavation, is discussed in connection with overbreak (p. 313).

Where a tunnel is to be driven in water-bearing rocks (i.e. below the water-table), groundwater will percolate into the workings and arrangements must be made to deal with it. Methods employing cementation, freezing, groundwater lowering, or compressed air working, may be applicable in different circumstances, but add to the cost of construction. Their usefulness in limiting the entry of groundwater into the workings will depend on the porosity and permeability of the rocks, and on the presence or absence of systems of joints. The latter are specially important in connection with limestones ; joints may be widened by solution in this type of rock (see p. 2), and they then allow the passage of much water.

The account of the construction of the Clyde Tunnel, west Glasgow, which was completed in 1964, illustrates many of the difficulties of working in water-bearing glacial deposits.[1] The latter included boulder clay, silts, sands and esker gravels, which lay above Lower Carboniferous shales and sandstones. As boreholes could not be sunk in the width of the river because of hazards to shipping, details of the under-river geology were obtained from a pilot heading driven in advance of the main excavation.

Pressure tunnels have been used to carry water under obstacles such as a deep river, or fracture zone, as in parts of the Catskill aqueduct for the supply of New York.[2] One tunnel was constructed at a depth of over 1000 feet, where the aqueduct crosses the Hudson River, which there flows over

[1] H. D. Morgan, C. K. Haskell & E. S. Pirie, *Proc. Inst. C.E.*, 30, Feb. 1965 (ppr. no. 6831).

[2] See reference on p. 320 (Berkey & Sanborn).

a hidden pre-glacial drift-filled gorge ; an exploratory boring in mid-stream penetrated drift to a depth of 765 feet without reaching solid rock, but the presence of granite at a greater depth was proved by trial bores drilled diagonally under the river from shafts on either side.   At the level chosen the tunnel was in sound granite throughout.

Stress conditions in rocks in tunnels.   When a tunnel is excavated the natural stability of the rock mass is disturbed, and there is a tendency for rock adjacent to it to move into the excavation.   New conditions of stress are developed in the rocks around the opening, and some of the load above the tunnel is transferred to the rock on either side of it.   This effect is known as *arching*, *i.e.* the capacity of the rock located above the tunnel roof to transfer part of its load to the sides of the tunnel.

With increasing depth from the surface, stress conditions gradually approach a hydrostatic distribution (p. 151).   The state of stress in the rock walls of an underground excavation may be found in several ways : electric strain-gauges can be cemented to the walls and the stress then

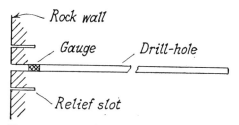

FIG. 133.—MEASUREMENT OF STRESS IN ROCK-WALL UNDERGROUND.

relieved locally by drilling shallow holes of larger diameter around them with a diamond core-drill.   The difference between gauge readings before and after the relief of stress gives a measure of the compression existing in the rock.[1]   Alternatively, the strain-gauge can be placed in a small diameter drill-hole, several feet long, the stress again being relieved by drilling a larger diameter hole to shallow depth around the first (Fig. 133).

In the " flat-jack " method, reference pegs are fixed in a rock-face, and a slot into which a flat hydraulic jack is inserted is cut in the rock. When the slot is cut the rock expands slightly into it (i.e. the pegs move together).   Hydraulic pressure is then exerted on the slot walls by means of the jack to restore them to their original position.   The jack pressure needed to do this is assumed to equal the tangential pressure in the rock face before the slot was cut.   By this method direct measurements of compressive stress can be made, in more than one direction if required, without assuming a knowledge of the elastic properties of the rock.

In the Snowy Mountains Scheme in south-east Australia, where large excavations for underground power stations have been made in the Tumut valley, estimates of horizontal pressure based on the vertical depth of cover and an assumed value for Poisson's ratio were found to be much too low.

---

[1] See, e.g., *Eng. News-Record*, 16 Oct. 1947, p. 93.

It was thought that the high tangential stresses which were encountered underground were due to *residual* tectonic stress in the fold-belt in which the work of excavation was carried out. Orogenic compression of the Palæozoic rocks of the belt had been relieved by the folding, but some residual stress still remained in the rocks at depth.

Overbreak. In hard rock excavation it is inevitable that some material is removed outside the perimeter planned as the excavated outline, and the amount of this material is known as *overbreak*. Its removal means increased cost for the work and, in the case of a lined tunnel, spaces between the outside of the lining and the rough rock surface must be filled. It is therefore desirable to reduce overbreak to a minimum ; the amount of overbreak is often small, depending on the nature of the rock which is being

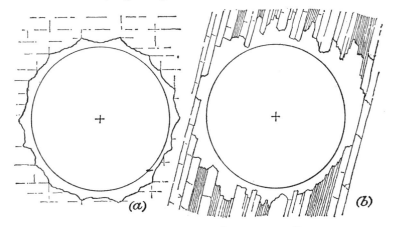

FIG. 134.—DIAGRAMS TO ILLUSTRATE OVERBREAK IN TUNNELLING.

(a) Tunnel driven against the strike, rock breaks evenly. (b) Tunnel driven parallel to strike, rock breaks badly. Excess of excavation over the circular outline is about 16 and 40 per cent respectively in the two cases.

worked, but in an exceptional case it may rise to as much as 40 per cent of the area of the planned cross-section (Fig. 134). Some of the factors on which overbreak depends are : size and spacing of shots used in blasting ; nature of the rock ; structures in the rock, such as bedding and joints, affecting the way in which it breaks ; relation between the direction of tunnel and the dip and strike of rocks.

The last point was well illustrated in driving the Lochaber water-power pressure tunnel, a large part of which was cut through schists (see below). Where the tunnel ran across the strike of the steeply dipping foliation in these rocks, a good cross-sectional shape resulted from the blasting, the rock coming out exactly to the outer ring of drill holes. Where the tunnel followed *along* the strike of the foliation, the dip then being steep across the tunnel, the rock broke badly to one side of the cross-section, which in places became almost rhombic (cf. Fig. 134).[1]

[1] " The Lochaber Water-Power Scheme and its Geological Aspect," by B. N. Peach, *Trans. Inst. Mining Eng.*, lxxviii, 1929–31, pp. 212–25.

Lochaber Water-power Tunnel. The Lochaber water-power scheme was developed for the purpose of generating electricity for the manufacture of aluminium at Fort William. It involved the construction of a 15-mile-long tunnel under the northern slopes of Ben Nevis, to carry water from the storage reservoir at Loch Treig to the pipe-line on the west slopes of Ben Nevis. The tunnel is lined with concrete and has an effective diameter of nearly 15 feet; 1¼ million tons of rock were removed during its construction, which was completed in 1929. The rocks passed through included a complex series of folded metamorphic types, mica schists, schistose flags, baked mica-schist and hornfels, and igneous rocks, granite and porphyrite. Rate of excavation varied according to the character and lie of the rocks encountered. Comparatively soft garnetiferous mica-schists (the Reservoir Schists) at the Loch Treig end were taken out over 1¼ miles of tunnel without difficulty, except where they were broken by faults, which necessitated the use of short lengths of cast-iron segmental lining for the tunnel. The position of many of these faults underground was predicted from surface evidence. Hard schistose flagstones (the Eilde Flags) followed the schists for a distance of 2 miles along the line of the tunnel, and progress in these highly quartzose rocks was very slow. They were followed in turn by 5½ miles of mica-schists (the Leven Schists), harder and more quartzose than the Reservoir Schists. The direction of their foliation varied in relation to the line of the tunnel, and it was in these rocks that the contrasted types of overbreak mentioned above occurred. The tunnel next traversed a mile of red porphyritic granite, succeeded by hard baked schists at the contact, and normal Leven Schists ; then a zone of calc-silicate hornfels (baked Ballachulish Limestone) led to another contact with the red Ben Nevis granite, here margined by fine-grained diorite, and the last three miles of the tunnel to the Fort William portal were driven in the igneous rock. The baked schist and the hornfels traversed at the igneous contacts were extremely hard rocks ; three sets of steel drills were sometimes needed to drill a single hole for placing the charges of gelignite, and the " pull " obtained from a round of firing in the hornfels was 4 feet, half the average for the whole tunnel.[1] Numerous dykes of porphyrite were crossed by the tunnel, and were associated with strong springs at their margins, the water from which caused difficulty in filling the concrete lining.

Throughout construction the tunnel was under the inspection of geologists and a detailed record of evidence was made ; valuable data was obtained underground which helped to corroborate and in places to correct the surface mapping. This part of the Lochaber scheme well demonstrates the important influence of the nature of rock encountered upon a drilling and excavation programme ; the geological factors affecting the whole scheme were studied in advance and are described in the papers mentioned in the footnotes.

Halkyn Drainage Tunnel, N. Wales. In the lead-mining district of Halkyn, Flintshire, an extension of an existing mines drainage tunnel

[1] " The Lochaber Water-Power Scheme," by W. T. Halcrow, *Proc. Inst. C.E.*, Vol. 231, 1930-1, p. 54.

was under construction during 1929–31. The new tunnel was 7 miles in eingth, of rectangular cross-section, 10 × 8 feet, and was cut throughout ln the Carboniferous Limestone formation. It provides an example of the way in which underground works may be hindered by incoming water. Previous mining operations in the district had encountered serious water difficulties ; the average flow throughout the year in the existing tunnel was 12,000 to 15,000 gallons per minute, part of this amount being due to percolation from rain and part coming from the River Alyn. The tunnel runs nearly north and south and cuts the limestone obliquely to its strike, which is north-west to south-east, with a gentle dip to the north-east. The limestone series contains beds of shale, and is cut by east-west veins and north-south fissures (called cross-courses). Progress of the work was at times seriously slowed up by heavy inrushes of water carrying large quantities of sand ; these occurred particularly at places where cross-courses intersected the tunnel at a very small angle. One group of fissures brought in water at the rate of 4000 gallons per minute, necessitating special timbering and delay due to removal of the sand. Under normal conditions the tunnel was advanced at the rate of nearly 30 feet per day, but at times was brought almost to a standstill.[1] This illustrates the point that circulation of water in limestone is through both joints and deep fissures connecting with surface water, it is often not possible to predict when workings will strike a water-bearing fissure and be temporarily flooded out.

Mersey Road Tunnel. As an alternative to a high-level bridge to connect Liverpool and Birkenhead, a scheme for the construction of a large sub-aqueous tunnel two miles in length, of which about ¾ mile lay under the River Mersey, received Parliamentary sanction in 1925. In order to accommodate four lines of traffic in one casing, instead of the usual two lines, a tunnel of exceptionally large diameter, 46 feet for the excavated outline, was necessary ; two pilot headings, one above the other, were driven from shafts sunk on either side of the Mersey, and the full circular section was opened up from them and lined with cast-iron rings. The space between the lining and the bare rock was packed with broken rock and grouted. The line of the new tunnel ran roughly parallel to the existing railway tunnel, constructed in 1886, and a little to the north of it (i.e. downstream, the river flowing nearly north).

The rocks shown on geological maps of the area are Triassic, Bunter and Keuper Sandstones, the outcrops of which are bounded by north-south faults and largely concealed by glacial drift. The sandstones dip gently to the east, and it was thought that the Middle Bunter Sandstone, a hard reddish-brown rock with few pebbles, which here occupies both banks of the Mersey, would be continuous under the river. The presence of a fault or faults along the estuary of the Mersey was probable on structual evidence. As far back as 1863 a Liverpool civil engineer, G. H. Morton, had published a geological section across the Mersey in which he showed the

---

[1] " Driving a Mines Drainage Tunnel in North Wales," by J. L. Francis and J. C. Allen, *Trans. Inst. Mining and Met.*, Vol. XLI, 1931–2, pp. 234–71.

strata broken by a fault beneath the river. This fault was met in the railway tunnel and eventually in the new tunnel, and occasioned little difficulty.

A more serious problem that had to be faced concerned the pre-glacial channel of the Mersey. Evidence for the existence of this old valley, buried below the drift, had been collected from records of wells and borings by Mellard Reade, who predicted in 1873 that the buried valley would be

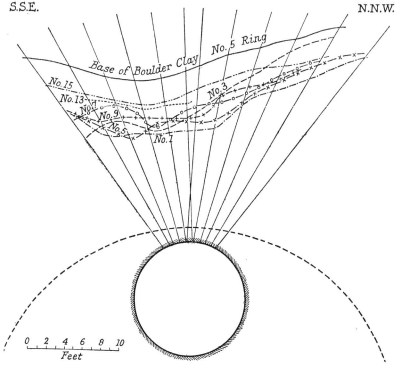

FIG. 135.—SERIAL SECTIONS ACROSS THE BURIED CHANNEL BELOW THE RIVER MERSEY.[1] Radial lines are drill-holes from upper pilot heading. Dotted line shows main tunnel outline.

found under the present bed of the Mersey, near its mouth. It was, in fact, encountered in the railway tunnel over a length of 200 feet, and had given considerable trouble through incoming water, so that a knowledge of its probable position and depth where it crossed the line of the new tunnel was very important. It was desirable to keep the whole of the under-river excavation in the sandstone. The buried valley had been found further upstream at Widnes, where borings to the north of the town went down to 130 feet below O.D. through glacial deposits before striking the rock floor. In the Liverpool area the channel appeared to be less deep. The geologists to the new tunnel, taking into account all the available evidence (here

[1] Fig. 135 is reproduced by permission of the Council of the Geological Society of Liverpool.

given in outline only), concluded that the buried channel probably deepened *southwards*, i.e. in the opposite direction to the present course of the river, and that the flow of the river had been reversed after the Pleistocene glaciation. The buried valley, therefore, would probably not be found at a lower level on the line of the new tunnel than in the old railway. This prediction, together with questions as to the length and gradient of the approaches, governed the depth of the under-river portion of the tunnel. As construction proceeded from the Liverpool side the lower pilot heading was kept ahead of the upper, and inclined borings to explore the ground ahead were drilled upwards from the heading. In this way the buried valley was located in advance of the main excavation ; some of the borings were taken up through the sandstone floor of the valley into the overlying fill of glacial gravel and a further 6 feet into boulder clay. From the data thus obtained, the profile of the channel was plotted at successive stages (Fig. 135). At one point the rock cover for the full excavation was only 5 feet, part of which was broken rock ; but the tunnel was driven throughout its length in sandstone.

Other considerations related to groundwater. As the strata were water-bearing sandstones, with a porosity of 16 per cent, water was pumped continuously from the headings via the Liverpool shaft, while construction was in progress, the maximum rate being 4200 gallons per minute. The pumping produced a local fall of 25 feet in the water-table, and was felt in neighbouring wells at least ¾ mile away ; the quantity pumped from the railway tunnel (which had no water-tight lining) was also reduced during the period of construction. The lengths of waterproof lining in the approaches of the new tunnel were controlled by the estimated position of the water-table after pumping ceased.[1]

Cementation in the Severn Tunnel. As an example of extensive grouting operations in fissured rocks, the work carried out during 1929–30 in the Severn railway tunnel may be briefly summarized.[2] Construction of the tunnel, which was completed in 1886, had been attended by great difficulties from incoming water, both groundwater and river water. Accurate geological records had fortunately been kept by the contractor throughout the work. The tunnel passes under the Severn estuary, through gently dipping Triassic marls and sandstones for the first 1½ miles at the eastern (Bristol) end ; these rocks are down-thrown against Coal Measures, which occupy about 2 miles in the central part of the tunnel and are overlain by Triassic marls in the last mile at the western end. Besides strong spring flow at one point (the " Big Spring " of Sudbrook), water from the River Severn broke through into the workings near the eastern end of the tunnel during construction, the water passing down open joints (and possibly faults) in the marl. These were sealed at their upper ends with clay deposited on the river bed and placed in position at low water.

[1] " The Geology of the New Mersey Tunnel," by P. G. H. Boswell, *Proc. Liverpool Geol. Soc.*, Vol. XVII, 1937, pp. 160–91.

[2] " Cementation in the Severn Tunnel," by R. Carpmael, *Proc. Inst. C.E.*, Vol. 234, 1931–2, pp. 277–89.

In 1924 and 1929 considerable trouble was again experienced from incoming river water, at about $\frac{3}{4}$ mile from the Bristol portal. Clay sealing was again tried, but it was decided to use cementation over a critical $\frac{3}{4}$-mile length of tunnel to strengthen the brickwork lining and to consolidate the ground between the tunnel and the river bed. Over 8000 tons of cement were injected through holes drilled radially through the brickwork, both above and below the tunnel. The existence of voids at the back of the brick lining, thought to have developed since its construction, was proved by the travel of injected cement and its appearance at other holes. At one point cement escaped up to ground surface, and at another up into the river-bed ; the latter occurred in the vicinity of the breaks-through of the river referred to above. The bed of the Severn was patrolled at low water to detect escaping cement. The work of cementation successfully reduced leakage into the tunnel to a small amount, and also reduced possible erosion of the marls by the action of circulating river water.

Bowland Forest Tunnel. With a length of $10\frac{1}{4}$ miles and a diameter of excavation of 10 feet, this tunnel forms part of the aqueduct conveying water to Manchester from the Haweswater Reservoir in Westmorland, completed in 1941. The tunnel took $3\frac{1}{4}$ years to build, and runs south-south-east from near Wray to Newton-in-Bowland, passing under the fells east of Lancaster through folded and faulted Carboniferous rocks. From the north portal the tunnel traversed the following rocks : first, about 2 miles of shales and mudstones ; in places the shales were incoherent, so that packing and concreting of the sides had to be carried out as the tunnel was driven ; next, about 1 mile of sandstone and 2 miles of coarse grits in which faults and fault-zones were present, and a further $2\frac{1}{2}$ miles of grits and shales (the Pendle Grit Group) which were folded into a broad anticline and syncline ; then over $\frac{1}{2}$ mile of shales (Bowland Shales) followed by a limestone (100 feet), and further shales ($\frac{1}{2}$ mile) which dipped steeply north, leading to an anticline in thick-bedded limestones (the Clitheroe Group of the Carboniferous Limestone). These limestones occupied the last $1\frac{3}{4}$ miles to the south portal.

The entry of water into the workings, mainly from faults and joints in the rocks, gave recurrent trouble, and pumping at the rate of 10,000 to 24,000 g.p.h. was necessary in sandstones. But at one fault $3\frac{1}{4}$ miles from the north end of the tunnel the influx of water was so great that pumping increased to 96,000 g.p.h., the water spouting horizontally from the tunnel sides under considerable pressure. Headings driven in faulted grits from the base of the Croasdale shaft (nearly 4 miles from the south portal, and sited in a fault-belt) again tapped large inflows of water, up to 84,000 g.p.h. By contrast, the upper part of the Pendle Grit Group was almost dry, owing to an increasing content of argillaceous material in the rocks and also to the large depth of cover (over 1000 feet).

At a point 24,500 feet from the north portal a spectacular event occurred, shaley beds in the roof of the tunnel splitting with great violence over a length of 200 feet, so that a " curtain " of water poured through the fissure along its whole length. This large inflow raised the discharge in one of the adits temporarily to 108,600 g.p.h., but it quickly ebbed, and ceased within 3 days.

It is considered that groundwater in the local grits and sandstones is not replenished below a depth of 700 feet. Below that depth, joints and fissures tend to close up and the rocks become impervious. On the other hand, major faults may carry surface water down to depths of 1000 feet or more, but such deep pockets of water are not necessarily in contact with the water in the zone of saturation. (This account is based on the paper by J. R. Earp, in Bulletin No. 7, Geol. Survey of Gt. Britain, 1955.)

Rock-bolting. This is a method of supporting rock in the walls or roofs of tunnels or other underground excavations by means of anchor bolts. The " slot and wedge " bolt is a steel rod of 1 to $1\frac{1}{2}$ inch diameter, commonly up to 20 feet in length, and slotted at one end to take a wedge. The bolt is placed in a drill hole of suitable length, and when driven the wedge develops friction against the side of the hole. A plate placed over the threaded outer end of the bolt is tightened against the rock face by means of a nut. Other types include expansion bolts, which have a shell that can be expanded against the side of the hole when the bolt is turned. And the perforated bolt, which consists of a split perforated sleeve around a central bar; the sleeve halves are inserted into the drill hole which is then filled with mortar. The bar is driven into the sleeve, forcing the mortar through perforations and filling the space between bar and rock. Adhesion is thus produced along the whole length of the bolt and is effective, for example, in sheared rocks.

Rock-bolts were employed to support the roof and walls of large underground power-station excavations in the Snowy Mountains Scheme, southeastern Australia, as in the Tumut no. 2 machine-hall where over 2000 bolts were used in the roof, with a spacing such that each bolt held an area of 11·6 sq. ft. The bolts are put in soon after a rock surface has been exposed, and wire mesh can be placed over the rock face, fastened to the bolts, to prevent falls of spalled rock. The bolts can be set in a pattern at regular intervals, and arranged so as to intersect main joints in the rock at right angles. The method saves time, as the work can proceed without waiting for concrete or other support to be placed, and is economical because the cost of the bolting is often about half that of other kinds of support (such as concrete beams).

Cameron Highlands Hydro-electric Scheme, Malaya.[1] Completed in 1963, this scheme diverts the headwaters of two rivers flowing east, the Telom and the Bertam, through a range of granite hills to the valley of the Batang Padang on the west side of the peninsula. More than three-quarters of the catchment of 66·8 sq. miles is jungle covered, with steep slopes and deeply weathered rock; the mean annual rainfall is 103·6 inches and is fairly evenly distributed throughout the year. The coarse porphyritic granite (and some finer-grained varieties) is much jointed, and on the hills both granite and schists (relics of the roof of the granite) are weathered in places to depths of several hundred feet. Examination of thin sections

---

[1] J. C. Dickinson and R. T. Gerrard, in *Proc. Inst. C.E.*, 26 Nov. 1963.

of the granite revealed many indications of strain, the quartz and felspar crystals often showing strain polarization and incipient fracturing. The relatively weak condition of this rock was confirmed by low crushing strengths found from 2½-inch core samples ; at the Jor power station site they ranged from about 6000 to 11,700 lbs./sq. in. During early investigations several rock cores, recovered from drill holes, disintegrated completely within a few days on the relief of pressure and exposure to air. Although the cause of this was uncertain, some opinion attributed it to the presence of montmorillonite. During tunnelling operations, however, similar rapid disintegration of the rock was not encountered.

Three tunnels (from north to south the Telom, Habu, and Bertam) total 15 miles in length ; low pressure tunnels are lined with concrete. In the Telom tunnel, 10½ feet diameter, the average thickness of overbreak varied from 7·7 inches in the north to 6·1 in the south ; incoming water amounted to 450 g.p.m. In the Bertam tunnel, however, working conditions were relatively dry ; flow from fissures occurred at a few points but was controlled by grouting.

The Jor power station was located at a depth of 860 feet below ground level, so as to provide a short length for the high pressure conduit (under 1880 feet head) and avoid the placing of large diameter pipes on the surface of steep hillsides which might be subject to landslips when jungle vegetation was removed. This location involved the excavation of a main chamber 80 feet high and some 270 feet long, the length being placed north-north-west, an orientation chosen with regard to prominent joint directions. The roof was lined with concrete, to give security against the possible opening of rock joints at a later date. Comparison with stress analysis data available from the Snowy Mountains Scheme showed the probability of tension occurring in the side walls of the chamber just below the roof arches, and these areas were secured by rock-bolting. Flat-jack tests [1] carried out in slots cut in the rock walls of the power station area gave values of 2250 lbs./sq. in. for horizontal stress parallel to the length of the excavation, and a vertical stress of 1650 lbs./sq. in. The latter was greater than the value estimated from the weight of overlying rock (1000 lbs./sq. in.). The site is located in a region of tectonic folding, where probably unrelieved stresses still remain.

SELECTED REFERENCES

BERKEY, C. P., AND SANBORN, F. J. " Engineering Geology of the Catskill Water Supply." *Trans. Amer. Soc. Civil Engrs.*, Vol. LXXXVI, 1923.
FOX, F. " The Simplon Tunnel." *Proc. Inst. Civ. Engrs.*, Vol. 168, 1907, p. 61.
LEGGET, R. F. " Geology and Engineering." 1962. Chapter 8.
SKEMPTON, A. W. " Long-term stability of clay slopes." *Géotechnique*, 14, no. 2, 1964.
SKEMPTON, A. W. " Some observations on tectonic shear-zones." *Proc. 1st Congr. Int. Soc. Rock Mechanics*, 1, Lisbon, 1966, p. 329.

[1] D. J. Kluth on " Rock stress in the Jor underground power station, Malaya," *8th. Int. Congr. on Large Dams*, Edinburgh, 1964.

SANBORN, J. F. " Engineering Geology in the Design and Construction of Tunnels." Berkey Volume, *Geol. Soc. Amer.*, 1951.

TERZAGHI, K. " Rock Defects and Loads on Tunnel Supports " Harvard Univ., Soil Mechanics Series No. 25, 1945-6.

KNILL, J. L., J. A. FRANKLIN and D. R. RAYBOULD. " A study of stress distribution around rock bolt anchors." *Proc. 1st Int. Congr. Rock Mechanics* (theme 7), 1966.

LANG, T. " Theory & practice of rock-bolting." *Trans. Amer. Inst. Mining Engrs.*, 233, 1962, p. 333.

GILMOUR, L. W., in Symposium on Tunnelling, *Inst. of Mining Engrs.*, 1959.

CHAPTER 16

SOME METHODS OF SITE INVESTIGATION

When a site has been selected as a possible location for engineering structures, a preliminary investigation is commonly made with the object of assessing the suitability of the site for the proposed works. The investigation is also a means of obtaining information on which the design of works, especially of foundations, can be based and possible difficulties provided for, and generally includes an exploration of sub-surface conditions. Alternatively, where the safety of existing works is in question an investigation may be needed. The availability of materials suitable for various purposes in construction can also be established by a preliminary survey. These matters are discussed in the present chapter ; among them are points which have been touched on earlier, but they are here collected together in summary, and a discussion of certain geophysical exploratory methods is added.

Preliminary Geological Surveys. It is generally agreed that a geological estimation of the conditions at a site is most usefully made very early in the development of a project. It is one of the first tasks to be undertaken. The survey will involve the examination of the ground in considerable detail, leading to the compiling of a geological map of the area (p. 281), on which the data obtained during the survey are recorded. In a country such as Great Britain much information is available from the published and unpublished maps of the Geological Survey, which should be consulted as a preliminary. A list of maps and other publications of the Survey is given in the Appendix (p. 335). Where published information is not available, geological reconnaissance mapping of the area will provide an outline of the surface geology, which can then be a basis for further detailed exploration. Aerial survey methods may be a valuable adjunct in the early stages. The recording of data on a geological map and the drawing of sections have been discussed in Chapter 12.

At an engineering site where excavation is to be made, and especially where deep excavation (or tunnelling) is involved, it is essential to obtain information about the sub-surface conditions. Auger holes, trial pits and trenches, headings, and boreholes are all useful in different circumstances, and can provide data which helps to build up a three-dimensional picture of the site when used to supplement the surface data. Augering is a simple method of putting down holes a few inches in diameter to depths up to 20 feet, in soft sediments (p. 250). Trial pits and trenches, in addition to providing samples of the deposits excavated, allow inspection of the rocks in the walls and floor over an area, and are useful when the walls stand without support. Boreholes allow much greater depths to be penetrated, and have been discussed on p. 285 *et al.* A hand rig is commonly used for boring vertically in soft sediments to depths of 70 or 80 feet ; for greater depths a power-operated rig is needed. Percussion and rotary methods of boring are used for penetrating harder rocks.

Different procedures are required at different types of site : thus, sites for dams, bridges, docks or buildings may need to have many closely spaced and relatively deep borings, from which the geological structure and variations in the sub-surface rocks can be determined. On the other hand, sites for railways, roads, canals, aqueducts, sewers and land drains, or coast defence works extend over larger distances and need relatively shallow borings along their course to give information about the geological deposits present and the groundwater conditions.

From data obtained in the above ways, sometimes in conjunction with geophysical surveys (p. 326), decisions can be made as to the best location of the works to be constructed, and the most suitable methods for carrying out the construction. The data should also yield information on matters such as the difficulty or ease of excavation ; the need for support (timbering, shoring) of the sides of the excavation ; and possible special provision to meet groundwater conditions (e.g. groundwater lowering). The presence and extent of buried channels filled with glacial or other sediments (p. 286), or of other undesirable features in a foundation, should also be made apparent.

In addition it may be necessary to obtain and test samples of the rocks at the site, and this is specially important in connection with the design of foundations. From the test results the bearing strength of the rocks and the stability of slopes can be assessed. Where there is considerable variation in the sub-surface deposits it is important that the least favourable conditions that may be present should be estimated. An assessment can also be made of the possible effects of alterations in existing conditions, brought about during construction : e.g. the lowering of the water-table through pumping, giving rise to possible settlement of the surrounding ground surface (cf. p. 17), or changes in natural drainage brought about by a rise in the groundwater level.

Boring and sampling methods. Apart from sampling at shallow depths, where a deeper hole is required boring methods are broadly of two kinds : (*a*) percussion, and (*b*) rotary. A drilling rig or derrick is used, to support the weight of the drilling rods.

In percussion boring the " bit " is suspended from rods (or a cable) and is jumped up and down, so that the rock is broken up by repeated blows. Water is added to the hole to keep the bit cool and make a slurry, and the debris removed by means of a baler. The pounded rock mixed with water forms a slurry, from which chips may be recovered for identification. The rate of progress of the boring, and the cost, varies according to the hardness of the rock encountered.

Rotary boring methods include mud-rotary drilling and core-drilling. In the former the bit is rotated, and is attached to hollow drilling rods through which a fluid mud is pumped continuously. The mud returns to the surface through the annular space between the rods and the hole, bringing with it small fragments of rock which can be screened out and examined.   The rods are usually in 20-feet lengths, and are successively added to the assembly as the hole is lowered.

Core-drilling uses a tubular bit with a lower cutting edge, which is rotated in the hole ; many forms of bit are available, some having a " crown " containing industrial diamonds or other hard abrasive, for penetrating hard rocks.   Diamond drills with a diameter of 2 to 4 inches are commonly used for sampling, or in exploratory bores from underground workings (cf. p. 317), and holes can be drilled at any angle.

As the bit is rotated, a core is cut out and enters a barrel mounted above the bit.   The length of the barrel controls the length of core which can be obtained at one time.   Water is circulated down the drilling rods to the bit, and returns to the surface bringing with it powdered rock and fragments produced in the drilling process.   The core is recovered by withdrawing the drilling rods and barrel, and is prevented from falling out of the latter by a spring clip.   Before withdrawal a core can be broken off from the parent rock without rotation ; in this way an oriented core is obtained from which the directions of structures in the rocks penetrated (such as the dip, in dipping strata) can be measured.   The cost of core-drilling is greater than for other methods, and increases greatly with increasing depth of the hole ; but the recovery of a core is a great advantage, as it yields information from depth and is a sample of the rocks drilled through. Friable rocks do not always yield a continuous core.

Sampling at an engineering site often involves the disturbance of the natural structure of the sedimentary deposit or other rock which is being investigated, but under some conditions undisturbed samples can be obtained.   In both soft sediments and harder rocks, relatively undisturbed samples are obtainable by coring, or (near the surface) by hand sampling. Disturbed (fragmented) samples are given by the sludge from rotary or percussion drilling, as described above, and from hand augering.   Special methods of obtaining undisturbed samples of clays, and of sands or other non-cohesive sediments, and for preserving the moisture content of samples, are described in text-books of soil mechanics.

Methods of Soil Mechanics.   The term " soil " as used by engineers includes all loose or uncompacted mineral and rock material, as distinct from " rock," which is compact and relatively hard.   Sands, gravels, silts, clays, and the products of rock-weathering are " soils " under this definition. To the geologist and agriculturist, however, *soil* is the surface layer of weathered rock mixed with organic matter from vegetation (humus), and the word has been used in that sense in preceding chapters, unless otherwise defined.

Soils, in the engineering sense, are distinguished principally by their low strength, and often possess a high water content ; for these reasons they require special consideration in the construction of works entailing their excavation, and in the design of foundations and slopes.   Geologically, such soils have been formed by the action of ice (glacial deposits), wind (dune deposits), rivers (alluvial deposits), the sea (beach deposits), and weathering processes, as discussed earlier in this book.   The science of soil mechanics, which can be regarded as a branch of quantitative engineering geology,[1] deals in the first place with the investigation of the mechanical and physical properties of soils ; and secondly, develops methods of using the results of these mechanical and physical tests in the design of civil engineering structures. It involves the quantitative study of unconsolidated sediments and related geological materials. There are now a number of good text-books of soil mechanics, some of which are listed on p. 334 and to which reference can be made. The following outline is intended only to indicate the methods and tests which are commonly employed in evaluating the properties of soils ; the general procedure being (i) sampling, (ii) testing, and (iii) analysis of the test results in relation to the specific problems under consideration.

Tests for the *index properties* of soils include mechanical analysis (by various methods, see p. 122) ; determination of the specific gravity of the solid particles in a soil ; determination of the natural water content from undisturbed samples ; evaluation of the liquid limit and plastic limit (the Atterberg limits) ;[2] and compressive strength determined on unconfined samples. The methods of carrying out these tests are described in books on the subject. The results of such tests allow comparisons to be made between different samples and different soils, and can be related to the behaviour of the soils in straightforward cases.

There are also tests for *basic properties* such as consolidation, shear strength, and permeability. These properties have a direct bearing on the behaviour of a soil at a site. Consolidation (or compaction) in a bed of clay in nature is brought about by the superposition of further deposits on the clay layer (p. 131). Its quantitative evaluation in the laboratory for a particular deposit gives useful information, e.g. in the design of founda-tions to be constructed in that deposit, or in the design of earth dams for which the soil is to be used as a material or " fill." The shear strength of a soil is an important factor in the design of foundations of many kinds, e.g. dam foundations, retaining walls, and road and runway subgrades. Permeability (p. 261) becomes important in excavations in sands, and in connection with earth dams and dam foundations generally. The technical details of these tests cannot be discussed here.

Geology as a science has, in turn, benefited from the development of soil mechanics techniques which has gone on since the publication of Professor K. Terzaghi's " Erdbaumechanik " in 1925 ; the studies have led to a better understanding of certain geological processes, as well as providing statistical data about them. Thus the Atterberg limits, which were first suggested by an agricultural scientist, A. Atterberg, in Sweden in 1913, and

---

[1] See discussion by A. W. Skempton, reference on p. 334.

[2] As the water content of a clay is increased during remoulding, the sediment becomes more and more plastic and eventually behaves as a liquid. The water content of the clay at which it ceases to be plastic and becomes a fluid is called the *liquid limit* ; the *plastic limit* is the water content at which the soil ceases to be plastic and becomes friable or brittle. These two values of water content express the shear strength of the material under different conditions. The numerical difference between the two values is called the *plasticity index*.

eventually introduced into soil mechanics by Terzaghi, have become a standard test in classifying cohesive soils (e.g. clays); and have further been correlated with the compressibility of natural clay formations,[1] and with the increase of strength which occurs with increasing overburden pressure.[2] The elucidation of the mechanism of landslipping in clays of different geological ages has been another result. And work on the consolidation of clayey sediments has made possible an understanding of the behaviour of different deposits in relation to their degree of consolidation under overburden pressures; the degree of loading which a deposit has undergone during its geological history can be estimated approximately from the compression curve for the material as found in the laboratory. It is useful to define broadly four stages passed through by argillaceous sediments during the process of consolidation : firstly *muds*, almost fluid materials which have been consolidated under not more than a few feet of overlying sediment; then *soft* to *firm clays*, plastic materials which can be moulded in the fingers, and which have been consolidated under overburdens varying from a few feet to several hundreds of feet in thickness; *stiff clays*, materials which can be moulded in the fingers only with great difficulty, and which have been consolidated under many hundreds or several thousands of feet. These clays often contain fissures, with an apparent random distribution, and if a large sample is dropped it will break into polyhedral fragments along the fissure planes; and lastly *shales*, materials with parallel laminations and which are brittle. If ground with water they may be reduced to a plastic mass; they have been consolidated under some thousands of feet of overburden (Skempton, 1944, *loc. cit.*).

Again, the effects of variations in the mineral composition and shape of particles on the properties of some soils, particularly clays and silty clays, is still being worked out; one example of such a correlation, for the Sasumua clay, has been described earlier (p. 297); and an instance of the change in permeability brought about by exchange of ions in the clay minerals of a deposit is referred to on p. 134. The above examples illustrate some of the contributions to geological knowledge which have accrued from the pursuit of soil mechanics in the last thirty years, quite apart from its main concern with matters pertaining to engineering construction.

Geophysical Methods. The various methods of applied geophysics make use of differences which exist in the physical properties of rocks and minerals. Only four properties have been used on an extensive scale, these being (a) the density of the rocks, (b) the magnetic properties (induced and permanent magnetism), (c) a combination of the elastic properties and densities, and (d) the electrical resistivities.

The density of the rocks modifies the magnitude and direction of the earth's gravitational attraction (acceleration due to gravity) and the methods based on this property are referred to as *gravitational methods*. The *magnetic methods*, employing the second of the above characteristics, make use of

---

[1] A. W. Skempton, " Notes on the Compressibility of Clays," *Qvart. Journ. Geol. Soc.*, 100, 1944, p. 119.

[2] A. W. Skempton, in *Géotechnique*, 1, 1948.

the local distortion produced in the earth's magnetic field by permanently magnetized minerals such as magnetite, or rocks carrying a heavy concentration of this mineral. The elasticity and density fix the speed with which a mechanical disturbance (usually due to the explosion of a buried charge) travels through the rock. By measuring the time taken by the shock, set up by the explosion, to travel to various points on the surface, it is possible to make deductions concerning the disposition, and sometimes the nature, of the rocks through which the shock has passed. The principles involved in this method are identical with those employed in the study of natural earthquake phenomena, and accordingly the artificial earthquake method is usually called the *seismic method*. Finally, those methods making use of the electrical resistivity of rocks and minerals are grouped under the heading of *electrical methods*. Of these four methods, the last two (seismic and electrical) may be specially useful at engineering sites, and a preliminary geophysical survey may yield valuable data quickly and comparatively cheaply ; it can supplement the geological data, and help to confine e.g. a drilling programme to the most promising areas. Underground structures, such as buried channels, can often be detected by geophysical surveys (e.g. the survey made for the Devon valley, near Stirling, reference on p. 236).

The Resistivity Method. This method depends on the differences in the electrical resistivities of rocks. The resistivity of a rock is defined as the resistance of a cylinder, of unit length and cross section, with the current flowing parallel to its length. The unit of resistivity is the ohm-cm., the ohm-metre, or the ohm-foot, according to the unit of length adopted in the definition. Unfortunately the resistivity of a rock is not a characteristic of the rock, but depends mainly on the conditions under which it occurs. The majority of mineral constituents are non-conductors of electricity, the current being confined to the saline solutions filling the interstitial spaces. Accordingly, the resistivity depends essentially on two factors, (a) the conducting properties of the solutions, which may vary from 10 ohm-cm. or less for high concentrations of salts, up to 100,000 ohm-cm. or more for fresh waters, and (b) the percentage volume of solutions in the rocks. This latter factor depends on the porosity if the rock is saturated, or on the grain size if the rock is above the water table where the moisture is retained against gravity by surface tension effects. Here a coarse gravel has a higher resistivity than a fine grained clay. It follows at once that rock resistivity tables cannot be compiled, but the following classification, depending on pore space, may be used as a guide.

(a) Crystalline rocks (low porosity).   50,000–1,000,000 ohm-cm.
(b) Consolidated sediments.   5,000–100,000 ohm-cm.
(c) Unconsolidated sediments (high   50–10,000 ohm-cm.
     porosity).

It should be appreciated that exceptions to this scheme often occur and only the order of resistivity, to be anticipated in any specific case, is indicated.

In a fairly small region, when the salinity is appreciably constant, the resistivity should allow a distinction between saturated and unsaturated rocks and also, in the zone of saturation, between rocks of differing porosity, e.g. it should be possible to locate the boundary between an unconsolidated formation and a compact sedimentary or crystalline basement.

To measure rock resistivities, four electrical contacts (electrodes) are made with the ground surface. There are various possible configurations of the electrodes, but that due to Wenner is usually employed. In this, the electrodes are placed in a straight line at equal intervals a known as the electrode separation (Fig. 136a). Between the two outer contacts $C_1 C_2$ a current I amps. is passed, and the resulting voltage V set up between the

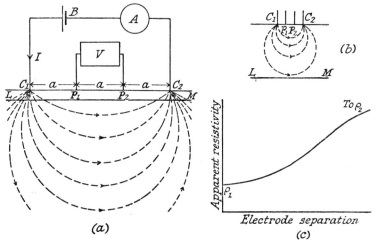

FIG. 136.—DIAGRAMS ILLUSTRATING ELECTRICAL RESISTIVITY METHOD.

inner electrodes $P_1 P_2$ is measured. From these observations the resistivity ρ of the ground can be calculated, for it can be shown that

$$\rho = 2\pi a V / I$$

if the ground is everywhere uniform. In practice, the resistivity is rarely constant throughout the area examined and the measured value is then called the *apparent resistivity*. When the current travels through the ground, it does not take the direct path from one electrode to the other, but spreads out and occupies all the volume available, following paths indicated by the broken lines. In uniform ground these current paths have a definite shape, with the result that the current penetration is proportional to the electrode separation. In non-uniform ground, the lines of flow are distorted, but there is still an increase in current penetration with increasing electrode separation, but the two are no longer proportional. Thus, by changing the electrode separation, the apparent resistivity can be measured to different depths.

The application of this is made clear by the case of a layer of resistivity ρ_1, and of uniform thickness, resting on a thick bed of higher resistivity rock (ρ_2). For electrode separations small compared with the thickness of the upper layer, it can be seen from Fig. 136b, in which LM is the interface between formations, that only a very small fraction of the current reaches the lower rock whose effect will be negligible. Thus the measured apparent resistivity is equal to ρ_1, the resistivity of the surface layer. For large electrode separations (Fig. 136a, LM again being the interface) nearly all the current enters the lower layer, and the measured value tends to ρ_2. As the separation is increased the measured value changes continuously from ρ_1 to ρ_2 as indicated in the graph (Fig. 136c). From the shape of the graph, the resistivity values and the depth of the common boundary can be calculated. The accuracy of the depth determination depends on how closely the actual conditions approximate to the ideal conditions used to develop the formula for the curve, in which the most important assumption is a constant resistivity in each of the two media involved. Estimates have been made to within 1·0 per cent, but generally errors up to 5 per cent are involved. It frequently happens that the conditions differ so much from the ideal case that theoretical interpretation of the observations is impossible. Under these conditions an empirical method is employed. At a point where the vertical rock sequence is known a resistivity curve is obtained, when certain features can often be associated with rock interfaces. In subsequent measurements in the same area similar features are assigned to the same boundary and the depth estimated from the electrode separation at which the features occur.

In making a series of measurements, the electrode system is expanded about the point at which the depth is required : that is, the distance a is increased by successive steps, and for each value of a the apparent resistivity is obtained. A graph of resistivity against electrode separation can then be drawn ; the method is also referred to as a " depth-probe." Another procedure is to maintain a fixed electrode separation and to move the system as a whole about the area, so that the region is examined to approximately a constant depth. Here, as the rock interface approaches the surface, the conditions become similar to Fig. 136a and a high resistivity is obtained, again assuming that the lower medium has the higher resistivity, while if the boundary is deep a low measured value is obtained. Thus it is possible to infer the variations in the depth of the interface from the changes in the measured values of the resistivity.

The equipment necessary for the measurements is simple. For shallow measurements up to 150–200 feet, a high-tension battery is usual for the current source, the current being measured with a multi-range instrument reading up to a maximum of 0·5 amp. The voltage difference between P_1 and P_2 is preferably measured with a portable potentiometer with a range of 0–200 millivolts. A suitable high resistance millivoltmeter can be employed, but it is not so satisfactory. The current electrodes are steel rods driven into the ground, but the potential electrodes must be specially prepared non-polarizing electrodes, to eliminate the contact voltage which would exist between a metal rod and the salt solutions in the ground. By introducing a double commutator into the circuit, Gish and Rooney eliminated the necessity of using non-polarizing electrodes, which are replaced by steel rods. There also exists a compact and portable instrument, the Megger Earth Tester, which is usually suitable for small-scale work. It is self-contained, incorporating a hand-driven D.C. generator, a double commutator, a current coil and a potential coil. The last two are mounted together in a magnetic field in such a way that the ratio V/I in the formula is read directly from the scale of the instrument.

As an example of the type of results which can be obtained by these methods, the survey in connection with the Lièvre Dam may be cited. It was proposed to construct a dam across the Lièvre River, some 15 miles downstream from Ottawa, and to conduct the water from the dam to a power-house about a mile away through a tunnel which had to be located everywhere in the solid rock. Before starting the project, it was necessary to know the subsurface conditions in the area between the proposed power station and dam to ensure that this last condition could be fulfilled. For this purpose, an electrical exploration was made of the area involved. The electrical conditions were favourable for an electrical survey, for the bed-rock was composed of Pre-Cambrian and Palæozoic formations, covered by a composite overburden of glacial drift, sand and clays, with fresh water sands, clays and gravels at the surface. In all, 63 depth determinations were made electrically at points separated by about 200 feet, and from the observations the contour lines of the bed-rock surface were constructed. The path of the tunnel was then selected, and along its length a series of boreholes were put down to confirm the electrical results. Agreement between the drilling results and the electrical depth determinations was good, but not perfect. Certain discrepancies could be assigned to the variable nature of the overburden. The problem was solved satisfactorily by the electrical method, since this showed that the overburden had everywhere a thickness small in comparison with the depth of the proposed tunnel.

Seismic Method. The basis of this method is the velocity with which a mechanical disturbance travels through a rock, the velocity changing appreciably from one rock to another. Thus for sands and clays the velocity is about 5000 feet per second, while in a granite it may be as high as 20,000 feet per second. Near the surface of the earth, abnormally low velocities in the region of 600 feet per second may be encountered. The mechanical disturbance is originated by the explosion of a buried charge, its size depending on the distances involved in the problem and the transmitting properties of the rocks. For small-scale work charges up to a few pounds are sufficient. The nature of the disturbance set up is quite complex, and three distinct mechanical pulses are produced, the P wave and the S wave, both of which travel outwards in all directions from the centre of the disturbance, and the Rayleigh wave, which is propagated over the ground surface only (see p. 163). Of these, the P wave has the greatest velocity and is the pulse usually observed in prospecting. When a P wave, or an S wave, is incident on a boundary between two rocks, it behaves in the same way as an incident light beam on a glass surface, part of the energy being reflected back into the first medium and part being refracted into the second medium. The angles of incidence i, of reflection r, and of refraction θ obey the laws of optics, and in particular for the angle of refraction

$$\sin i / \sin \theta = V_1/V_2$$

where V_1 is the velocity on the incident side of the boundary and V_2 the velocity on the other. If V_2 is the greater velocity, the angle of refraction is greater than the angle of incidence, and there will be a certain critical value of the latter for which r is 90°. In this case the refracted pulse is transmitted along the boundary with the greater velocity. In addition to this reflection and refraction, there is also a change of type, for an incident P wave sets up reflected and refracted S waves as well as corresponding waves of its own type. Consequently, at a point near a boundary there are a large number of pulses arriving from an explosion, and in general, as they do not arrive in any particular sequence the arrivals are difficult to identify.

For this reason prospecting makes use of the first arrival, which of necessity must be a P wave over the whole length of the path taken.

The method of utilizing these waves is best illustrated by a simple case, in which a uniform surface layer of thickness H and velocity V_1 rests on a thick lower medium of velocity V_2, the lower medium possessing the greater velocity. An explosion is detonated at a point O (Fig. 137), which for simplicity will be assumed to be a point on the surface. On a straight line passing through the

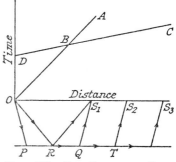

FIG. 137.—TIME-DISTANCE GRAPH (OBC) for seismic waves at a buried surface (PT).

explosion point, a series of geophones S_1, S_2, S_3, etc. (electrical instruments for detecting the ground movement), are laid out at suitable intervals. The time taken for disturbance to travel from O to the various geophones is measured, and a time-distance curve constructed. The wave can reach the detector from the explosion by one of three paths, the direct path OS_1, the reflected path ORS_1, or the refracted path $OPQS_1$. If the work is carried out with first arrivals only, the reflected path, which is always greater than the direct path and is covered with the same velocity V_1 is automatically eliminated. For the direct path the time/distance curve is a straight line OA passing through the origin and from its slope the velocity V_1 can be determined. For the refracted path the pulse travels down to the boundary with a velocity V_1 and is incident at the critical angle. After refraction the pulse travels along the boundary with the velocity V_2, and at all points along the boundary energy leaves the lower medium at the critical angle and travels up to the surface where it influences the instruments there. At short distances, the indirect refracted path lags behind the direct path due to the delay in travelling down to and up from the lower boundary. Since the part PQ of the path is covered at a higher velocity, this delay is ultimately made up, and at sufficiently large distances the pulse following the refracted path is the first arrival, leading to the portion BC of the time-distance curve. This portion is also a straight line, for the time difference between the first arrivals at S_1 and S_2 corresponds to the path difference QT ($= S_1S_2$) covered with a velocity V_2. From the slope BC, therefore, the velocity V_2 can be calculated. The intercept OD on the time axis, made by the line BC, gives a measure of the lag of the indirect path behind the direct path and from it the depth of the boundary can be calculated from the formula

$$H = V_1V_2\, \Delta T/2\sqrt{V_2{}^2 - V_1{}^2}$$

where ΔT is the intercept on the time axis. With suitable modifications the method can be extended to multilayer problems and also to the case of inclined boundaries. In all cases, however, it is essential that the velocity in any layer should be greater than the velocity in the layers above it.

For best results, the velocities in the two layers must differ appreciably and show a sharply defined boundary. Where the bed-rock is compact, unweathered and free from fracturing with a loose uncompacted overburden no difficulty is experienced. Where the bed-rock is weathered and the overburden reasonably compacted it may be impossible to locate the boundary. As a result granitic areas are rarely suitable for this type of investigation. Again if the bedrock is not fully consolidated and the over-burden, say, a compact glacial drift, difficulty may be experienced. Fortunately it is found that many of these conditions rarely persist over the whole of the site, and the method suitably applied will supply certain information.

Using a small survey party of three men to locate shot points and stations, and four labourers, it was found that some 80 shots per day could be fired at a cost of about \$100 and requiring the full time of a computer (Shepard and Wood, 1940). For a preliminary survey two to three days' work in the field is usually sufficient. To carry out the same work by drilling would cost some three times as much as a seismic survey and take a considerably longer time. For more detailed work, a study of a dam site in New York State showed that the seismic survey cost 10 per cent as much as the cost of drilling, but in many cases the seismic method is not considered suitable for the more detailed programme (see also Robertshaw and Brown, reference on p. 334).

To obtain wave arrivals which have travelled through the lower formation, the distance between shot point and detector must vary up to about four times the depth of the lower boundary. In practice three or four detectors are laid out at intervals of 30–40 feet, and a record taken using a small charge buried about 3 feet deep, a short distance from one of the detectors. The shot point is then moved by 20–50-feet steps, the size of the step being controlled by the problem, and further records are taken. On the trace of the ground motion the shot instant or time of firing is recorded together with time marks at intervals of 0·01 second, so that the time of travel can be read to the nearest 0·001 second. The type of time-distance curve obtained is shown in Fig. 138, which shows three straight lines corresponding to three layers of rock in the area. These layers consist of a top soil having a velocity of 1110 feet per second, an intermediate layer of 3170 feet per second, and bedrock (in this case sandstone) having a velocity of 8210 feet per second. From these velocities, and the intercepts on the time axis, the depths to the boundaries have been calculated as 6·8 feet and 16·4 feet respectively. It will be seen that on the graph, arrivals

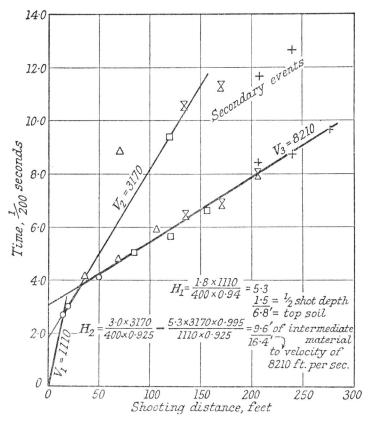

FIG. 138.—TYPICAL TIME-DISTANCE CURVE FOR A 3-LAYER PROBLEM.

other than the first are shown, and in fact the velocity of the intermediate layer has been obtained using some of the secondary events. Frequently the existence of one or more intermediate layers is not revealed by the first arrivals and errors will arise in the depth determinations if they are ignored. By using later arrivals their presence is often revealed, but it may be impossible to obtain an accurate value for the velocities involved, the results suggesting a continuous increase of velocity with depth. When these conditions exist, it is found convenient to assume two intermediate layers, and by judicious selection of the velocities, the selection being guided by the time-distance results, the depth to the bed-rock can be determined without any serious error.

The above is a brief sketch of the main methods which have been satisfactory in solving certain problems arising in engineering projects. Other problems can be solved by their application and other examples will be found in works listed below, which also give a more extended treatment.

SELECTED REFERENCES

Code of Practice No. 1. "Site Investigations." British Standards Institution, 1957.

TERZAGHI, K., AND PECK, R. "Soil Mechanics in Engineering Practice." 1962. Wiley & Sons, New York.

TRASK, P. D. (Ed.). "Applied Sedimentation." 1950. Wiley & Sons, New York. Chapter 5: Principles of Soil Mechanics as viewed by a geologist, by C. A. Kaye.

SKEMPTON, A. W. "Soil Mechanics in Relation to Geology." *Proc. Yorks. Geol. Soc.*, 29, 1953, p. 33.

COOLING, L. F., AND SKEMPTON, A. W. "A Laboratory Study of London Clay." *Journ. Inst. C.E.*, 17, London, 1942, p. 251.

DAPPLES, E. C. "Basic Geology for Science and Engineering." 1959. Chapter 2: Soil Materials.

HEILAND, C. A. "Geophysical Exploration." Reprinted 1963. Hafner.

ROBERTSHAW, J., AND BROWN, P. D. "Geophysical Methods of Exploration and their Application to Civil Engineering Problems." *Proc. Inst. C.E.*, 4, London, 1955, p. 644.

D.S.I.R. (Road Research Laboratory): "Soil Mechanics for Road Engineers." 1955. H.M. Stationery Office, London.

APPENDIX

PUBLICATIONS OF THE GEOLOGICAL SURVEY OF GREAT BRITAIN

The Geological Survey became the Institute of Geological Sciences in 1966. The following summary includes most of its publications ; a full list of maps and memoirs is available on application.

1. MAPS

(a) *Small Scales*

The British Isles, 25 miles to the inch. Colour printed. 4th edition, 1957.
Great Britian, 1 : 625,000 (about 10 miles to 1 inch), in two sheets. First published 1948, revised 1957.

The Coalfields of England and Wales.
The Iron Ores of England and Wales. } Scale, 1 : 1,000,000
The Chief Limestones of England and Wales.

(b) *Quarter-inch Scale* (1 : 253,440)

England and Wales. 19 sheets. Printed in colour, not all available.
Scotland. 17 sheets, of which 11 are published, printed in colour.
Ireland. Sheet 2 (Antrim and Donegal).
Geophysical maps : gravity survey and aeromagnetic.

(c) *One-inch Scale* (1 : 63,360)

England and Wales : *New Series*. The country is covered by 360 sheets, colour printed, not all of which are published. Each sheet covers an area 18 × 12 miles. Solid and Drift editions are available for many sheets. Special sheets are also available on this scale of the London District, Oxford, Bristol, Nottingham, the Isle of Wight, and the Isle of Man.

Old Series. The country was covered by 110 sheets, hand coloured, each taking in an area 35 × 23 miles. These maps are available for reference.

Scotland : 131 sheets (not all published), colour printed, each covering an area 24 × 18 miles, and the following special sheets : Isle of Arran, the Assynt District, the Glasgow District.

Northern Ireland : Sheets 8 (Ballycastle) and 35 (Dungannon) have been issued, in Solid or Drift editions.

(d) *Six-inch Scale* (1 : 10,560)

Geological maps of the Coalfields, and certain other areas (including the London district and Edinburgh) are published, coloured or uncoloured. Also certain sheets in Northern Ireland.

MS. copies of maps of areas which have been geologically surveyed on the scale of 6 inches to the mile are deposited for reference at the offices of the Survey in London, Leeds, Edinburgh, and Belfast.

2. SECTIONS

A series of horizontal sections on the scale of 6 inches to the mile, illustrating the geological maps, and of vertical sections on the scale of 40 feet to the inch, showing details which cannot be given on the horizontal sections, were published at the time of issue of the *Old Series* one-inch maps.

3. MEMOIRS

(a) *General.*

Summary of Progress of the Geological Survey (issued annually).

Bulletins. Research papers are published in this series, which was begun in 1939. Recent issues (1957 onwards) contain reports on new boreholes and geological data at certain engineering sites.

Attrition Tests of British Road Stones. (1929.)

Chemical Analyses of Igneous Rocks, Metamorphic Rocks, and Minerals.

(b) *Economic Memoirs.*

Special Reports on the Mineral Resources of Gt. Britain. This series deals with metalliferous ores, refractory materials, oil shales, and other economic products. (For coal, see under District Memoirs.)

(c) *Handbooks and Guides.*

British Regional Geology. A series of 18 handbooks covering the whole of Great Britain (listed on p. 238 of this book). Each volume contains a condensed and illustrated account of the region with which it deals.

Guides to various models, and lists of the gemstone and fossil collections, in the Museum of Practical Geology, South Kensington, London.

(d) *District Memoirs.*

England and Wales : Memoirs describing the geology of a number of districts, such as Anglesey, the Isle of Wight, the London District, the Forest of Dean. Coalfields are dealt with in a special series of memoirs.

Scotland : Memoirs dealing with the geology of a number of districts including Arran, Edinburgh, Glasgow, the N.W. Highlands, Skye, Mull.

Scottish coalfields form the subject of a series of economic memoirs.

(e) *Water Supply Memoirs.*

These are arranged by counties, and describe the water supplies from underground sources. Lists of wells are included. (Issued up to about 1924.)

(f) *Sheet Memoirs.*

England and Wales : (i) In explanation of Old Series 1-inch maps. The memoirs are numbered to correspond with the map numbers. (ii) In explanation of New Series 1-inch maps. Most of the New Series sheets have an accompanying memoir ; but for some areas which are covered by District Memoirs (for example, coalfields), no separate Sheet Memoirs are issued.

Scotland : Memoirs accompany the 1-inch maps and bear the corresponding sheet number, except where the area is covered by a District Memoir or other publication.

(g) *Water Supply Papers.*

Short memoirs on water supply were published as a temporary war-time measure, and are now available for reference. These pamphlets are being revised and re-issued as " Water Supply Papers " (1964 onwards).

INDEX

Names of fossils are given in italics